REALMS OF WATER

Original Title
DE KRINGLOOP VAN HET WATER
Published by
N. V. Leopold Uitg., The Hague

Revised version translated by
May Hollander

Realms of Water

SOME ASPECTS OF ITS
CYCLE IN NATURE

by

P. H. Kuenen

Professor of Geology
University of Groningen, Netherlands

LONDON
Cleaver-Hume Press Ltd.

CLEAVER-HUME PRESS LTD.
31 Wright's Lane, Kensington,
London, W.8

JOHN WILEY & SONS INC.
440 Fourth Avenue,
New York 16, N.Y.

First published 1955

Printed in Great Britain
by Western Printing Services Ltd., Bristol
and bound by Key & Whiting Ltd., London

FOREWORD

WATER has a dual claim to be regarded as a unique and very remarkable product of Nature in that, firstly, it is the only inorganic fluid which occurs in appreciable quantities and, secondly, it is the sole substance to be found in the natural state as a solid, a liquid and a vapour. Water is, therefore, directly responsible for nearly all visible movements in inanimate Nature. Hurrying clouds and foaming waves, seething waterfalls and the slow rise and fall of the tides, dancing snowflakes and downpouring rain, floating icebergs and drifting ice-floes, creeping glaciers and eddying rivers—all are manifestations of the urge impelling this restless wanderer to be on the move.

When we consider, in addition to this visible movement, the invisible peregrinations of water below ground, its predominance over all other elements combined, in the uppermost few miles of the earth's crust, its ubiquity in living vegetable and animal tissues as well as in the vast majority of goods provided for daily consumption, the study of water and its ways can hardly fail to engross us.

Another journey undertaken by water on this earth—familiar to us from our school days, even though we are precluded from following it directly in some of its stages—is that cycle which begins with the evaporation of water from the seas and ends with its return thereto by way of discharging rivers.

In the ensuing pages I have tried to give an account of the scientific facts pertaining to this cycle in a form intelligible to the non-expert and, I hope, useful to the student of the natural sciences. I have had occasion to touch on many ideas of the past, exploded by more recent knowledge, and have endeavoured to demolish some common misconceptions such as the alleged existence of underground streams in all sorts of unlikely places, and of springs at the summits of mountains; or the belief that every river has its source in a spring or glacier.

The absence of acknowledgments to individual research workers and sources of information may cause some surprise. Their omission was dictated by the wish to spare the majority of my readers unnecessary tedium and to limit the weight of the book. Notes are often felt by a non-specialist to be an irksome distraction from the main theme. Moreover, no bibliography, however comprehensive, could do full justice to the assistance, equally valuable and valued, derived from the work of countless others in fields of research only secondarily associated with ours, in whose debt we nevertheless stand for their contribution towards the sum total of knowledge. Some references and the sources from which the illustrations were taken are given at the end.

The utmost possible economy has been observed in the use of technical terms, and it is believed that all of them are sufficiently explained in terms familiar to anyone with but slight acquaintance with science.

My colleagues should know that this is not intended to be a text-book and I have therefore not attempted to present the subject in full, nor yet to maintain a nice balance by assigning to each section precisely that measure of treatment which the theoretical importance of the matter would seem to demand. In choosing my material, I was guided largely by what I esteemed likely to interest a beginner or a keen amateur in our branch of science. It may be that the sub-title suggests the true theme of the book more aptly than the main title, for the term "cycle" is to be understood figuratively and the subject matter includes aspects of water in free Nature, such as the tides, which have nothing to do with that cycle.

Not one of the complementary disciplines here represented is dealt with in its full scope; nor should the reader expect to find a short outline of oceanography or geology any more than of meteorology or geomorphology, for only some sections of these sciences come within the province of our subject. Indeed, resisting the temptation to digress too far, I have even found it necessary to ignore certain topics such as the rôle of water in animate Nature.

P. H. KUENEN

CONTENTS

LIST OF PLATES

9

ACKNOWLEDGMENTS

THE author gratefully acknowledges permissions from the following sources to adapt
illustrations from the books here indicated by authors and referred to in more detail in
the bibliography at the end.

The Macmillan Company of New York (*Hobbs;* figs. 83, 89, 101).
American Association of Petroleum Geologists (*Trask, Fleming* and *Revelle;* fig. 40)
Touring Club Italiano (*Bertarelli and Boegan;* plate XIV)
McGraw-Hill Book Company Inc. (*Bentley and Humphreys;* plates IX, X)
C. Boysen, Hamburg (*Schott;* figs. 14, 39)
Haynes Inc., St. Paul, Minn. (*Bauer;* plate XIV a)
Springer-Verlag, Berlin (*Defant;* figs. 30, 31; *Paulcke;* fig. 64; *Thorade;* figs. 11, 12)
Gebr. Borntraeger, Berlin (*Krenkel;* 128, 129)
Versluys, Amsterdam (*Jong;* figs. 50, 63)
F. A. Brockhaus, Wiesbaden (*Flaig;* plates XI (*a*), XII (*a*))
Wereldbibliotheek, Amsterdam (*Escher;* figs. 115, 140, 173)
American Geographical Society, New York (*Davis;* fig. 59)
B. G. Teubner, Stuttgart (*Davis;* figs. 79, 80, 84, 102, 153, 154, 158, 176)
University of Chicago Press, Journal of Geology (*Zernitz;* figs. 179, 183, 184)
Bruckmann, Munich (*Dircksen;* plate II 6)
Ehrhardt Film, Hamburg (Plates I, V (*a*), XVI)
Keystone Press (Plate II (*a*)).

I

Introductory

The Cycle of Water

If it were possible to trace the careers of all the water-molecules on earth from the earliest times, it would be found that no two were alike. The opportunities for adventure open to such a molecule are circumscribed; but just as writings of limitless variety result from the different grouping of a very small number of letters and symbols, so are the life-histories of all water-molecules composed of a very restricted range of possible episodes.

Thus one will evaporate from the surface of the sea and rain back into it many times in succession before it is engulfed at the Pole in a submerging stream and drifts through the dark depths of the ocean, year upon year, until it eventually emerges at the Equator or at the opposite Pole. Meanwhile, a neighbour molecule, which had also taken a few turns at rising from and falling back into the sea, has been wafted higher into the atmosphere and, now transformed into the constituent of a snowflake, has landed on a glacier. Years later it may sweep towards the valley in the glacier stream or evaporate from the tongue of ice, only to return to earth again, this time, maybe, flung down in heavy rain upon a desert, from which it may evaporate at sunrise and return as dew at night again and again.

Elsewhere, water penetrates many hundreds of feet into the earth's crust and follows long, tortuous paths until it spurts upwards in a hot spring or unobtrusively makes its appearance in the bed of a river, flowing with the latter towards the ocean. Most water that goes underground, however, eventually evaporates at the surface again, or else is absorbed by vegetation and is thus returned to the atmosphere. Another considerable contingent may have travelled only a little way between sand and particles of clay before oozing into a brook and sweeping rapidly out to sea.

There are, again, prisons, as it were, in which the molecules of water may be trapped. They may be held between grains of sand at the bottom of the sea and smothered there under growing accumulations of deposits. If such be their fate, it will be millions of years before they are released; not until the

sea-bed has been raised up to mountains and these in turn have been worn
down by the teeth of time. Then, carried along by the creeping ground-
water, a few of those drops of water, which have been imprisoned for whole
geological periods, will at last make good their escape. Molecules which are
caught up as crystal water in weathering minerals are imprisoned in far
smaller but no less escape-proof cells. Their liberation will not come until
mountain-forming forces have pushed them deep down into the earth's
crust, whence the heat will drive them out once more. Then again there is
stagnant water deep down in Norwegian fjords or the Black Sea which,
through lack of circulation, becomes foul and saturated with hydrogen
sulphide and semi-decayed organic remains.

Most of the water absorbed by plants or animals is set free again within
twenty-four hours, but those particles which are pressed into service for the
building of cells have a much longer period of enforced rest.

In the foregoing summary we have reviewed all the major experiences
which fate may have in store for a molecule of water in its life on earth.
Though minor incidents and digressions may vary the pattern in many ways,
it cannot justly be said that the choice of possibilities for a water-molecule's
career is extensive! In whatever sequence the events occur and however
varied the pattern may be, again and again we come up against the same
ineluctable *principle of a cycle*. No matter whether this cycle takes a long or a
short time to complete, whether it is a complicated or a simple one, the outcome is always the same: water returns to its point of departure, the ocean.

By far the majority of molecules are congregated in the oceans and it is
the exception rather than the rule for some to escape for a comparatively
short period full of exciting variety and activity until, having completed their
cycle, they return to that same huge reservoir.

The mere evaporation from the sea and immediate return to it is called the
short cycle. There is an even *shorter cycle*, however, namely condensing in the
atmosphere and evaporating again without having reached the earth's surface. What we call the *long cycle* also includes evaporating from the ocean,
but in this case the moisture is precipitated upon dry land. The vehicle of
such water in its return journey to its point of departure is a river. If the
route is via a glacier, we might distinguish this variant as the *longest cycle*.

But apart from these "official" excursions, there are innumerable escap-
ades such as convection currents in a lake or the sea, circular paths through
wave-movement, escape from a river overflowing its banks, only to ooze back
into it through the ground, and so on. We have already seen that involun-
tary periods of rest may be imposed and often a cycle is embarked upon but
not completed. Thus a molecule which evaporates from terra firma is

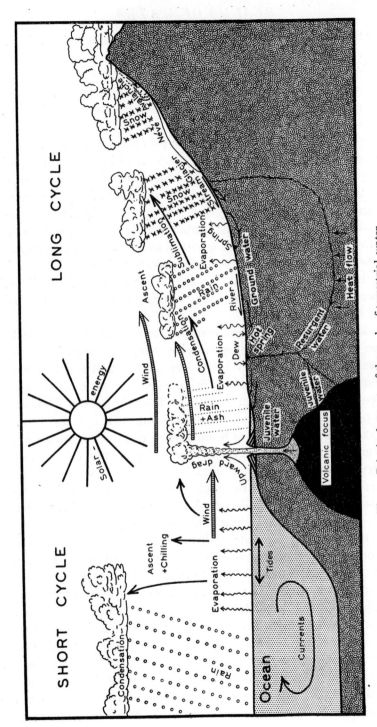

Fig. 1. Principal aspects of the cycle of terrestrial water.

retracing its steps, as it were, and as it may quite possibly fall as rain into the sea, it may reach its point of departure by reversing the route along which it has already travelled. If glacier ice flows straight into the sea, thus by-passing the segment of the cycle in the river, or if the ice evaporates and thus even the interlude in the sea is omitted, one might say that, metaphorically speaking, it cuts across the circle as by a chord.

If we consider for a moment this cyclic principle by which water is governed, we shall soon realise that many aspects of inanimate and animate nature will have to be studied to gain some insight into what happens to water on this earth. We shall have to dip into meteorology, oceanography, geology and even consult pedology and biology. Nobody can be a specialist in all these subjects at once. The author is fully aware that he will often have to trespass on other people's territory and feels uncomfortably certain that he will get stung by many an unsuspected clump of nettles in the process. His plea will then have to be the wide field which his subject covers, even though he has passed over entirely the rôle of water in living matter.

In the following pages we shall consider the various stages of the longest cycle, one by one, not concerning ourselves with the divagations or oscillations of particular molecules. When water condenses, it will be a matter of indifference to us that one portion of it has recently evaporated from a plant, another part from a lake and the remainder from the oceans. Ground-water will be a point of consideration as the main source of supply for rivers but is, in turn, supplemented by rivers from time to time. Many other examples could be given of molecules forgetting, now and then, that they are supposed to be hurrying along on a cyclic course.

Theoretically, the point in the cycle from which we start is immaterial. Before discussing rivers, ground-water has to be considered, before that there is snow and before snow the vapour in the atmosphere, and so forth.

Seeing that about 97 per cent of all the water on earth is collected in the seas and oceans, this enormous mass is scarcely affected by evaporation or by the rivers flowing and the rain falling into it. Of the remaining thirtieth part, one-third is locked up in snow and glaciers, while two-thirds constitute the fresh water of rivers and lakes and the ground-water in the soil. The water floating in the atmosphere amounts only to a fraction of one per cent (*ca.* 1/2000 per cent). We shall ignore the water physically and chemically combined in clays and other weathering products; quantitatively it is negligible and has, moreover, been shunted, so to speak, into a siding.

Since, then, a molecule spends on an average thirty times as much of its time in the sea as in the other, less staid section of the circuit, it seems obvious that we should start with the oceans. But before coming to grips with oceanography, we must look at some of the properties of water as a natural product.

The chemist denotes the water-molecule by the symbol H_2O—two atoms of hydrogen with one atom of oxygen. Nowadays we hear of various forms of water, because one, two or three elementary molecules can be strung together into larger units. Moreover, chemists have discovered different kinds of hydrogen and oxygen atoms, that is to say, in addition to the normal kinds, there occur in nature in minute quantities, atoms possessing the same chemical properties but of slightly greater weight, the heavy isotopes so called. Fortunately we do not have to concern ourselves with these variants, as they play no noticeable part in nature. In point of fact, "heavy water" in somewhat larger concentration appears only in isolated, saline lakes or inland seas like the Dead Sea, because it evaporates less readily than ordinary water and has therefore always tended to remain behind in the never-ending process of inflow and distillation which goes on there in the desert. That the far less volatile salts which the Jordan, like every river, carries along were concentrated in an even greater degree, will easily be realised.

Water is the most extraordinary of all compounds known to science and it is precisely these departures from the normal which fit it so eminently for the dominant rôle it plays in the nature by which we have our being.

Water when purified by distillation is an odourless liquid which, taken neat, has an offensively insipid taste. It is virtually the only inorganic substance in nature which can occur in the liquid state under normal conditions of temperature and pressure; for the same reason it is the only natural product found in three states of aggregation in the open, viz., solid, liquid and gaseous. If we except earthquakes, land-slips and volcanic eruptions— in which, as a matter of fact, water as vapour often plays a conspicuous part —it may be said that there are only two "auto-mobile" substances in inanimate nature, air and water. Thanks to its greater specific gravity and internal friction, water takes the lion's share of all transport on earth. Waves and currents carry not only sand and clay in the sea, but shift great masses of rock on the shore, while a predominant proportion of marine organisms not held fast to the bottom can only be moved from place to place by submitting passively to the action of the water. On the continents the most assiduous vehicles are rivers and glaciers, which move immense quantities of coarse and fine rock fragments and compared with which the wind is a mere lazy dilettante.

It is a curious fact that water derives its kinetic energy (except that due to tides) entirely from the action and movements of the atmosphere, while in the background the sun as the primary source of energy is responsible for all displacements.

The supply of nutrients to and in vegetation is likewise effected by water in the form of solutions, and the passage of food within the animal body also depends upon this substance which is indispensable to life. In this connection, we may mention yet another property of water, namely that of being able to dissolve a larger variety of substances, in greater amounts, than any other liquid. Is it not a most remarkable circumstance that the only liquid always available in nature should at the same time possess this tremendous solvent power, by means of which plants and animals alike are enabled to build up the exceedingly intricate structures of their bodies? For there are innumerable inorganic and organic substances that have to be transported to create a living organism and keep it functioning. What would be the chances of the subsistence of any form of life on earth if water had as little solvent power as, say, paraffin oil?

The capacity of water to dissolve almost every component of the earth's crust, even though sometimes in only a minor degree, is responsible for the universal denudation of all rocks by "the elements". Were it not for this property, mountains would wear down but little and the rivers would carry only a very small burden. In the result, the formation of sedimentary rocks such as sands, clays and limestones would not have played that predominant part which it has in the history of the globe. Briefly, the geographical appearance of our earth would have been totally different.

Admittedly, humic acid, carbonic acid and oxygen are also powerful agents in this chemical weathering, but always in the dissolved form. Figuratively they might be compared with the tools enabling the cabinet-maker to ply his trade: man's capacity to grasp and hold is primary; his implements are secondary. Equally, that property of water which enables it to grasp its tools (corrosive fluids) is the primary necessity, and this immensely enhances the solvent effect upon the rocks.

It is the same thing with surface tension, that of water being greater than of any other fluid. In the physiology of the cell this property is one of incalculable importance; while in inanimate nature it governs drop formation and, therefore, precipitation. Surface tension is active in the formation of both small and big waves and thus the action of the sea upon coasts and the sea-bed. To pour oil upon the troubled waters is not a mere figure of speech for, as we know, oil does subdue the fury of the waves, one reason being its small surface tension.

We have now to consider the solid state of aggregation, ice. Glacier ice, icebergs, snow and frozen sea-water have played a mighty part in the history of the earth and ice is sometimes a very active contributory factor in the denudation of rocks. When water solidifies it expands, a property which it shares with very few substances, such as bismuth and silver. As a result, when water in cracks and fissures freezes, it acts like a wedge forcing the blocks of rock asunder. Think, too, how different conditions would be in the oceans if ice sank instead of floating! (Fig. 2.) Ice melts under pressure, because it then shrinks and therefore gives. This property comes into play with the flow of glaciers and prevents the solid precipitate from accumulating endlessly upon the mountains and at the Poles. This is very much more

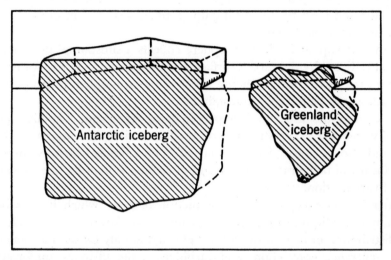

Fig. 2. Floating icebergs (exaggerated vertically). The Antarctic, composed of barrier-ice, is tabular and about four-fifths submerged. The Arctic, composed of glacier-ice, is tooth-shaped, about six-sevenths submerged and carries moraine débris at the bottom.

important for the development of the world around us than the mere opportunity for skating, which depends upon the same principle.

No substance has as great a capacity as water for absorbing or transmitting heat. The heat of vaporisation, hence the quantity of heat required to convert water or ice into vapour, is greater than that of any other substance, while both the heat of fusion of ice and the specific heat of water are surpassed only by those of ammonia. The value of this enormous thermal capacity can scarcely be over-estimated. It is inextricably mixed up with our daily lives. It costs more fuel and time to bring water to the boil than to heat other liquids through just as many degrees. Conversely, hot water cools more slowly and therefore gives off more heat than all other substances, which is why hot-water bottles keep warm for so long; it also obviates the necessity of hastily swallowing our hot toddy or of putting it into the hay-box between sips to keep it warm.

This property radically affects the thermal economy everywhere. It moderates temperature fluctuations, not only of the sea and adjacent lands, but of all areas on earth. Even in the desert the formation of dew tempers the nocturnal chill, just as the sublimation of snow, and its melting at a later stage, even out temperature-contrasts in the colder regions and on the summits of mountains. The ocean currents carry an enormous mass of heat to the polar regions, thus allaying the rigours of the arctic climate. The tremendous heat of vaporisation keeps the evaporation of water within reasonable limits and prevents the drying up of inland seas and lakes in the intervals between the rainy seasons.

The water vapour in the atmosphere collects a substantial percentage of the heat radiated by the earth's surface and reflects it. So it is to water again that we owe part of the hot-house effect of the atmosphere, without which the earth would be too cold to sustain life.

These properties also come into play in living organisms. The high specific heat of water acts as a restraint upon the fluctuations of temperature in the body and also, of course, has a similar effect on animals which live in water. The efficacy of perspiration as a means of cooling is likewise due to its great heat of vaporisation.

Water is also exceptional for conduction of heat, which it does better than any other liquid substance except mercury. Although the conduction and distribution of heat in the sea are effected mainly by the movements of water—currents, convection, and turbulence—the ultimate uniformity is attained only through conduction. In the animal body too, conduction is for ever manœuvring to attain uniformity and thus to avoid dangerous extremes.

A strange thing happens when water contracts on cooling. Shrinkage continues down to 4° C., after which expansion again sets in, which means to say that water at 4° C. is not only heavier than warmer water but than colder water too. As a result, rivers and lakes in frosty weather cool down to 4° C. and then begin to freeze at the surface, whereby the deep water is protected from greater cooling and the surface freezes more and more.

Most people are unaware that the properties of sea-water in this respect are totally different. However, the heat economy of the deep sea and that of the surface water, and hence the climates on the continents, would be quite different if sea-water reacted to cooling in exactly the same way as fresh water. Not only is the freezing point of sea-water lower than that of fresh water, viz. about $-2°$ C., but contraction on cooling progresses steadily thus far. Therefore the heaviest sea-water is that which is just about to freeze. The fact that sea-water, unlike fresh water, does *not* depart from the normal laws in this respect means that in winter the sea at the Poles may cool down, before freezing, to 6 degrees lower than fresh water, which would only drop to below $4°$ C. at the surface. This heavy, cold sea-water sinks and fills the ocean, with the result that the deep sea has a far lower temperature than it otherwise would. This promotes oceanic circulation, which tends not only to equalise the climates at all latitudes, but improves the ventilation of deep-sea water. Oxygen is supplied; carbon dioxide, nutritive salts and lime are transported and are made available to new life elsewhere in shallow waters.

The compressibility of water is very slight. There is a superstition among seamen that a corpse buried at sea sinks only to a moderate depth and there remains drifting unto all eternity. Unconsciously they imagine that the immense pressure in the depths compresses the water into a heavy fluid in which all objects float for ever. The facts are that, not only are all submerged objects themselves compressed in equal or greater measure (wood to such a degree, indeed, that it loses its buoyancy and begins to sink), but the compressibility of water is too insignificant to be tangibly manifest. For all that, the slight compression which does exist is responsible for the fact that sea-level is 100 feet lower than it would be if water's compressibility were nil. Were its compressibility suddenly to cease, two million square miles of land would be flooded—more than twenty times the area of Britain.

Pure water is fairly transparent. If it were not, plant life would only be possible a little below the surface of the sea and of fresh-water basins. It is not an easy matter to explain briefly the significance of the minute electrolytic degree of dissociation of water and of the fact that the dielectric constant exceeds that of all other liquids. Both properties are fundamental factors for living organisms because they strongly affect all solutions in water. The whole of inorganic nature, too, is radically influenced by them, notably through the properties of sea-water and the action of ground-water in the denudation and alteration of rocks at greater depths.

It would be possible to discuss the whole cycle of water from the point of view of its exceptional properties which have just been considered and which are briefly set out below. Over and over again one would be tempted to point out how closely the processes of nature are related precisely to the uniqueness of these properties and that no other liquid, if it had chanced to be available instead of water in such quantities, could have taken over the tasks of that medium. Even if water had deviated a little less from the normal standard for substances in the universe, our globe would have remained a heavenly body as devoid of history, as dead as the moon.

But we must not pursue this teleological approach to our subject any further. Rather should the facts with the theories pertaining to them be allowed to speak for themselves.

PROPERTIES OF WATER

Property	Compared with other Substances
Quantity in outermost 5 kilometres of the earth.	3 times that of all other substances together 6 times that of felspar, the next in abundance
State of aggregation	Almost the only inorganic liquid present in nature and the only substance occurring in all three states of aggregation
Solvent power	More general than that of any other fluid
Surface tension	Highest of all fluids
Expansion on freezing	Very exceptional
Expansion on elevation of temperature	Greatest density of pure water at 4°, of sea-water at freezing point of − 2°
Thermal capacity and heat of fusion	After ammonia the greatest of all fluids and solids
Heat of vaporisation	Greatest of all substances
Thermal conductivity	Greatest of all liquids except mercury
Transparency	Very considerable and almost equal for all visible rays
Electrolytic dissociation	Very small
Dielectric constant	Highest of all fluids

II

Water in the Oceans

Oceanography as a Science

The scientific study of the oceans, which is known as oceanography, is a latecomer among the disciplines; so late, in fact, that it is still unrepresented at most universities. Ever since man has sailed the seas, he has taken note of the tides, waves, currents, the constitution of and the life within salt water. All these matters come within the province of oceanography, but it was not until a few decades ago that the oceans began to be studied from purely scientific motives.

The fact that the study of oceanography depends in large measure upon the undertaking of costly expeditions places it in a class apart from the other natural sciences. While it is true that the navies of seafaring countries produce sea-charts, that regular observations are made, and even that sea-borne laboratories exist for the benefit of the fisheries, and that accurate soundings have to be taken before transoceanic telegraph cables can be laid, there are nevertheless numerous aspects of the seas and oceans inviting investigation, which routine expeditions must necessarily ignore. Thus only those in pursuit of scientific knowledge for its own sake have hitherto wanted to know what conditions prevail in the depths of the oceans; and the answers to their questions can only be provided by researches pursued aboard a ship specially equipped for the purpose. It is, however, an expensive business to equip, man and run even a small sea-going vessel. The cost of a well-equipped deep-sea expedition for a year may be two hundred thousand pounds or more, especially if the salaries of the scientists during the preparatory work and the subsequent task of drawing up the reports, plus the cost of publication, are taken into account. It is scarcely surprising, therefore, to find that only a very limited number of such voyages on the grand scale have been undertaken. Reconnaissance of the deep sea started in earnest eighty years ago with the "Challenger" expedition. In those days, interest was mainly centred upon the mysterious life of the dark, cold deeps of the oceans. The specimens of rare animals and plants were snatched from their habitat by various means known to deep-sea fishing, including trawls at all depths and dredge-nets dragged along the sea bed. Although investigations were made into the deposits on the ocean floor as well as the temperature and constitution of deep water, in those days the tools available for this kind of work were on the whole rather inadequate. Hence, physical and chemical oceanography continued perforce to play a secondary part.

In the last three decades, physical and chemical researches applied to the sea have turned the tables on biology and are rapidly overtaking it. This is largely thanks to the perfecting of technical aids such as sounding instruments, current meters, thermometers, and chemical methods; but the economic and military importance of physical oceanography has also been a powerful stimulant.

A growing number of oceanographical institutes and marine laboratories have been established and these are engaged on extensive programmes of marine research.

Deep-sea Soundings

The movements of oceanic water are governed largely by the shape of the sea floor; the depth and morphology of that floor are, therefore, fundamental points of enquiry. In early times, seamen used some primitive device, like a stone on a line, or a long stick, for depth-sounding, that indispensable accessory to the art of navigation. No one troubled to plumb the depths farther out at sea, curiosity as to this non-utilitarian piece of information still, apparently, being dormant.

It was not until 1521 that Magellan tried to sound the depth of the Pacific Ocean. When, in the middle of this great stretch of water, he failed to touch bottom after paying out 2300 feet of line, he drew the conclusion that he had come upon the deepest spot on this earth. Had he known, there were depths five times as great within a few miles of his native shore. In 1773 Phipps plumbed 4000 feet in the Arctic and Ross was able to show in 1840 that the depth of the South Atlantic Ocean was more than 13,000 feet.

When considerable depths were sounded with the old-fashioned type of plumb-line, the tremendous weight and great frictional resistance of the line with the water made it almost impossible to tell when the lead had reached the bottom. It was not until well into the second half of the nineteenth century, when thin steel wire was used instead of hempen line, that this moment could be established with certainty.

Nowadays, soundings are taken with some heavy instrument attached to thin steel wire, which is paid out over a measuring wheel until the lead touches bottom; the length of the submerged wire is then read off. As this operation takes anything from one to two hours in normal oceanic depths, with the vessel having to keep stationary in the meantime, the reason for the paucity of depth soundings is not far to seek.

A highly significant advance was made when the *echo method* came into practice after the First World War. The underlying principle is the emission of a sharp sound signal from a moving ship and reception, by means of a kind of telephone placed under the water line, of the echo reflected by the sea floor. As the speed of the sound on its double journey is known, all that is required is to measure the time which elapses between the emission of the signal and the reception of the echo. The speed under water being about 5000 feet per second, the interval for a depth of, say, 10,000 feet would be 4 seconds (see Fig. 3).

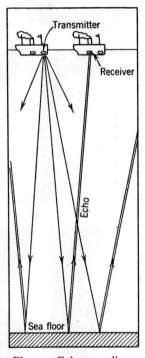

Fig. 3. Echo-sounding.

It will at once be evident that one of the main technical problems was to produce a signal powerful enough to make an echo audible above the noise of the waves and of the screw even after travelling several miles. Then again, the interval measured must be accurate to within 1/20 second if it is to measure depths accurately to within 100 feet. This is about the degree of accuracy obtained by wire soundings in oceanic depths. To equal this by the echo technique, both the apparatus used and the personnel serving it have to meet the most exacting standards. It will be obvious that even greater accuracy is required in shallower waters. In coastal waters, no seaman would venture to rely on echo soundings unless he were confident that they were accurate to a few feet. The result of recent refinements is the production of wholly automatic instruments capable of drawing a continuous line representing the bottom profile along the entire route.

The very considerable expansion of our knowledge of submarine topography, thanks to echo-sounding, is well exemplified by the work of the Dutch *Snellius* Expedition in the Moluccan Seas about 1930. When the expedition set out, the ascertained wire soundings in water deeper than 600 feet within the area to be explored numbered 3000. On its return, this number was increased by upwards of 30,000 echo soundings (Fig. 4).

Before the outbreak of World War II, the U.S. Coast and Geodetic Survey had completed a truly impressive programme of echo soundings. A

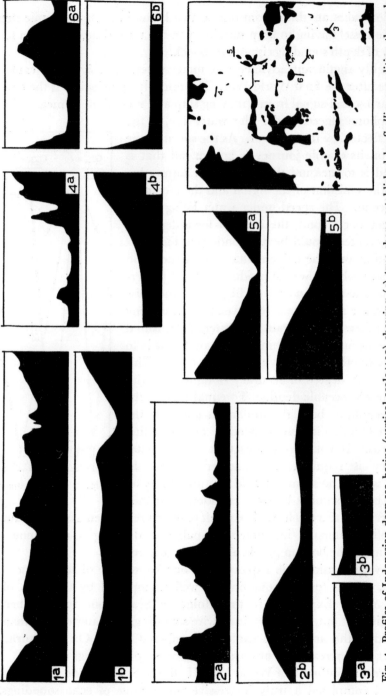

Fig. 4. Profiles of Indonesian deep-sea basins (vertical scale × 10) showing (*a*) true shape established by *Snellius* expedition through echo-sounding compared with (*b*) supposed profile based on previous wire soundings.

survey was made, with a very close network of depth soundings, covering stretches 100 to 200 kilometres wide along both ocean coasts of the United States. Thanks to a variety of new techniques, the accuracy of location attained was of a very high order. We now know that the continental slopes dropping down to the deep ocean floor are cut by dozens of huge valley clefts; but it required a *large number* of soundings combined with the *utmost precision* of siting and depth determination to map these ravines. Admittedly, earlier lead-line soundings had indicated the existence of some such submarine canyons, but it was echo-sounding which revealed their multiplicity, precipitousness, depth and continuance right down to the ocean floor.[1]

There is another highly curious way in which depth can be measured; it consists in using two deep-sea thermometers, one being exposed to, the other shielded from, the pressure of the water. If these two thermometers are let down to just above the sea bed, the unprotected instrument will register too high a temperature, because the pressure of the sea-water will force the mercury out of the bulb into the tube. The difference between the two readings is, therefore, a measure of the pressure to which the instruments have been subjected and, accordingly, of the depth. Experiment has shown that this method produces the most accurate results of all deep-sea soundings, but, as it is only practicable on a scientific expedition, it cannot be adopted for general use.

The Configuration of the Ocean Floor

Observations made in the last few decades present a very different picture of the ocean floor from that previously conceived. When all we had to go upon were a few, widely-scattered, random tests, the topography of the land below the waters gave the impression of being exceedingly monotonous. Flat expanses, the size of half a continent, appeared to be relieved by only minor undulations. Only here and there was the picture enlivened by so-called deep-sea trenches, oblong troughs usually situated along the outer edge of island chains, and by the submarine canyons which we shall mention in the last chapter.

Owing to the short relative distances between modern echo soundings, no significant unevennesses of the deep-sea floor escape detection, and in number, precipitousness and height they exceed all expectations. Although, owing to the absence of the erosive action of streams, and to the levelling influence of the deposition of mud, the submarine landscape cannot be marked by the finer kinds of relief found on dry land, its surface is on the whole little less variegated. Even in the depths we come across long mountain ranges with

[1] The origin of these canyons will be dealt with in Chapter VII.

valleys and ridges, troughs and plateaus. Many islands prove to be merely the summits of volcanic giants or enormous mountain massifs which, in relation to the surrounding area, match the mightiest continental mountains in point of height, extent and diversity of shapes.

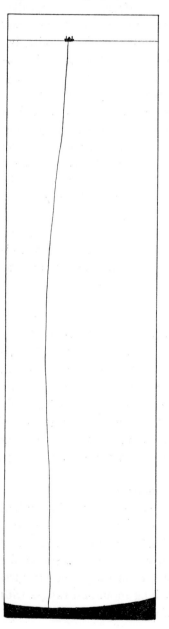

Moreover, the deep sea presents some topographical types that are absent on land. These are, primarily, the deep-sea trenches to which reference has already been made. They are elongated depressions with a gently curved axis, some 100 miles wide, increasing gradually in depth from the ends and sides towards the centre. The majority of these troughs reach depths of roughly 30,000 feet and the Mindanao Trench along the east coast of the Philippines sinks to well over ten kilometres (= 33,000 feet) below sea-level (Fig. 5). This means to say that the loftiest mountain on earth could easily be engulfed in the greatest depths of the sea.

In the second place, a great many truncated cones have been found, obviously decapitated volcanoes. They have been called guyots. Waves must have been the executioners after the volcanoes had become extinct. At a later period, these plateaus must have subsided to the present depth of about six thousand feet or even more.

Finally, the continental shelf is another typical submarine form of relief, which will be described presently.

Main Features of Submarine Relief

A regional description, however concise, of the shapes of the oceanic floor would detain us too long; a few generalities will therefore have

Fig. 5. H.M.S. *Willebrord Snellius* (drawn to double scale) taking the deepest wire sounding ever performed, on 16th May, 1930, in the Mindanao Trench (33,500 feet).

to suffice. A very important ridge stretches from north to south following the middle of the whole Atlantic Ocean and is known as the Mid-Atlantic Ridge. The distinguishing features of the Pacific Ocean are discrete elevations culminating in the Hawaii Islands and the innumerable atolls and islets of the Coral Sea. There is a complicated system of ridges in the western area of the Indian Ocean. Few soundings have as yet been taken in the North Pole basin, but drift expeditions across the Arctic Ocean have encountered only moderate and uniform depths. The bed of the Antarctic Ocean is also for the main part unexplored. So far as is known, the depth is normal and the submarine landscape tranquil.

It has also been discovered that the oblong deeps on both sides between the Mid-Atlantic Ridge and the continents are subdivided into roughly diamond-shaped basins by oblique cross-ridges. The large, flatter basins between the submarine ridges are more than 17,000 feet below sea-level.

By far the most complicated sea floors occur within and around the Indonesian and West Indian archipelagos. In this respect the Moluccan Archipelago carries off the palm (Fig. 6). Rounded and oval basins and trenches, the latter partly strung out in long chains, encircle the island arcs. Detached volcanic cones shoot upwards from submarine ridges or from the flat centres of the basins, some of them projecting far above sea-level. In addition to these ridges, there are plateau-shaped elevations, some of these being broken up by secondary depressions.

Another important feature of the ocean floor is that everywhere along the coasts of the continents with their islands, like Newfoundland and Great Britain with Ireland, there is a narrow to very wide strip of platform known as the continental shelf. This platform slopes gradually towards the open sea until at the edge the depth reaches 300 to 600 feet. Then comes a comparatively steep gradient, the continental slope, which leads down to the ocean bed. Shelf and slope together form the continental terrace. Although the continental slope is much steeper than the shelf, dips exceeding 4° or 5° are seldom encountered. Hence a car could easily be driven up from the deep-sea floor on to the shelf almost anywhere. When studying a coloured deep-sea map, it should be borne in mind that the slopes are far more gradual than the customary impressive colour scales are apt to suggest. Conversely, we should not forget that we tend to over-estimate the slopes on dry land and, as has been stated, ultimately submarine topography is in a general way comparable with the grosser continental features.

The Field of Oceanographical Research

What, it may be asked, are the natural phenomena which come within the province of oceanography? Depth soundings, which we have just been considering, constitute one item of investigation. Another is marine life, both vegetable and animal, the species that occur, their horizontal and vertical distribution, their conditions of life, and the communities they form. One of the principal tasks of the oceanographer is to ascertain the tempera-

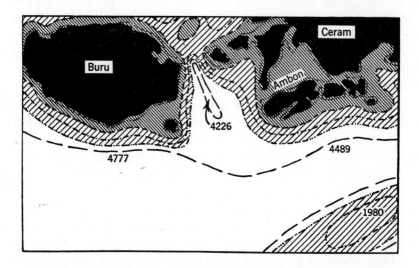

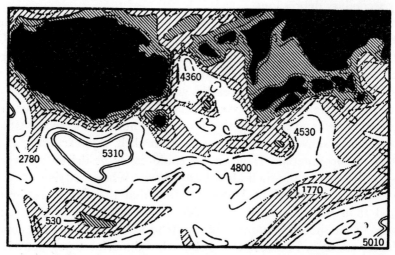

Fig. 6. The Manipa Strait between Buru and Ceram, showing (top) simple submarine relief formerly assumed on the basis of a few dozen wire soundings and (bottom) the more complicated relief established by several thousand echo soundings taken by the *Snellius* expedition. The fault formerly thought to mark the strait has turned out to be a basin with an old submarine volcano in the centre.

tures of the water, not only at the surface, but at all depths and over the whole expanse of the seas. What he needs to know in addition to the mean temperature at every point is whether these values fluctuate. The composition of sea-water at every point, i.e. floating particles, salt content and dissolved gases, is another important item of investigation. The sediments deposited on the sea floor, both deep-sea accumulations and the products laid down on the shelf and in inland seas, are as much the concern of the oceanographer as of the geologist. The former must also occupy himself with the meteorology of the layers of air above the sea, because of the interaction between the atmosphere and the hydrosphere. This relation is manifested in evaporation and precipitation, in temperature, in currents as the result of the wind, in wave action and in the drift of icebergs. The last chapter in the study of the seas comprises the movements of water, including the currents, the tides and the wash of the waves.

It will be seen, then, that oceanography not only covers a wide field, but is concerned with very divergent branches of research. The chemical, physical, biological, geological, meteorological and nautical aspects have to be studied by methods proper to each of these sciences, and only specialists trained in these various disciplines can do the job. No single individual at the present time could command the whole domain of oceanographic science. It follows that a general summary, such as the present work is intended to be, must necessarily bear the impress of the compiler's particular specialisation in one of the ancillary sciences. Lack of space, moreover, will compel us to ignore some of the contributory subjects altogether; among these will be marine biology and sedimentary deposits on the sea floor. More particularly, we shall concentrate on the state and movements of the ocean waters.

Deep-sea Observations

The aspects of oceanography mentioned in the preceding paragraph can be explained more easily once we know how marine scientists come by the facts they use, and the degree of accuracy with which those facts may be credited.

Needless to say, the observations made at the surface are the easiest to carry out. No special instruments are required, nor does the vessel have to remain stationary while the work is going forward. As, moreover, many of these observations, especially those concerned with the currents, have navigational value, they have claimed the attention of plain sailors from the earliest days of seafaring. We are, indeed, indebted almost entirely to the practical art of navigation for such details as we possess of the direction, strength and variation of the great ocean currents and tidal currents.

The procedure is first to determine the course and speed of the ship in relation to the water by the use of compass and log. Starting from a known position, it is then possible to predict the location of the ship at any given moment. If the reckoning or the taking of bearings then discloses a different location, the discrepancy must be due to the current (Fig. 7). From this it is an easy matter to derive the velocity and direction of the current. The result of one such observation naturally lacks precision, but the average of innumerable records obtained along the busier traffic lanes provides a very reliable standard.

Nor are mariners by any means indifferent to the salinity and temperature of the surface water. The position of a vessel can occasionally be verified

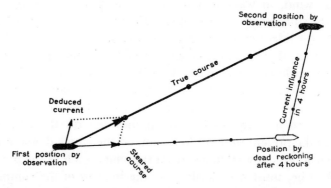

Fig. 7. Derivation of the current from two successive reckonings.

by scooping up a bucketful of water and determining these two properties, particularly in regions, like the estuaries of great rivers, where these properties exhibit marked variation from place to place. The temperature of surface water can easily be measured in a bucket to within tenths of a degree. For more accurate determination of the salinity than a rough estimate, it is, of course, necessary to carry samples to a shore laboratory if there are no special facilities on board; and when it comes to finding the content of the greatly diluted nutrient salts for plants and of dissolved gases like oxygen and carbon dioxide, the demands become even more exacting. We have, in fact, now entered the realm of scientific expeditions, so the moment has come to consider how greater depths can be made to divulge their secrets.

The procedure may best be illustrated by taking an example and describing how the *Snellius* deep-sea expedition went to work in the Moluccas. On arrival at the "station", the ship is stopped and a wire sounding is taken. A weighted tube is fixed at the end of the wire for the purpose of scooping a sample out of the soft bed so that the sediment on the bottom can be examined. Just above this sampler, the wire also carries a water-scoop or water-bottle with a thermometer attached, with the double object of measuring the temperature and obtaining a sample of the water immediately above the bottom.

Meanwhile, the depth is verified by echo-sounding and the biologist, using nets of very fine mesh, collects the minute organisms floating in the upper-most layers of water.

Next comes an oceanographic test arranged in a series. A strong metal wire is paid out, to which several—say ten—water-bottles with thermo-meters are attached at intervals. When it is hauled up again, the water can be analysed and its temperature read at each of the levels sampled. Since, generally speaking, the properties are slower to change with depth at deeper levels than nearer the surface, the spacing can be widened towards the lower end of the wire. If ten bottles should prove to be insufficient, two or more series can follow in succession, taking samples from progressively deeper layers. Fig. 8 illustrates how a vertical section through a deep-sea basin finally appears packed with data, while the close net of stations laid by the *Snellius* in the Molucca seas is clearly seen in Fig. 9.

The reader who is anxious to have technical details of the water-bottles and deep-sea thermometers should refer to the relevant literature. It must

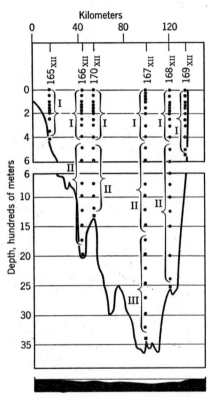

Fig. 8. Vertical section through the Flores Sea (exaggerated; correct proportions below), showing the points where the *Snellius* expedition determined the temperature and took samples of the water. (After van Riel, *Snellius Report*.)

suffice here to point out that the temperature, which varies from 0° to 30° C., can be measured to within 1/100°; the salinity, which is commonly in the neighbourhood of 3½ per cent, can be determined to within 2/1000 of one per cent, and the gas content, e.g. of oxygen, which varies from 0 to 4 c.c. per litre of sea-water, can be established down to ± 2/100 c.c. by a simple chemical titration.

In addition to the observations obtained at normal oceanographic stations, it is necessary to make direct measurements of current and to add constantly repeated series at fixed points. It is to supply this information that anchor stations are established. The vessel must be equipped with a cable several miles in length to enable her to lie at anchor in water of oceanic depth. By means of current meters, the direction and strength of the currents can then

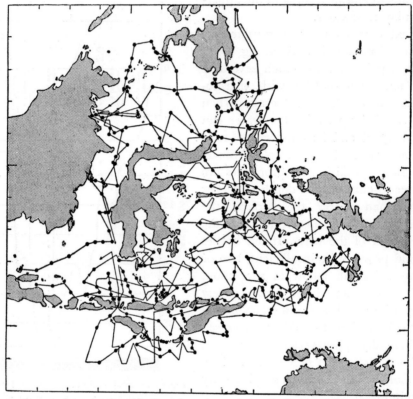

Fig. 9. Routes (greatly simplified) and stations of the *Snellius* expedition in Indonesian waters. (After van Riel, *Snellius Report.*)

be determined at any required level between the surface and the floor. These meters give readings which are accurate to within centimetres per second if sufficient time is allowed. As, however, the ship yaws at the anchor cable and does not, therefore, answer to the ideal of a fixed point of comparison, the results cannot be taken at their face value. The meter readings of currents flowing at less than a foot per second are liable to show figures significantly in excess of the true velocities.

Anchor stations are also utilised for the estimation of *internal wave move-*

PLATE I

The cycle of water is seen in one view. The sea, into which rain is falling from mirrored nimbus clouds; snow on the mountains; the Langjökull Glacier reaches the sea in a dark, sharply defined front. (*Photo Ehrhardt.*)

PLATE II

(a) The "Bore" ascending the River Severn in England. (*Photo Keystone.*)

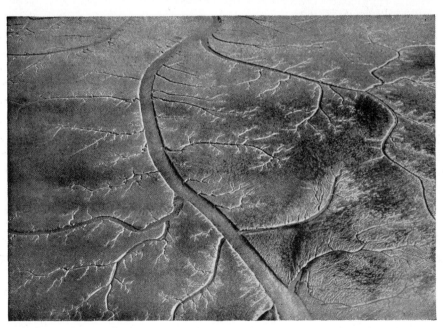

(b) Vascular pattern of channels in a tidal marsh, seen from the air. (*From Dircksen.*)

ments in the water. When serial observations of temperature and salt content are repeated at short intervals for twenty-four hours, there is found to be a wave-like displacement of the various layers of water, often with the same rhythm as that of the tidal movement. The amplitude may range from a few feet to hundreds of feet. These up-and-down movements of the particles of water are the result of internal waves, some of them of a tidal nature.

In shallow water, current meters have been suspended from a tripod placed on the bottom. This allows the currents to be measured with much greater accuracy, and it has been found that irregular flow of quite considerable velocities occurs in varying directions. This is ascribed to enormous slow eddies in the sea-water.

A new development in oceanographic research is the application of methods by which currents can be measured, temperatures taken at depth and bottom samples collected while the ship is under way. Like echo-sounding, the first mobile technique to be devised, these new methods save an immense amount of time. Instead of disclosing the average conditions during a long period, they present an almost instantaneous picture for a large area, or else a vastly more detailed picture. Oceanography appears to be breaking into a run!

Tides

Having touched on the tides, let us consider this fascinating subject somewhat more closely. Next to waves, the tides are the most striking movements of sea-water and affect shipping more, almost, than anything else. In the rhythmical ebb and flow of the tides on the beaches, it is predominantly the vertical movement which strikes the observer and aids or thwarts the youthful architects of sand castles. But we see something very different when we watch the sea on rocky shores broken up by bays, or at the mouths of rivers, the entrances to inland seas, etc., or if we pay a visit to a tidal mud flat. In such places the vertical movement of the water is transformed into tidal currents, which are liable to run at high speeds. On a flat shore, where the range of the tide is also considerable, the water may come rolling in with such terrifying speed that the unwary stroller has to run for dear life. One can imagine what such currents involve for shipping in seaports on tidal waters some distance from the coast. Apart from the direct impulse given to the ships, the dredging and silting action in the waterway and harbour basins very materially affects the conditions at these ports.

It had been noticed in very ancient times that the run of the tide stands in close relation with the phases of the moon. Up to a couple of centuries ago, predictions as to the level and time of the tide in harbours and estuaries had nothing more concrete to go upon than years of accumulated practical experience. Then the first tide gauges were installed, since when readings have been taken from them at regular intervals.

In 1870 there were still not more than a few dozen trustworthy tide gauges in constant operation. By 1900 the number had increased to over 200, and before World War II to well over 400.

At present, many stations use self-registering tide gauges. These provide an accurate, continuous record of water levels. Lightships lying off the coast use current meters and pressure gauges resting on the bottom, the latter registering the depth of the water, hence the level of the tide.

The reason why short-term observations do not suffice to show the tidal movements at the point in question is that wind and barometric pressure have considerable influence upon the water level; varying haphazardly, as they do, they obscure the picture of true tidal movement. This cannot be ascertained to within half an inch until the average for a series over some ten years has been found. Then, the level of the water can be predicted for any future moment (always subject to the intervention of the erratic factors mentioned) on the basis of the phase of the moon at the period in question.

The establishment of tidal movement is closely associated with that of mean sea-level. Devices for this purpose operate as follows. A large drum, open at the top, is connected by a small opening with the surrounding sea. The impulses of waves, and even of the tide, are too brief to cause any noticeable fluctuation of the water level in the drum. Nevertheless, the amount of water eventually accumulated in the drum can never be either more or less than that which is exactly in equilibrium with the mean level of the surrounding water. Readings need only be taken once a day. Fluctuations will then be found to occur due to the weather and the season. Thus, even if the averages at Marseilles diverge from month to month by more than a foot, the annual averages there vary by only a few centimetres. With this device, then, it takes many years to establish mean sea-level at the point of observation, but when it has ultimately been found, its accuracy is all the greater. By combining all the recorded observations scattered over the earth, it has been discovered that in the past half century the level of the sea has risen by two or three inches as the result of recession of the glaciers.

Alternatively, sea-level at widely separated points can be compared by levelling. It has thus been shown that the sea on the Pacific side of the Isthmus of Panama is 6 inches lower than on the Atlantic side. The level of the Mediterranean at Marseilles is 7 inches below that of the Atlantic at Brest.

The force which causes the tides is the gravitational attraction of the moon (and, in a lesser degree, of the sun), combined with a centrifugal force generated by the rotation of the earth around the common centre of gravity of the moon and earth. Right opposite the moon, this tidal force is directed vertically upwards towards it; on the other side of the earth, directly away from it, i.e. likewise upwards relative to the earth's surface. Everywhere between these two points the force is directed obliquely and therefore possesses a component in a horizontal sense.

When at its maximum the tidal force is only 1/9,000,000 of the gravitational force, and the weight of a heavy man standing directly under the moon is reduced only by the equivalent of one drop of sweat.

It is, for all that, the weaker horizontal component which pulls the seas to and fro and raises and depresses the tides. These forces produce a mountain of water opposite the moon and at the antipode and a depression encircling the earth in between. The whole of this system revolves slowly with the moon in a lunar month and, as the earth rotates far more rapidly around its own axis in the meantime, each point on its surface is carried past a tidal wave and tidal trough twice in every 24 hours.

As the moon does not stand in the plane of the equator, a point on the earth passes alternately closer to and farther from the tidal mountain every 12 hours. Consequently, the two tides per 24 hours are of unequal height and, if local conditions accentuate the difference, only a single wave may be noticeable in the 24 hours. Then there will be a high and a low tide only once a day instead of twice.

In addition to this daily inequality, there is also a fortnightly one which is due to the varying combination of lunar and solar tides, for the sun also exerts a tidal force. Although the sun is far larger, its influence is only half that of the moon by reason of its enormous distance from the earth. Now when the sun and moon are on a straight line running through the earth, i.e. at full and new moon, their tidal forces operate in conjunction, and amount to one and a half times that of the moon alone. At first and last quarter, the forces oppose each other and all that remains is half the force exerted by the moon. Hence, in the latter case—that is, at *neap* tide—the difference between high and low water will only be a fraction of the range at the *spring* tides of full and new moon.

Seeing that both the size and direction of the tidal forces are known with such precision, the level of the tide at every point of the earth could easily be calculated if the earth were surrounded by nothing but a deep ocean. As things are, however, the continents divide the seas into basins of capricious shapes and the depths vary to such an extent that the tidal waves encounter all sorts of obstructions in their course round the globe. This complicates the problem so enormously that it is debatable whether it can ever be fully solved.

Tides in Closed Basins

A closed basin is the simplest case. The vertical component is everywhere equal and therefore has no noticeable effect; the horizontal resolved force is likewise uniform in direction and magnitude and its action therefore uncomplicated.

The smaller the basin, the weaker the tides must be. A lake about eight miles in length will have tides of less than one millimetre, whereas the Black Sea produces just under 4 inches and the Mediterranean 12 inches. A disturbing complication may, however, arise which can, perhaps, best be

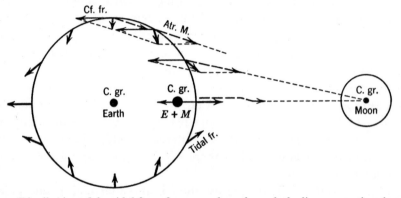

Fig. 10. Distribution of the tidal force for every plane through the line connecting the earth with the moon. The tidal force arises from the centrifugal force and the gravitational attraction of the moon.

illustrated by comparing the basin with a tub of water. The water in the basin may oscillate like water in a tub. Now, if the tub is tilted gently by one handle, the water will remain at rest, but if the tub is moved up and down with the same rhythm in which the water tends to oscillate, the amplitude will increase progressively until the water eventually starts to spill over. If the movement is further accelerated, the water will become nearly quiescent once more, apart from a few wavelets. Another fact which emerges is that the larger the tub, the slower is the rhythm with which the water swings to and fro.

In this comparison, our hand is the counterpart of the tidal force trying to generate a tidal wave in the lake. If the natural period of oscillation of the water in the basin is very short, the tidal force will be able to pull the water tranquilly in the required direction, in which case the measured and calculated tides will be identical. In our example, this corresponds to the gentle tilting of a small tub. But should the period of oscillation of the water approximately coincide with the period of the tidal force, i.e. reversing direction every six hours, then there will be greater amplitude than was calculated. This may be compared to the manual movement intensifying the rocking of the water in the tub in its own rhythm. The natural period, or rhythm, of a basin depends on its length as well as its depth. The longer and shallower it is, the slower its rhythm will be. This period for the Lake of Geneva, which is deep, is 74 minutes, whereas for that of the equally long, but vastly shallower, Lake Balaton or Platten-see in Hungary, it is roughly ten hours. The tidal force is in fact resonant in the latter and the tide actually generated is half an inch high, whereas it would be no more than one-twelfth of an inch if the only factor were the force itself. Lake Erie has a natural period of 14 hours, and 3-inch tides, whereas Lake Baikal, in Siberia, in spite of being twice as long, has a period of only 4½ hours, due to its far greater depth; there is no resonance whatever and the tide is less than one inch.

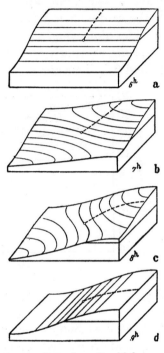

Fig. 11. Rotation of a tidal wave during successive hours in a non-oblong basin (Black Sea type). (After Thorade.)

Not only is the natural period of a basin accurately computable; it can also be observed. Besides the tidal forces, factors such as propulsion by the wind or varying barometric pressure may push the water in a lake aside, thus causing it to oscillate. These oscillations are quite capable of dominating the tide altogether, in which case they will exhibit the natural period of the basin. The amplitude in some lakes is liable to be very considerable, as dwellers on their shores know only too well. These apparent tides are known as *Seiches* in Lake Geneva, where the amplitude with a period of about one hour may be more than one metre—ten times quicker and hundreds of times higher than the tide there. If the tide is observed in a rounded basin, like the Black Sea, there is seen to be a revolving wave, running clockwise in the Northern Hemisphere (see Fig. 11).

When we turn to basins freely communicating with the oceans, we find that, in addition to their own tides, they are invaded by tidal waves rolling in from the open sea. A simple example is that of the Red Sea, because its communication with the Indian Ocean is provided by a single opening at the southern extremity. The rise and fall of the sea-level outside the Straits of Bab-el-Mandeb forces a wave through this portal and right through the Red Sea up to Suez, where it is thrown back to return southwards. These opposed series of waves combine to form what may be termed a "stationary wave". The combination with the tides of the basin itself produces for most harbours double to treble the amplitude which would ensue from the intrinsic tides alone (Fig. 12). But, between the coastal strips with vertical tides, there are areas where the movement consists mainly of horizontal currents to and fro. Thus the vertical run of the tide in the Gulf of Suez is nearly one

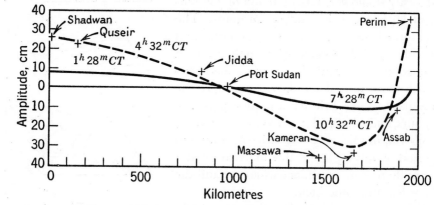

Fig. 12. Tidal range in the Red Sea. (After Thorade.)

foot, at Port Sudan the movement is purely horizontal, at Kamaran the amplitude registered is again one foot, but always in the reverse sense compared with Suez. At Assab there is again a horizontal water displacement and in the mouth at Perim the vertical amplitude is one foot and a half.

Among the more peculiar tidal phenomena may be counted the currents that run in the Euripos Channel, the narrows between the large island of that name and the mainland of Greece. As early an observer as Aristotle was struck by the erratic behaviour of the currents in this passage, only 130 feet long and wide, as he stood watching them at Chalkis (Fig. 13). For 22 days of the month, strong tidal currents run there normally twice a day. As the tides in the wide arms of the sea to the north and south of Chalkis are not of exactly the same height, the water is forced at the rate of 10 miles an hour through the narrow channel between them. During the other days of the month, however, near first and last quarter (i.e. during the neap tides), the currents behave in the most capricious manner. After flowing steadily in one direction for 12 hours in succession, they will suddenly change direction several times in an hour. Aristotle compared the movement of the sea to a swinging pair of scales, which, in essence, is the actual explanation. For oscillations of the "seiche" type occur in each of the arms individually and in its own rhythm. The swings of level are high enough to dominate the weak neap tide, raising the water higher now at one end of the channel, now at the other. Sometimes the wind dominates the seiches and drives the waters in one particular direction for a longer period. Many had cudgelled their brains to account for this strange behaviour before the correct answer was found in quite recent times.

Among other stretches of water notorious for their tides right down the ages is the Strait of Messina. Here the current may run at as much as six miles an hour, with streamers of foam and boiling eddies intensifying the dramatic effect. Threatening as the waters may appear, their menace to shipping is negligible and the poets of old had to avail themselves of their full quota of professional licence to raise the passage between Scylla and Charybdis to the status of an heroic achievement.

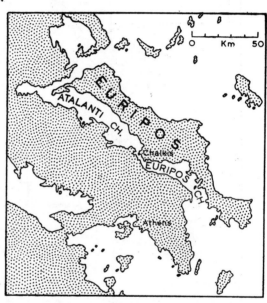

Fig. 13. Euripos Channel and neighbouring waters.

Tides of the North Sea, the Atlantic Ocean and Elsewhere

The tidal movement of the Red Sea can be fairly accurately calculated, but it is hardly feasible to work out the manifold mathematical details of an ocean-adjacent sea like the North Sea. Not only is the shape complicated and the depth small and variable, but oceanic tides can penetrate easily in two places. For all that, it has proved possible to explain the complicated phenomena, in broad outline at least.

With the help of countless current measurements and the data from the tide gauges along the shores, a general picture has been evolved (Fig. 14). A tidal wave, entering from the north, presses on southwards at great speed and with marked amplitudes down the British coast and at a far slower pace and with small range past Norway and Denmark. Whereas spring tide reaches 15 feet along the western shore, less than one foot is registered in southern Norway. The Wash shows a maximum with 23 feet amplitude. A couple of anti-clockwise eddying tides develop in the southern region, reinforced by the tidal wave coming from the Channel.

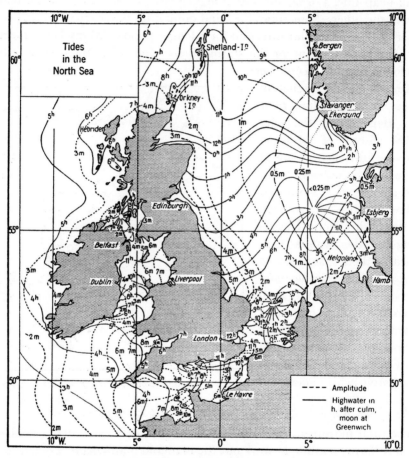

Fig. 14. Tides in the North Sea. (After Schott.)

It appears that this complicated picture is due in the main to the influence of the earth's rotation around its axis (Coriolis force) upon the tidal wave coming from the north, while in addition the basin is comparatively shallow and is rounded in shape.

The tidal current running up the Channel is forced to the right by this same Coriolis force, thus causing the high-water levels along the French coast to exceed those of southern England. Conversely, the ebb current is forced away from the French coast, causing the most pronounced low waters on that same side. The rotation of the earth is thus responsible for the moderate tides on the northern shores of the Channel contrasting so strangely with the excessively high tides on the opposite side.

The tides in the mouth of a river are totally different in character. There must be a gradual transition from the normal tide at the coast up to the tranquil uninterrupted current of the inland river. The farther up we sail, the shorter will be the duration of the inward-flowing tide and the longer the persistence of the outflow. The amplitude, moreover, decreases until first there is only a minor retardation of flow during the rising tide, without any reversal of direction and, finally, even this effect ceases and we arrive at the waters beyond the range of all tidal action.

In wide, funnel-shaped estuaries, an enormous volume of water swings to and fro. This scours a deep channel, which often provides a good fairway for some distance inland. At the same time, the incoming tide is forced through an increasingly narrow passage and must therefore increase in height. Fantastic amplitudes may result. The world's record is held by the Bay of Fundy on the east coast of North America, where the maximum difference between high and low water at spring tide is no less than 50 feet, and greater still if the wind happens to lend a hand.

Some river mouths are famous for a tidal wave which advances up the river like a foaming wall. This occurs on a small scale on the Severn, where it is called the "bore". A similar phenomenon was the "mascaret" at the mouth of the Seine, before shallow sandbanks there had been removed by dredging.

There is a bore on a gigantic scale in the Amazon and also in the Chiang Tang Kiang (the estuary on which stands Hangchow) in China, where, at flood tide, a raging mountain of foaming water some 20 feet high comes crashing up these wide waterways at a speed of over 12 miles an hour. The thundering roar can be distinctly heard a dozen miles away and it need hardly be said that small boats are battered and crushed like so much matchwood by this monstrous, mobile waterfall. It is the shoals at the mouths of these rivers, as well as the funnel shape, which cause the ordinarily harmless tidal wave to rise to such dangerous steepness. Owing to the great friction along the bottom, the lower part of the wave is held strongly in check and, as the water advances, the steepness of its front is thus maintained.

The tides in the oceans, on the other hand, are still very incompletely understood. We have only water gauges and current measurements along the borders to go upon, but in these shallow coastal waters the tidal waves are greatly distorted and therefore reveal little as to the state of affairs in deep water. It would not be correct to say that neither current measurements nor level readings can be taken in the open ocean, for not only can observations made on oceanic islands produce an almost undistorted picture, but measurements at anchor stations or with pressure meters on the ocean floor are, theoretically at least, feasible. Before a complete set of data has been obtained by this means, however, the moon will have swung round the earth a very considerable number of times. It can be safely postulated, however, that the range is not more than two or three feet.

The tidal movements in the Malay Archipelago are very singular indeed. Here the islands constitute formidable obstacles, involving highly complicated reflection of the waves and resonances in the separate basins with natural periods of oscillation. In many places, the water rises and falls once only in 24 hours, this being called a *diurnal tide*. Low-water is then apt to persist for a very long time, giving way briefly to a rapid rise and subsequent fall of high-water. The converse also occurs. Along some coasts the amplitude is very small, but along others it measures many feet. Strong currents are encountered in a number of straits, e.g. between the Lesser Sunda Islands. With the rapidity of a mountain stream, the water gushes through the strait between Taliabu and Mangole, to the east of Celebes. Here the current may run at as much as ten knots, against which smaller ships can hardly make headway.

No more eloquent example of the vagaries of the Indonesian tides could be found than that of the area in the vicinity of Surabaya. There are two outlets from the harbour along the island of Madura to the open sea, the Westgat towards the north and west, the Oostgat towards Bali, etc. In the Westgat there is an almost undeviating diurnal tide as far as the vertical movements are concerned, but the horizontal currents are semi-diurnal. In the Oostgat, however, both the vertical and horizontal movements are semi-diurnal. At Surabaya itself, the vertical movement is of a complicated type.

It was a remarkable feat when astronomers and hydrographers, each calculating the friction which is caused by the tides from laws and data appertaining to their individual disciplines, arrived at compatible results. Appealing to ancient observations of solar eclipses and other relevant facts, the astronomers were able to show that the rotation of the earth is not constant, but is subject to gradual retardation in addition to periodic variations. This means that the days are lengthening by degrees at a very slow rate, in fact by about one second in 120,000 years. From this length retardation of rotation of the earth about its axis, a value was derived for the consequent drag. This check must be the friction in sea-water during the tidal movements, when the rotatory energy is converted into heat. The figure found was $1 \cdot 39 \times 10^{19}$ erg/sec.

The hydrographers went to work along different lines. They computed the friction which tidal currents experience, especially in comparatively shallow seas, starting from the Irish Sea. It was not possible to include all the small arms of the sea, like the Norwegian fjords; nor could the influence of pack-ice be taken into account, though energy is undoubtedly dissipated there also. So when it transpired that the hydrographic calculation without these omissions produced a figure which was 80 per cent of that found by the astronomers, it was hardly an exaggeration to declare the results to be in perfect agreement.

Interaction between the Atmosphere and the Ocean

So strong is the influence of the oceans upon the atmosphere and vice versa, that they cannot be considered independently. In some respects the hydrosphere and the atmosphere react in the same way to the many identical influences which affect both. In others, their natures are so different that their reactions are totally dissimilar. They are alike in flowing from regions of higher pressure to areas of lower pressure on the same level and, in doing so, both undergo the deviating influence of earth's rotation. Both are heated by the sun's rays and cool down chiefly by radiation. A small portion of the atmospheric gases is dissolved in the oceans; a fraction of the water rises as vapour and mingles with the air. There are, on the other hand, quantitative and even qualitative differences. The atmosphere transmits solar radiation, but water does not; hence, this energy is captured, predominantly at the surface of the earth and sea, and is converted to heat, a fact more fully discussed in the next chapter. The result is that the atmosphere is heated from below upwards and is brought into labile equilibrium. Again and again, great volumes of air are heated and consequently expand and rise upwards, making room for cold air coming from elsewhere. Thus the stable stratification of the air, with the heaviest particles underneath, is constantly being undermined by solar energy and in this manner convection currents are formed. Nor should we leave out of account the varying degrees in which the air is heated at different latitudes, for it is upon these differences that the great atmospheric systems of circulation depend.

What happens to the oceans is the reverse. The water is heated from above and conduction is so slow that it is virtually a negligible factor. As a result, the stable stratification with the cold and heavy water below is accentuated by solar radiation, because the uppermost layer is rendered even warmer and lighter than before. The coefficient of expansion of water being much smaller than of air, the difference in density between arctic and tropical water is small. It cannot lead to noticeable exchange by flow at those enormous distances in the thin, top layer of the oceans. And only in this top layer are differences in density produced by the climates. Accordingly, the powerful circulation met with on the ocean surface is secondary, for, being initiated by the wind, it is an indirect consequence of atmospheric circulation. The different temperatures of water are manifested principally by the fact that the heavier water of the poles seeks lower levels, where it moves very slowly. The warmer water, on the contrary, travels along the surface and is sped along by air currents.

Here again, however, we encounter a difference between water and air, viz., the far greater thermal capacity of water. Water requires 3000 times the quantity of heat that air does to effect an equivalent rise of temperature.

As the warm tropical water tends to float on top, warm water is constantly being driven by the wind to colder regions, whereas movements in a contrary sense are rare. Hence, the sea is constantly carrying huge masses of tepid water to the polar regions. Thanks to the large amount of stored-up heat in that water, the climate, i.e. the surrounding air, becomes much warmer. Actually, the total *amount* of heat carried to the Poles by the atmosphere is very much larger than that brought by the water; but, owing to the quicker cooling of the air and the variability of its movements, local influences are far less noticeable. A warm sea current is able, during an entire winter, to maintain the temperature of the air within a wide radius many degrees above the average for that particular latitude. As we shall see presently, the best-known example is the North Atlantic Current, which in January keeps the temperature in Britain 15°, and in Norway as much as 20° to 25° above what it would otherwise be.

For further details on such phenomena, the reader should consult an atlas including maps showing marine currents, wind systems, air temperatures and pressures, water temperatures, barometric pressures, and salt contents in their regional distribution. As to the oceans, Schott's brilliant standard works provide lucid descriptions of these geographical aspects of oceanography and meteorology. The main thing for us is to understand the principle of these phenomena, as illustrated by an example.

As far as the interplay between air and sea-water is concerned, there is no more impressive system on the whole globe than that presented by the "Gulf Stream" and the atmosphere in its vicinity. It also shows how a system of constant winds keeps the ocean currents in motion.

These trade winds (the cause of which will be studied in Chapter II) are the most persistent winds on earth, blowing all the year round from the

N.E. in the Northern Hemisphere and from the S.E. in the Southern Hemisphere. By them the surface water on both sides of the Equator is driven westwards in two mighty equatorial drift-currents, a southern and northern branch (Fig. 15). Water is driven from the African to the South American side, is replaced by that from north and south, and from the depths; it is, above all, this deep water which accounts for the low temperature of the coastal waters around that part of Africa.

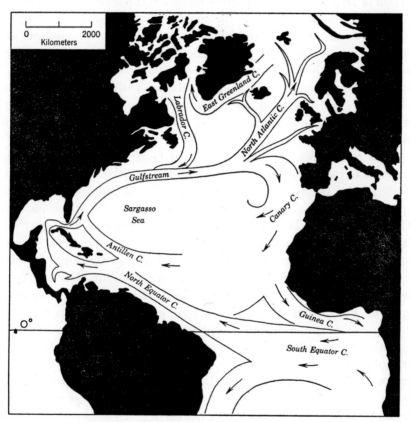

Fig. 15. Currents in the Atlantic Ocean during Winter.

As the north coast of South America crosses the Equator obliquely, it intercepts almost the whole mass of water, which it guides towards the north-west, to the West Indies. Here there is a bifurcation, one branch—partly fed by other currents—flowing along the north-east coast of the Antilles until it reaches Florida, while the bulk enters the Caribbean Sea, debouching thence via the Gulf of Mexico into the Atlantic Ocean again. At Florida the two branches reunite to form the Gulf Stream, which now flows in a north-easterly direction along the coast of the United States.

Farther north, the Gulf Stream sheers off from the coast to the south of Newfoundland and cuts right across the Atlantic Ocean, largely as the result of the incursion of the cold Labrador Current from the north, which pushes the warm Gulf Stream water aside. It is at this juncture that the predominating westerly winds take an active part in driving the warm water in the direction of Ireland. While a portion wheels to the south, washing the western shores of Southern Europe, the main bulk proceeds on its course and strikes the coasts of Scotland and Norway. Finally, this mighty current divides again and dies out in the Arctic Ocean near Iceland, Jan Mayen, Spitsbergen and Nova Zemlya. Non-professionals use the term "Gulf Stream", an easy one by which they embrace a whole system of coherent sea currents, even when they are referring to these extreme tentacles in the north; but in nautical circles it is called the "North Atlantic Current" from Newfoundland onwards.

It has already been pointed out that the Gulf Stream radically changes the climate of north-western Europe. This fact may be better realised when we consider that the Swedish harvest, for instance, is said to depend upon the temperature of the Gulf Stream during the preceding winter; and the rainfall in Great Britain has been related to the temperature of the water in the vicinity of Newfoundland in the previous year. On this basis, long-term weather forecasts can sometimes be made for north-west Europe. It will also be evident that the thermal economy of the North Atlantic Ocean is entirely subservient to this current system if we look at its far-flung branches and tongues on our current chart. For a full appreciation of this tremendous natural phenomenon, however, it is necessary to include in the total picture the depth down to which the moving current reaches so as to find the discharge of water.

In the straits to the south of Florida, its measured speed at a depth of 800 feet was found to be as much as $2\frac{1}{2}$ miles per hour, while speeds of nearly 6 miles an hour have been recorded at the surface. In the open sea, the flow reaches to a depth of about 3000 feet. The significance of these figures is brought out by comparison with other ocean currents. Whereas the Gulf Stream at Florida owes its origin to a difference in level of the surface of the sea—a pressure gradient—almost all other currents on the surface are the result of drag exerted by the wind. They therefore reach no deeper than about 300 feet and consequently have a far smaller discharge than the Gulf Stream. The main branch of the latter carries water from the Gulf of Mexico into the Atlantic Ocean about a thousand times as fast as the Mississippi pours it in. It has thus some 25 times the joint drainage of all rivers on earth, transporting to the ocean one and a half million tons of salt per second, a rate which would fill all the cargo vessels in the world in less than half a minute.

At its maximum, off the coast of New England, the Gulf Stream has more than double this discharge. There is only one other current of equal power in the ocean and that is the Antarctic Circumpolar Current, which sweeps round and round the far south of the world.

Wind and Tides in Relation to the Enclosure of the Zuider Zee

The damming of the Zuider Zee in the Netherlands raised problems of universal interest in connection with wind-driven surge and tides. When the plans began to mature, the opinion was voiced that the dam would greatly increase the heights to which the water might rise in gales, necessitating an increase in the height of the dykes. When, therefore, in 1918, it was finally decided to build the dam, a committee was appointed to report on this possibility and it set to work under the inspiring chairmanship of the great physicist H. A. Lorentz. At the end of eight years, the result was set down in a report unique of its kind. It deals with the tides and storm-driven surges under the original conditions, and with the modifications expected to be caused by the dam. Of no other large area in the world has the complicated behaviour of the tide been studied with such meticulous care. The velocity and direction of the current in every channel have been calculated for every hour of the day. There is a record of the water level in the whole area for every moment. Fig. 16 shows the precision with which all the phenomena at a given time can be indicated. One hour before the moment to which the chart refers, the water in the whole region of the Wadden Sea (as this water between Friesland and North Holland is termed) was still falling, and the tidal wave coming from the south in the North Sea had approached the second island. But, although, on the chart, the water is already rising some distance inside the islands and the tidal wave is rapidly travelling inwards, it will be seen that the water in half the area, including even the tidal inlets, is still moving outwards. This is due to inertia: the ebbing waters, rising as they go, continue to flow for some distance against the pressure gradient, for it takes time to reverse the flow of their great mass.

It is easy to see that the obstruction formed by the dam must impart greater amplitude to the tide, because the water can no longer escape to the inland sea. But it is not so obvious why the strength of the current in the inlets should also increase. It would be reasonable to expect the water displacement at the entrances to the Shallows to decrease now that the basin of the Zuider Zee no longer participates in the absorption of the inflowing and outflowing tidal water; yet it was predicted with absolute confidence on the basis of the computations that, owing to the presence of the dam, the incoming and outgoing currents would increase in strength, by as much as one-third in the southernmost inlet, and by one-fifth in the next one. This is due to the existence of two waves, one entering and the other reflected

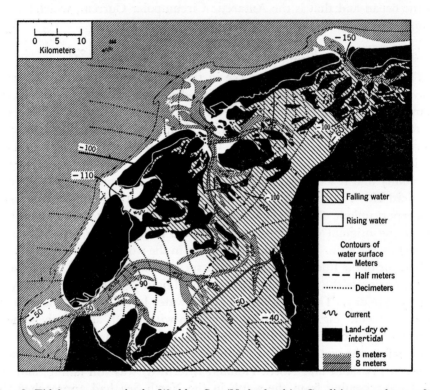

Fig. 16. Tidal movements in the Wadden Sea (Netherlands). Conditions two hours after the moon's transit of the meridian, on 31st May, 1919, at 4 p.m. as calculated by the Lorentz Committee.

from the shores. These two interfere with each other but, owing to the dimensions of the undammed Zuider Zee, the opposed waves cancelled each other out more completely than they do now. With the dam, the reflected wave returns to the inlets of the sea sooner than it did under the previous conditions.

Storm levels after the closure cannot be ascertained by the mere addition of the tide to the influence of the wind. If wind raises the water to a higher level, the tidal wave meets less resistance in the deepened water than norm-

PLATE III

(*a*) Storm swell beating on the rocky coast near Tenby, South Wales.

(*b*) Storm swell eroding dunes near Tenby.

PLATE IV

(a) White surf-bands show how the wave-forms are modified by the shape of the bay. Manorbier, South Wales.

(b) An eroded plateau which has risen is once more eaten into by the sea so that a new plane of erosion is formed 75 metres lower. Tenby.

ally. As a result, the amplitude of the tide increases, but at the same time the propagation of the wave is accelerated, which means that at every point high-water will be advanced in time to some degree. Allowance has to be made also for the influence (Coriolis force) of the earth's rotation, which tends to deflect a current towards the right in the Northern Hemisphere. One result is that the surface of the current in the sea inlets stands aslant, e.g. 4 inches in the Vlie, the second from the south.

The calculations showed that the vertical movement of the tide would increase by 60 per cent at the eastern end of the dam, viz., from 42 to 66 inches. The increase in height of strong spring tides (which was the main point at issue, since the height for the dyke depended upon this) was forecast as 14 inches at the eastern and 18 inches at the western end.

We now come to the influence of storms. This cannot be as reliably predicted as that of the tidal forces, because storms vary so much in character and chance also comes into the picture, whereas tides are governed by immutable laws, complicated though these be. For this reason, all the notorious gales of the preceding century were analysed in detail. The duration, strength and direction of the wind in each storm were noted and a schedule was made of the tides on those dates. All available records relating to the height to which the water had risen in storms around the Zuider Zee, the Wadden Zee and the North Sea were assembled and sifted and recorded on a chart. In the south-eastern part of the Zuider Zee the water sometimes rose above 10 feet, in the south of the Wadden Zee, 8 feet, and on the northern coast of Friesland as much as 13 feet. And to this must be added the surge of the waves.

The result of this study showed that the gales of 1825, 1877 and 1894 were the most dangerous for the area outside the enclosing dam of the Zuider Zee and for these a computation was made of how the currents must have run as the result of the action of the wind. The next task was to derive by calculation the height which the water would have reached in these storms if the Zuider Zee had been closed in, taking into account both wind-driven surge and tidal forces.

Finally, the committee set itself the question whether there was reason to fear in the future a conjunction of meteorological conditions more dangerous than those which occurred on those occasions in the preceding century. The distinguishing feature of the gale of 1877 had been the hurricane force of the wind, though the water levels in the North Sea had not been exceptionally high. In 1894, on the other hand, the wind had gradually raised the water level in the North Sea beforehand, with the result that far more water had already entered the inlets. The question now to be answered was

D

whether a hurricane like that of 1877 could occur following upon great piling up of the waters of the North Sea, thus causing even higher water levels on the Frisian coast and along the enclosing dam of the Zuider Zee. Fortunately it transpires that the possibility of such a conjunction can be completely ruled out.

The 1825 gale brought to most places water levels of a height never since exceeded, the reason being its duration, from 3rd to 5th February, in conjunction with a very high spring tide. The enclosing dam would not have altered the picture so much in this storm as in the 1894 gale. If a wind blows

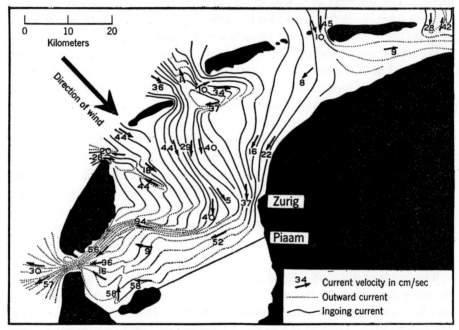

Fig. 17. How the currents in the Wadden Sea would have run in the gale of 22nd–23rd December, 1894, at 3 a.m., if there had been an enclosing dam at that time.

long enough, the resultant raising of the water level reaches a certain maximum, because owing to the gradient of the surface a compensatory reflux is generated. The condition is then stationary, and through any vertical section the amount of water moving forward above is the same as that retreating below. At that stage a partition could be let down through any section without affecting the water levels on either side of it. In a gale of *short* duration, a strong current was constantly sweeping through towards the Zuider Zee and if a partition could have been put down suddenly at the site of the present Zuider Zee dyke, the result must have been a piling-up of water on the seaward side. But in 1825, and particularly in the four-day gale of 1895, conditions came very close to the stationary state, with the highest possible levels for the prevailing force of the wind. So that if a partition in the form of the projected dam had been set up then, there would have been only a moderate rise, if any, against it.

The gale of 1894 was marked by exceptionally high levels of the North Sea, before the gale began, and a very strong current running towards the Zuider Zee. Hence an enclosing dam would have caused considerable rise of water level in the southern basin of the Wadden Sea. This, in fact, appears to have been the most dangerous of all the storms of the last century in its implications for the dyke. The Committee felt justified in assuming that it represented the maximum threat, so it was most carefully studied. Two small charts included in the report show the currents as they must have run during the gale, and as they would have run if the dam had already existed. The difference is very marked; and one of the striking facts is that in 1894 the water came swirling in through all the inlets, whereas now (see Fig. 17), under the same circumstances, a powerful outgoing current would pass through the most southerly entrance. The many details provided by these charts bear witness to the astonishing precision with which the Committee succeeded in treating its problems; subsequent observation has shown how accurate the results were.

These wind-driven currents are also affected by the earth's rotation around its axis. For the current entering the Zuider Zee basin, the surface along the Frisian coast was depressed and that on the western side raised. The dyke obstructs this current and abolishes the difference, so allowance has to be made for levels on the Frisian coast 8 inches higher than before.

The analyses of past storms revealed another remarkable fact, viz., that during the gale of 1863 the force of the wind towards the eastern side of the Zuider Zee basin was so great that a large area of the sea bed on the opposite North Holland side must have stood bare.

After prolonged calculations and study, the Committee drew up a chart of its predictions, which Fig. 18 reproduces in simplified form. An extra foot or two had to be added to these figures when designing the dam, because the deeper water produces higher waves and, therefore, greater surge against it.

In the twenty years of the dam's existence the predictions of the Lorentz Committee have been borne out in a truly remarkable degree. Here are a few examples. The tidal range at Den Oever increased from 85 cm. to 153 cm., while the prediction was 155 cm. The figures for Harlingen are: from 127 cm. to 174 cm., the predicted figure being 168 cm. More eloquent testimony to the Committee's achievement could scarcely be found.

Turbidity Currents

There is an entirely different type of current, called turbidity current, to which we shall also have to give our attention. It was not until quite recently that scientists began to realise that these may have played an important part in the modelling of the sea floor. They arise when sediment is locally churned up, raising the density of the water to higher values than that of the surrounding clear water. Under the influence of gravity, the heavy water will flow down any available slope and spread out on a horizontal floor.

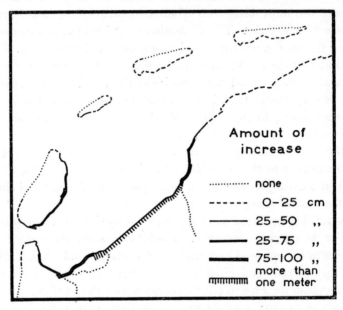

Fig. 18. Increased high-tide levels to be expected in gales along the coasts outside the Enclosing Dam of the Zuider Zee as estimated by the Lorentz Committee.

Turbulence due to the flow will tend to keep the sediment in suspension until the flow comes to a standstill. Either the churning effect of storm waves or a slide of mud on a steep submarine slope may trigger off a turbidity current. Once well started, the current may begin to erode the bottom and it will gradually increase in size on its way down the slope.

It is not surprising that, although turbidity currents can be easily generated in a pond or aquarium, natural ones have never been observed. But a huge turbidity current charging down the continental slope, faster than the swiftest rivers on land, appears to have caused the snapping of submarine telegraph cables after an earthquake in the Atlantic. There is also much indirect evidence of their activity. Thus many mysterious coarse sands found in the oceans, right out on the deep-sea floor, are evidently the deposits of turbidity currents, because no other force could have carried the materials out there from the coast. These sands are characterised by a special structure called "graded bedding", in which the grain size varies regularly from coarse at the base to fine at the top. Experimental turbidity currents also form this typical kind of bedding. The currents appear to have been rare phenomena, occurring once in a few hundred or even thousand years at a given locality. Yet their significance in transport and deposition in deep water is greater than that of any other mechanism. In a later chapter, they will be invoked in an attempt to explain the origin of submarine canyons.

Waves

The formation of waves is yet another result of the interplay between the atmosphere and the sea. We are so accustomed to the sight of a gentle breeze ruffling the face of the waters and of a storm wind whipping up foaming crests, that we never pause to enquire why the air should not prefer to skim over a smooth surface, and contrary to what it actually does, suppress already existing waves. In fact, it is not an easy question to answer.

Let us first examine the motion taking place in a wave in deep water. Each particle revolves in a vertical circle. Starting at the top, as the wave crest passes it moves forward, reaching the bottom of the circle as the wave trough arrives, thence back up to the top in the next wave crest (Fig. 22). The size of these circles decreases downwards. At depths equal to the distance from crest to crest, the motion is already imperceptible.

When a vertical column of water is considered, it is found to undergo curious distortions and to sway back and forth like corn in the wind. At the moment when a crest passes, the column is tall and thin; it then inclines in the direction of propagation and returns to the vertical as the trough reaches the spot. At that moment the column is at its shortest and thickest, after which it stretches, bending in the opposite direction (Fig. 22).

It follows from the above that the wave *shape* is propagated, but that the water merely circles up and down. Actually, there is a *slight* forward movement; and it is this which enables a ball to be retrieved from a pond by throwing stones into the water beyond it, when the waves will gradually propel it back to the bank.

There appear to be three more or less distinct actions involved in the creation of waves by wind. In the first place, frictional drag causes the water to move along with the wind; and, as we have seen, this forward movement is part of the wave motion. In the second place, the air moving over a crest is accelerated and rarefied and at the same time sucks the wave up; in the

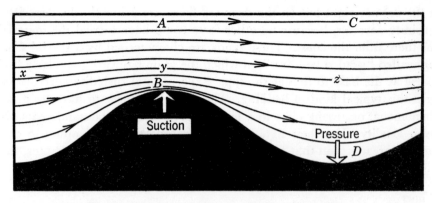

Fig. 19. Forces exerted by air current on wave form.

trough it is slowed down and compressed, thus forcing the water down (Fig. 19). Finally, the wind tends to form an eddy behind the crest of the wave (Fig. 20). This results in a downward push of the wind against the rear of the wave, like the action of a cyclist's pedal, speeding up the particles in their circular motion.

The size of the waves increases with the force of the wind. By size is meant the height (vertical distance from trough to crest) and length (horizontal distance between successive crests); we may leave out of account its extent measured along its crest. But the bigger the waves are, the faster do they travel onward. Contrary to what might be expected, wind can generate waves which travel somewhat faster than the moving air itself. This is because the wind, being faster than the circular motion, can accelerate it, in spite of the fact that the wave *shape* outruns the particles of air. When, however, the velocity of the wave has grown to nearly one and a half times that of the wind, it can increase no further and at that juncture the wave has likewise reached its maximum size in that particular wind.

It is not only the velocity of the wind which governs the size of waves, but also the length of time it acts upon them. The transfer of energy from wind

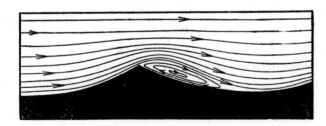

Fig. 20. Formation of a counter-eddy in the air behind a pointed wave.

to wave is a slow process and in a storm it takes many hours for the maximum size to be attained. To attain this, waves require enough space to run before the wind the whole of that time. In other words, the "length of fetch", i.e. the up-wind distance to the coast, is an important factor. On a pond or lake, the growth of the waves at increasing distance from the lee shore is obvious. The very largest storm waves require lengths of fetch of a thousand miles or so.

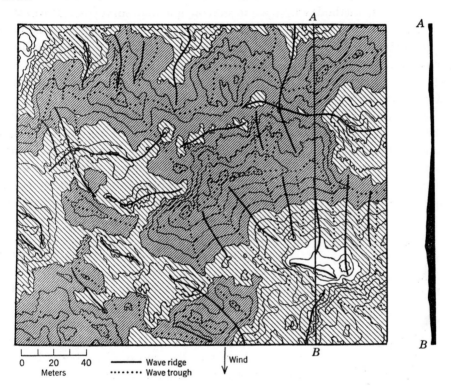

Fig. 21. Complicated wave pattern with two predominant directions, one perpendicular to the prevailing wind. (Based on Schumacher.)

Fascinating as storm waves may be to the poet or artist, the naval architect, the film producer or the scientific observer, even the confirmed land-lubber is not without a certain curiosity as to the potential size of such awesome mountains of water. The average height does not appear to exceed 30 to 40 feet, but individual waves may attain 70 to 80 feet. To estimate, when aboard ship, the height of the waves, one should climb the rigging up to where the crests can just be seen on the horizon when the ship is in the trough of a wave. The highest wave on record was observed in the North Pacific;

its carefully estimated height was 110 feet, the equivalent of a ten-storeyed building. These colossal giants are only encountered during prolonged gales of hurricane force in the wide ocean. They speed along at 50 miles an hour and outrun the fastest steamers afloat.

A far more accurate picture of the sizes and shapes of waves can be obtained by making stereoscopic exposures with telephoto cameras fixed to the mast. At home a contoured map can be constructed from these photographs by the methods employed in stereoscopic map surveying. It will then be realised how erratic are the undulations of the sea. It requires the most careful scrutiny to make out the crest or trough of a wave in the jumble of irregular, crenellated contours and there is little if any visual evidence of a clear system of alternating parallel crests and troughs (Fig. 21). The highest wave so far photographed measured 50 feet.

The energy in a wave increases both with its height and its length, but the internal friction increases with steepness. Hence a long, low wave containing the same amount of energy as a short, high one, will travel much farther before dying out. Thus, of all waves generated in a storm, the short, steep ones must, with distance, be progressively engulfed by the less conspicuous but more persistent long waves which, travelling at high speeds over the widest expanses of ocean, are so often witness to some far-off storm.

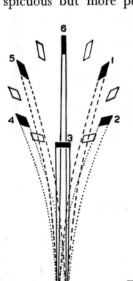

The latter type of wave is not maintained by the wind; it is called "a swell" (Fig. 23). Waves built up, or at least maintained, by the wind are called "wind waves". They have more pointed crests and carry "white horses" as soon as the wind exceeds some 20 feet per second. The greatest length of wind waves is about 1000 feet, but swell has been observed with two or three times that length.

Breakers

Waves which are being raised by the wind cannot attain more than a given degree of steepness, i.e. when their height approximates to one-tenth

Fig. 22. Changes in the shape of a column of water as a wave passes. Deep water; each interval 1/6 (1/12) of the wave period. At moment 0 (=6), just when the wave-crest is passing, a column of water has the shape shown; one-sixth of the wave period later, shape 1, etc. The trough of the wave is passing at moment 3. The internal transformations are also clearly indicated by the successive blocks.

Fig. 23. In a calm on the equatorial ground-swell. After a photograph taken from the lifeboat. (Count von Larisch.)

of their length. As the gradient of the flanks steepens, the shape changes and the top of the waves becomes progressively narrower and tapering, while the trough (Fig. 25; Plate III, 1) becomes ever broader and flatter. If the water piles up higher and more steeply still, the wave "breaks" at the crest and foaming "white horses" are hurled forward into the trough. As the tips may be whipped off by the wind, it looks as though the white caps are torn from the wave by wind pressure, but actually the internal circular movements of the particles of water constitute the principal cause.

Surf on the beach is a somewhat similar phenomenon. When a wave reaches shallower water, free circular movement of the particles begins to be impeded by the sea floor. The particles right at the bottom can no longer revolve in circles, but are restricted to a to-and-fro movement, while the contiguous particles above them follow an elliptical path (Fig. 20). It is not so much friction along the bottom as restriction of free motion

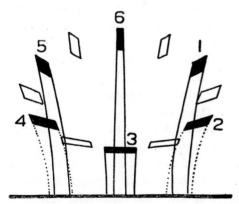

Fig. 24. Changes in the shape of a column of water as a wave passes. Shallow water; each interval 1/6 (1/12) of the wave period (see legend of Fig. 22).

that influences the wave approaching shallow water. This factor becomes noticeable when the depth is half the wave length. Hence a long wave begins to "feel bottom" before a short one.

The nearer the wave comes to the shore and the shallower the water becomes, so much the greater is the restriction of movement and the retardation of the propagation of the wave. As a result, however, the crests of successive waves are packed closer together, as would the lines of a marching column if those in the van slowed down. This shortens the waves and they therefore become steeper while, concomitantly, their height increases, sometimes to more than double what it was far off-shore. Moreover, the crest begins to catch up with the preceding trough, thus rendering the front steeper and finally even concave. This soon culminates in a bodily forward plunge of the crest in an elegant curl (Fig. 25). Usually waves break before the wave height equals the average depth of water.

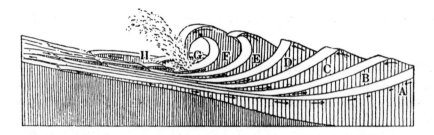

Fig. 25. Diagram of the development of a plunging breaker. (After Davis.)

The ideal "plunging breaker" just described, which discharges its energy in a sudden rush, is formed from swell on an even, smooth beach. Wind waves tend to form "spilling breakers", which run in with a foaming crest spilling down the front of the wave and dissipating the energy over a wide zone along the beach. Most sandy beaches are fronted by off-shore sandbars, on which breakers tend to form, the waves then continuing to the next bar or, as the case may be, the beach. Here, the character of the waves is radically altered after breaking. The water advances in a steep, foaming front some little distance up the beach as "swash". Instead of revolving in a closed circuit, the water particles have shifted towards the beach and in the process have expended their energy. Some now trickle through the beach sand, thus eventually returning to the sea, while the remainder run down the slope back to the sea, not as a wave movement, but as "back-wash" (Plate III, 2).

As a rule, breakers face the shoreline squarely, even if the wind is blowing

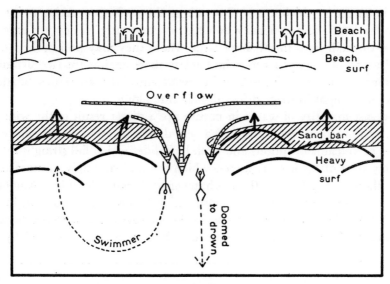

Fig. 26. Breakers with concomitant currents on a sandy seashore with sand-bars.

obliquely. One end of a wave approaching the shoreline at an angle will reach shallow water before the other end, and its progress will therefore be retarded. The wave front will tend to swing round, for the deep-water end will continue to advance faster as long as the wave is not parallel to the shore.

A glance at Fig. 27 will make it clear that an island or tongue of land causes the wave fronts to close in, whereas they fan out in a bay.

The transport of water by waves and swash raises the level against the coast. This piled-up water finds its way back in two kinds of current, viz., the undertow, which is a slow general current sweeping along the bottom,

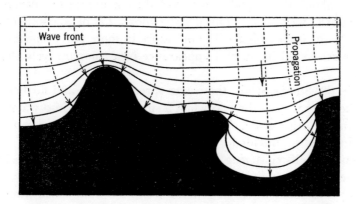

Fig. 27. Distortion of wave crests around a cape and in a bay.

and rip currents, which are outflows along the surface occurring at intervals along the beach and generally flowing intermittently. They are especially vicious through gaps in off-shore bars, where they may pull bathers out to sea. Instead of attempting to swim back to shore against the rip current, the swimmer should allow himself to be swept out and then return beside the rip, where a slight in-shore drift will help him along.

The vast majority of waves in nature are a direct result of the wind, but the largest of all owe their origin to a very different cause. Submarine earthquakes or volcanic eruptions and even landslides which fall straight into the sea may start off enormous waves, which are unfortunately misnamed *tidal waves*, though they have nothing whatever to do with the tides. Among the more notorious tidal waves are those which followed the eruption in 1883 on the volcanic island of Krakatoa, in the narrow straits between Java and Sumatra, while the shores of Japan have been repeatedly ravaged by tidal

Fig. 28. The scar of a land-slip on the south coast of Buton, near Celebes, which must have caused a tidal wave in prehistoric times.

waves initiated by earthquakes. The Krakatoa waves were 100 feet high when they swept up the adjacent coasts, penetrating many miles inland across the flat coastal region, dragging ships with them and tearing off huge masses of rock from the coral reefs and casting them up on the beach. When played out, these flood-waters flowed back into the sea, carrying every movable object with them. This disaster took a toll of 30,000 lives and it is due only to the incredible fertility of nature in those parts that the ravaged landscape recovered its normal appearance in a comparatively short space of time.

Outside the Sunda Strait, the waves spread farther and farther over the ocean, the same way as they do when a stone is thrown into water, only on an immensely larger scale. They soon became too long and too flat to be seen plainly by the unaided eye, but subsequently the traces of the waves were found on self-registering tide-gauges. It transpired that the Krakatoa tidal waves had passed right round the globe.

Having considered waves in general, let us see what storm waves can do when they batter the coast. When a fairly large wave comes up against a steep incline or perpendicular object, like a quay-wall or a bluff, much of the live force is concentrated in a portion of the summit of the wave and a curtain of water is sometimes flung vertically upwards to enormous heights, e.g. up to 120 feet against the quay-wall at Cherbourg in a severe storm. As it comes thundering down, this mass of water, possibly carrying boulders it has swept up with it, possesses terrific destructive force.

During a gale in 1860, a bell weighing 300 lb. was wrenched off its support 100 feet above sea-level in the Bishop Rock lighthouse and a door at 195 feet was broken open at Unst in the Shetland Islands. During a storm in 1902, great masses of water were flung more than 200 feet above the level of the sea at Tillamook Rock lighthouse, on the coast of Oregon. Eight years previously, a block of stone weighing 135 lb. was hurled in a gale through the roof of the lightkeeper's house, well over 100 feet above sea-level.

The stupendous force of storm waves was dramatically illustrated during the tempest of 1877, when a solid mass of concrete weighing 2600 tons was ripped from the breakwater at Wick, in the north of Scotland, and tumbled into the harbour entrance.

Mention should be made, in conclusion, of a peculiar type of wave which, though invisible, betrays its presence in another way under certain circumstances. Seamen call, or used to call, this "dead water". If a slowly moving ship, say a sailing vessel, entered the mouths of certain rivers or fjords, she was liable to encounter such strong resistance that she was scarcely able to make any headway. A slightly faster ship would experience none of this. As it turns out, this riddle is fairly easily solved. A thin layer of fresh water is then resting on the salty sea water and at the interface a ship can stir up strong internal waves which are invisible at the surface. A great deal of energy is absorbed, with the result that the progress of the ship is retarded. But a vessel moving faster than the speed of propagation of those waves cannot disturb the interface. A speed of about 4 miles an hour is sufficient for a vessel to pass unimpeded on her way.

Evaporation, Precipitation and Gas Exchange

Atmosphere and hydrosphere also interact by evaporation and precipitation, and by absorption and emission of gases by water. But here the effects are not confined to the immediate surroundings of the interface. As we shall consider the atmosphere, the next phase in the cycle, in the following chapter, we shall here treat these phenomena only in so far as they affect the sea.

Evaporation increases with the temperature, the wind and the dryness of the air. At the Poles the cold limits it; inside the Tropics the humidity, and on the Equator the calms as well. The greatest evaporation takes place from seas surrounded by deserts, or at any rate hot, dry regions. There is consider-able evaporation from the Mediterranean, but less than from the Red Sea, the desert sea *par excellence*.

Precipitation will have our full attention in the next chapter. All that need be pointed out here is the evident fact that it is bound to be pronounced in humid regions; nor will it require much perspicacity to understand why rain will seldom fall in a sea surrounded by desert lands. Hence, wherever evaporation is strongly marked, there will be little compensating precipita-tion. So far as the Mediterranean is concerned, it should moreover be borne in mind that few important rivers, bringing fresh water from afar, empty into it. In this respect the Red Sea is in an even worse position, for it receives virtually no fresh water at all.

The ratio of the various salts dissolved in the sea is always constant. On an average, 1 kilogram of sea-water contains 35 grams of dissolved solids. Little as this may appear, so enormous is the volume of water in the oceans of the world that, if all the salt dissolved in it were collected and spread upon the continents, they would be covered with a layer 500 feet thick.

In all basins where evaporation exceeds precipitation, the loss of water will cause an increase in salinity. If the basin is shut off, the process may proceed to the point where salts are precipitated: first gypsum, then rock-salt and finally the potassium and magnesium salts. This often happened in the geological past and explains the origin of the salt deposits now found in the earth. Notwithstanding their solubility, they were preserved down the ages by the deposition of impermeable clay on top, followed later by many other sediments.

The outcome is very different if there exists an open communication between the evaporating basin and the wide ocean. Before conditions in, e.g., the Mediterranean, can be understood, however, some of the physical properties of sea-water will have to be considered. The specific gravity of sea-water depends upon two factors, salinity and temperature. The colder the water, the heavier it is. This applies to fresh water only down to 4° C., below which temperature it again begins to expand and, therefore, becomes lighter. There is no such limit for sea-water, the specific gravity of which steadily increases down to below 0° C.

Together with the salt content, the weight per litre increases steadily to saturation point, ruling out any further accumulation of salt. The percentage of dissolved gases contained in water has no noticeable influence upon its specific gravity, though their solubility does to some extent depend upon the salinity and particularly upon the temperature of the water. It may be assumed roughly that, at the surface, sea-water is in equilibrium with the atmosphere. Consequently, the maximum amount of atmospheric gases is dissolved which can be contained in it under the prevailing conditions.

We need not concern ourselves with nitrogen, because there can be neither consumption nor supply of this gas at depth. But oxygen and carbon dioxide behave in quite a different manner. The former is consumed by marine fauna and in the process of decay. The longer a mass of water is cut off from atmospheric supply, the lower will the oxygen content become. Conversely, therefore, the time taken by a certain mass of water to travel from the surface to its present position can be deduced from this same oxygen content. In point of fact, the total amount of this gas dissolved in all the oceans is negligible compared to that concentrated in the atmosphere.

In most respects, carbon dioxide is the antipode of oxygen. Animal organisms *produce* this gas, whereas plants *consume* it. It is, moreover, highly soluble and its total content in oceanic waters is sixty times that of all the carbon dioxide in the atmosphere. The output of carbon dioxide in the past fifty years by human combustion of coal and crude oil represents something like 10 per cent of what is in the atmosphere and there is some basis for fearing that this increase might tend to assume objectionable proportions. However, 98 per cent of this increment is re-absorbed by sea-water and the ultimate increased proportion in the atmosphere is still, therefore, not worth speaking of.

Circulation in Basins

As labile equilibrium in a mass of water is not lasting, any water of which the density at the surface has increased through cooling or evaporation must sink and change places with warmer water or less saline water from elsewhere. In the simplest case, convection occurs and deep water in a basin takes the place of the descending surface water by direct exchange, as in the Baltic in winter. Although the water near the bottom contains the largest amount of salt, the water at the surface cools down to such an extent that it becomes even heavier, and a reversal takes place throughout the basin. This is a distinct economic gain, for the decay of dead plants and animals has greatly enriched the water at the bottom with nutrient salts which, through this reversal, will feed the minute, floating vegetation at the surface in the Baltic next spring, which, in turn, means good hauls of fish. That these factors really are interrelated is clear from the fact that the catch of fish is disappointing when this "overturn" of the waters has failed to occur in the preceding winter. This happens sometimes when several coincident factors combine to make the surface water lighter than that at the bottom.

The deep water of the Black Sea is too saline to be displaceable by the winter surface water. The narrow, shallow passage through the Bosphorus and Dardanelles to the Mediterranean is inadequate for proper ventilation of its deeps. The deep water therefore stagnates, the stored-up oxygen has been consumed and, finally, normal life came to an end. Only sulpho-bacteria are left, which break down proteins and generate hydrogen sulphide, a poisonous gas which dissolves and fouls the deep waters. This is not the only unventilated basin. Among others known to exist is Kau Bay between the northern arms of the island of Halmahera in the Moluccas (Fig. 29). Nothing sinister is betrayed at the surface, where the water is clear and

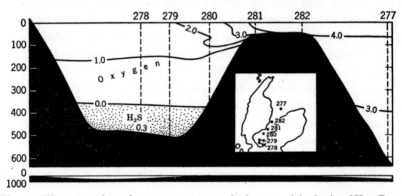

Fig. 29. The contaminated, stagnant water at the bottom of the basin of Kau Bay. Below: Vertical section to true scale. Oxygen in cu. cm. per litre water Depths in metres; station numbers *Snellius* expedition at top.

healthy, with seaweed, fish and other animals leading a perfectly normal existence; but below is the house of the dead, for any animal venturing into those waters impregnated with hydrogen sulphide is doomed. There are no living carrion-eating creatures on the bottom and the corpses of vertebrates are preserved in the soft black or green mud. Once the organic remains have decomposed, a perfect skeleton is left behind; many fine fossils exhibited in museums owe their conservation to just such unventilated basins in the geological past.

A great many Norwegian fjords, or portions of them, stagnate at depth, behind shallow sills. The surface water of many of these basins is fresh or brackish, which makes it difficult for the heavier sea-water to pass over the sill into the interior. Foul water then collects behind the sill in the depths. In course of time, this becomes warmer and warmer until it finally changes places in the winter with the surface water which has become cold and heavy; or else at a given moment, outside clean, salt water of lower tempera-ture pushes through. In either case, the stale water, malodorous with hydrogen sulphide, drains off. The process then begins all over again: the fresh supply of oxygen in the new water is gradually consumed and hydrogen sulphide begins to accumulate in the depths. The frequency of this periodic spring cleaning depends on various factors, and in most cases is not known.

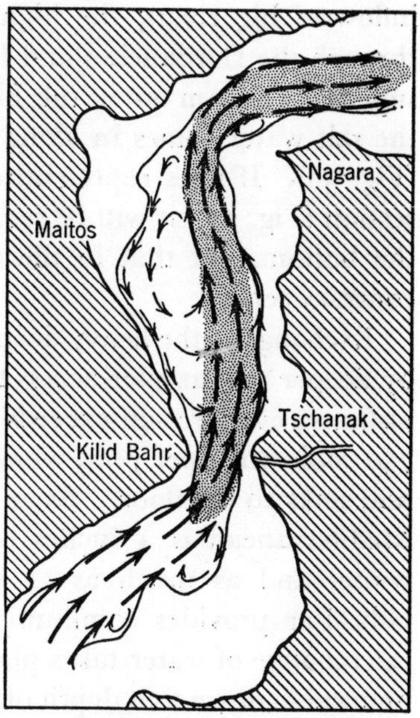

In some basins there is an intermediate layer of ordinary sea-water, well provided with oxygen, between the contaminated salt-water layer below and the fresh water at the surface. Normal marine life subsists precariously in this intermediate zone, where even floating seaweed is to be found. This exhibits a highly interesting adaptation to its environment, in that its bladders contain moisture, which prevents it from rising into the covering layer of fresh water, where it would be killed.

Fig. 30. Dardanelles with undercurrent at 50 metres depth; in dotted area, bed consists of gravel. Eddies along the sides. (After Defant.)

Quite independently of the stagnant deep basin, the shallower layers of the Black Sea show a vigorous exchange with the Mediterranean. Thanks to the predominance over evaporation of precipitation combined with the

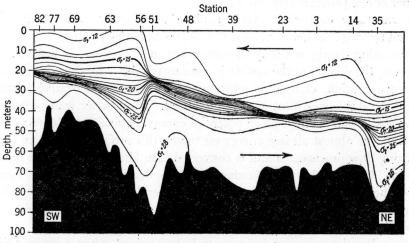

Fig. 31. Section (vertical dimensions greatly exaggerated) through the Bosphorus with specific gravity of the water (September 1917). (After Defant.)

E

inflow of big rivers, the highly saline Mediterranean water streaming in through the Dardanelles and Bosphorus is diluted. Lighter water flows in a superficial stream out of the Black Sea at the rate of 6 feet per second, while the salt water comes in along the bottom at the rate of $2\frac{1}{2}$ feet per second (Fig. 30). If lines representing equal salt content are drawn in a vertical section (Fig. 31), it will be seen that they approximately follow the shapes of the bottom, but that in the uppermost layers the water undulates in the contrary sense.

Exchange of the heavy deep water of many basins is, however, facilitated by deeper and ampler access to the open ocean. In the Mediterranean, for instance, evaporation exceeds precipitation plus drainage from the land by 750 cubic miles per year, which means that the surface water becomes heavy and sinks to the floor. As an additional result, the level of the water in the Mediterranean is 4 inches below that outside the Strait of Gibraltar in winter and as much as 12 inches sometimes in summer. The Strait of Gibraltar provides communication with the Atlantic Ocean and a lively interchange of water takes place over this sill (Fig. 32). At the surface, and noticeable down to a depth of 300 feet, a current running inwards at a speed of $2\frac{1}{2}$ miles per hour feeds cool water of low salinity from the open ocean. At almost double this speed, the deep water, warmed but changed by evaporation to a relatively heavy brine, flows outwards over the sill. The incoming current must compensate both for the outgoing stream and the residue of evaporation. Both streams must, on the other hand, carry the same amount of salt; otherwise the Mediterranean waters would either become fresher and fresher or else progressively saline.

It was stated above that a labile equilibrium of water cannot be durable. Accordingly, it is generally found that water becomes progressively heavier at increasing depth, not only in basins, but in the oceans themselves. As, however, the density at the surface is constantly subject to disturbing factors (e.g. evaporation, change of temperature, dilution by currents), in many places the stable stratification is undermined. The heavier water may then lie on top in places and is given potential energy. This energy (derived from the sun, like almost all free energy on the earth's surface) is used up in the resulting flow downwards and is converted into kinetic energy and heat of friction. On the other hand, reduction of the density would not, of course, impel the water to sink, but would give it a tendency to spread to the sides over heavier water, with the result that layers which stood *side by side* would now stand one *below* the other.

Then, in other cases we have neutral equilibrium, when a basin is filled with water of uniform specific gravity, with no component tending either to

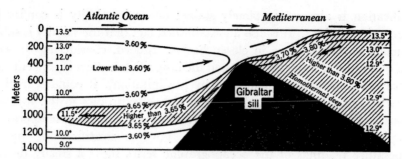

Fig. 32. Flow of saline, warm water from the Mediterranean basin through the Strait of Gibraltar towards a floating "delta" at 1000 metres depth in the Atlantic Ocean.

rise or sink. Such a condition prevails more or less in that portion of the Mediterranean basin which lies below the level of the Gibraltar sill. The water in virtually any deep-sea basin is likewise of uniform composition and temperature below the level of the lowest spot on the rim.

Whereas, generally speaking, it is the salinity of basins which actuates convection and other forms of transfer, differences in temperatures are an additional important factor in the great oceanic basins. Records of the temperature and composition from the surface of oceans downwards show that the

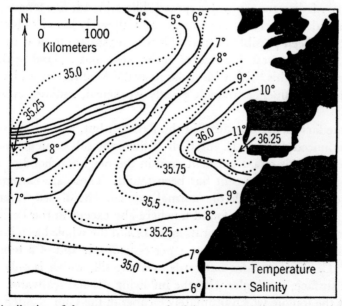

Fig. 33. Distribution of the temperature and salt content (in thousandths) in the Atlantic Ocean at a depth of 3000 feet in front of the Strait of Gibraltar. The tongue of warm saline water stands out clearly.

stratification is almost completely stable; hence instability is confined to horizontal variations. It is also an established fact that the salinity is subject to smaller variations than in closed basins. Indeed, considering the enormous quantities of water involved and the insignificant effect of concentration by evaporation (which is balanced by precipitation), it could scarcely be otherwise. But the ocean stretches from the sultry tropics to the icy polar regions and is therefore exposed to a wide range of changing temperatures. This is the factor, therefore, which governs stratification, and the temperature readings of the oceanographic series show a steady decrease from the surface down to the floor.

What, it may now be asked, happens to the warm, but salty, water flowing through the Strait of Gibraltar over the sill towards the open? It would be strange indeed if, after combined densifying and heating, this current chanced to have exactly the same density as the ocean water at sill level. It is in fact considerably heavier, and is accordingly deflected downwards and pursues its course towards a far lower level. As it does so, the contiguous water becomes progressively colder and, therefore, denser until, at about 3000 feet, a balance is at last struck between the high salinity of the basin water and the low temperature prevailing in the ocean. Here the submarine river debouches into what we may call a "fluid delta". At this level, the warm, salty Mediterranean water spreads like a broad, flat tongue, mingles by degrees with the surrounding waters and ultimately loses its identity. For all that, it has been possible to trace this waning stream to near the Canary Islands in the south-west, the Azores in the west, and Ireland in the north-west. The area of this "delta" is as large as the Mediterranean itself and it may be that its influence, though greatly weakened, radiates even farther afield.

The same factors are operative in the Red Sea but, as we have seen, in a more pronounced degree. In the Gulf of Suez the salt content may rise in summer to upwards of 4·1 per cent, and in the neighbourhood of Perim at the southern exit 3·7 per cent has been found. These are extremely high percentages compared with the normal salt content of sea-water (round about 3·5 per cent) and are found nowhere else except in the Persian Gulf. The water, heavy through evaporation, sinks and the whole basin is therefore filled with water containing about 4 per cent of salt and of a temperature above 20° C. As it streams outwards over the sill, which is only 500 feet below the surface, it mingles with the inflowing normal sea-water, with the result that the tongue which ultimately escapes in the Gulf of Aden contains only 3·7 to 3·8 per cent of salt. As with the other tongue, a balance is not struck until it reaches a depth of 3000 feet.

Conditions are different in the deep basins of Indonesia, where, in spite of the high temperature, precipitation and evaporation are pretty well equal; circulation, therefore, depends on other factors in this region.

The Economy of the Ocean Basins in the Far East

It is interesting to observe that there are three distinct movements of the waters in the basins of the Moluccas; they are the tidal motions, the currents in the superficial layers and the ventilating currents in the deep wells of the basins below the level of the sill. The tidal movements, having already been briefly discussed, need not delay us now, once it has been noted that, generally speaking, they comprise to-and-fro movements, at all levels, and are not, therefore, instrumental in the ultimate supply or drainage of water. They are superimposed upon the currents we are about to deal with, as the

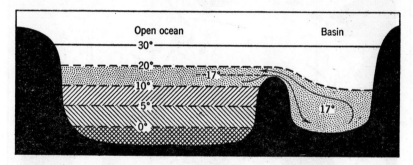

Fig. 34. Diagrammatic vertical section to show how a basin is filled from the ocean with cold, heavy water of a given temperature, depending on the depth of the sill.

motion of a ship's machinery is superimposed upon its forward movement. For all that, tidal movements attain locally to greater velocity than the progressive current.

It has been pointed out that there is a stable stratification of the oceanic waters, with the heaviest layer at the bottom, and, in conformity with this law, the density of the oceans surrounding the Malay Archipelago increases steadily to depths of several thousands of feet. However, as the straits between the islands are of limited depth, the deepest ocean waters are not in direct communication with the basins, which are filled with ocean water coming only from the level of the deepest point in the rim (Fig. 34).

This is simple enough, but complicating factors are the irregular shapes and, more especially, the linking together of the basins. Fig. 35 shows how contorted is the path along which deep water has to pass in penetrating to all deeps in the Molucca Sea. Thus, the water in the Savu Sea, to the north of Timor, does not come from the adjacent Indian Ocean, exchange here being obstructed by the sill at 2900 feet. The communication with the Pacific is considerably deeper, viz., 6000 feet. In spite of the far greater distance of 3000 kilometres and the circuitous route, it is *Pacific* water which penetrates to the depth of the Savu Sea (Fig. 36). Owing to its lower temperature (3·2°), it has a considerably higher density than the water in

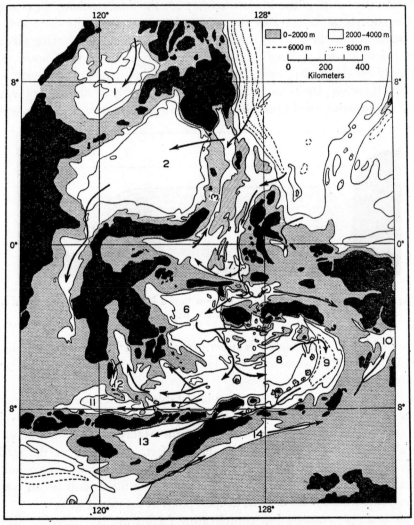

Fig. 35. The filling of the Indonesian deep-sea basins with water from the Pacific Ocean (top right). The deeps on both sides of Flores (marked 11 and 13) are ventilated by water from the Pacific, flowing for more than 2000 miles from basin to basin (see next figure).
(After van Riel, *Snellius Report.*)

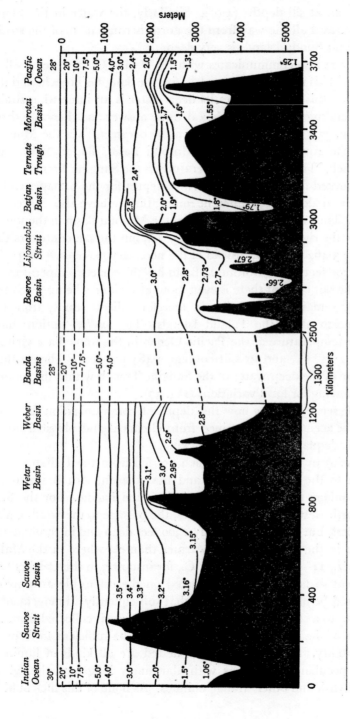

Fig. 36. Vertical section (greatly exaggerated) to show the successive influx of cold Pacific water (from right). Coming from the ocean, it passes through the Molucca Passage to the Banda Sea and, via the Weber Deep, into the Savu Basin. The water from the Indian Ocean is held back by the high bar of the Savu Strait (farthest left). The thin line below shows the actual range of the section to scale (see preceding figure).

the Indian Ocean at sill depths (4·0°). Similarly, the water in the Flores Sea has had to travel all the way from the north because none of the straits between the Lesser Sunda Islands is very deep.

The Celebes Sea also communicates with the Pacific Ocean over a sill of 4790 feet depth. This route passes over a basin, the Sangihe Trench, and the path along which this basin receives its deep water is an interesting study. The existing soundings do not provide a definite answer and there are three alternatives (Fig. 35), viz., (1) straight from the ocean, (2) via the Morotai Basin, or (3) the roundabout way of Morotai Basin, Batjan Basin and Gorontalo Trench. The recorded temperature in the Sangihe Trench could always be accounted for by assuming certain depths for the passages which have to be followed along these different routes; but we have also to account for the salinity. Thus water at 6400 feet from the Morotai Basin in the south-east might have the right temperature of 2·15° C., but the salt content of this water would be 3·462 per cent, instead of the necessary percentage of 3·465. The water at 7700 feet in the Gorontalo Basin has the correct temperature of 2·15° C., but the salt content there is even more at variance, being 3·461 per cent. The only remaining possibility is, therefore, direct supply from the ocean to the north along the Talaud Islands. The *Snellius* stations have shown that the temperature of the Pacific Ocean in the immediate vicinity at 6600 feet is 2·15° C., and its salt content 3·464 per cent. These values agree with those of the deep water of the Sangihe Trench within the margin of error and allowing for local variations (Fig. 37).

This example serves to show how the depth of communication between the basins can be accurately ascertained from chemical and physical observations, even if adequate soundings are lacking.

The only basins in the Moluccas which are fed from the Indian Ocean are the trench to the south of Timor and the adjacent Aru Basin to the north-east, all others receiving their water from the Pacific. For the Sulu Basin in the north-west near the Philippines, the passage to the South China Sea is the deepest, but it is long and only 1300 feet deep and in consequence the deep water in the Sulu Sea is far warmer than elsewhere in the Malay Archipelago, viz., 11° C. as against 3·4° C., for instance, in the Celebes Sea.

Our argument so far has been conducted on the ostensible assumption that a basin need be filled once only and that subsequently all movement in the water comes to a standstill. The biological specimens collected from the greatest depths of the basins would, in themselves, be sufficient to disprove any such possibility. Among the catches netted are all kinds of luminous deep-sea fish, peculiar red lobsters with alarmingly long tentacles, glassy transparent jellyfish and other strange animals. As none of this life could be sustained without oxygen, obviously the water at these depths must be ventilated in some way. Were it not so, the stock of dissolved oxygen would be exhausted and an unwholesome atmosphere of hydrogen sulphide would be produced as in the Black Sea and Kau Bay. Moreover, the heat of the earth could only be dissipated by conduction. For this to happen, it is calculated that the temperature of the bottom water would have to rise to about 700° C. before there could be a sufficient gradient. Clearly, then, it is by circulation of the water that the earth's heat is dispersed.

It is easily deducible from the *Snellius* measurements that oxygen is consumed, for its percentage in the basins falls in proportion to the distance from

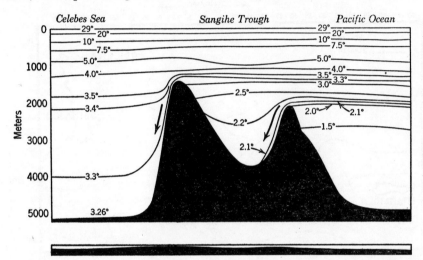

Fig. 37. Vertical section (with true proportions shown below) to demonstrate the influx of cold Pacific water into the Sangihe Trough and the Celebes Sea.
(After van Riel, *Snellius Report.*)

the open door to the ocean. During the waters' slow passage from one basin to the second and possibly to a third and fourth, marine life and the decay of organic matter progressively replace oxygen by carbon dioxide.

What information we have as to the force of these incoming currents is scanty enough. The only strait in which significant observations have been made is that of Lifamatola to the south of the Gorontalo Basin (Fig. 35). This has to ventilate the Banda Basins and all their ramifications. An anchor station was maintained on the sill by the *Snellius*, current-meter readings being taken at various depths (Fig. 38). These showed that, from about 5000 feet to the bottom at 6000 feet, there is a current running towards the southeast—hence a ventilating stream—at the rate of about two inches per second. This is not very fast, admittedly, but, thanks to the huge cross-section, an enormous quantity of water enters the Banda Basins. There is a diurnal influx of roughly 10 cubic miles and if this quantity is divided into the capacity of the basins, it will be seen that it takes from one to two centuries for complete exchange to be effected. The absorption of oxygen must be very slow indeed, as it is known that even the Savu Sea and Flores Trench right at the far end of the chain of basins contain quite a fair amount of this gas.

But, although it is obvious that ventilation of the deeps is accomplished, it is quite another matter to explain how it is brought about. What are the

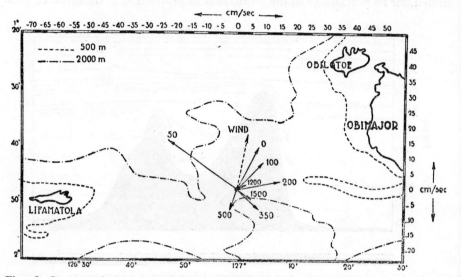

Fig. 38. Current velocities (apart from the tidal currents) at various depths (metres) in the Strait of Lifamatola, north of Buru. (After Lek, *Snellius Report*.)

sources of energy to keep these ventilating currents flowing? Or, to put it differently still, where does the heat come from which warms the cold water flowing in over the sills, so that it can expand, rise and find its way out again at a higher level?

The energy must come from three sources, viz., the heat emitted from the interior of the earth, tidal forces and the conversion of oxygen to carbon dioxide. Present knowledge is insufficient to show which predominates. Nor do we know how and whither the water escapes from the deep basins again; whether by general, gradual rising, by local incidental upwellings or along an unvarying path of constant flow.

Sufficient emphasis has been laid upon the fact that the ventilation of the Indonesian deep-sea basins is a *conditio sine quâ non* for normal life down to the floors. But this renewal stamps its mark upon another phenomenon as well. The uppermost couple of hundred metres of water are the habitat of innumerable unicellular organisms, many of which form a test of calcium carbonate. At death, these tests sink and come to rest on the bottom. Although volcanic ash, in addition to clay and other waste denuded from the land, dilutes this rain of lime, the tests would always constitute an appreciable proportion of the sediment, in fact would often predominate, were it not for their vulnerability to solvent action. Once the protective coating of organic material has decayed, they are so powerfully attacked by water that lime, if present at all, is found in only minute quantities in the majority of bottom samples. Seeing that the rain of lime never ceases, the process of solution also apparently continues with unabated persistence, from which, again, it may be inferred that the water never becomes saturated with lime. This, of course, can only hold good if the contents of the deep basins are constantly being renewed with unsaturated water.

The Sulu Basin provides an opportunity of verifying the effect of circulation upon the lime content of deep-sea muds. It will be remembered that ventilation there is very inadequate, so it is not surprising to learn that the percentage of lime in the sediments on its floor is much higher than that found in the Celebes Sea with its excellent circulation. In the former sea the percentage of lime is 40 to 50, whereas in the latter only 0 to 2 per cent is found below about 13,000 feet.

Circulation in the Ocean

Having learned how the currents at the surface of the Seven Seas are generated by wind, evaporation and tide, and how basins like the Mediterranean and the deep-sea trenches in Far Eastern waters are ventilated, let us now turn to the great circulation in the oceans down to the floor. The Atlantic must be our subject, since this is the only ocean of which full enough details are available for an adequate picture.

The main features of the circulation in the Atlantic are to be found in the outline shown in Fig. 39, where the curvature of the earth's surface has been eliminated and the height is greatly exaggerated in proportion to the length. If drawn true to scale, the height would be even less than the thickness of the thin depth lines, or, taken the other way round, the section would, at the height given, have to be 200 yards long!

Those familiar with meteorological charts, with their shifting areas of high and low pressure, entailing changes in direction and force of the winds, may be surprised to find that, for the oceanic basins, a fixed system of currents can be shown to exist which is valid for all seasons and any year. We

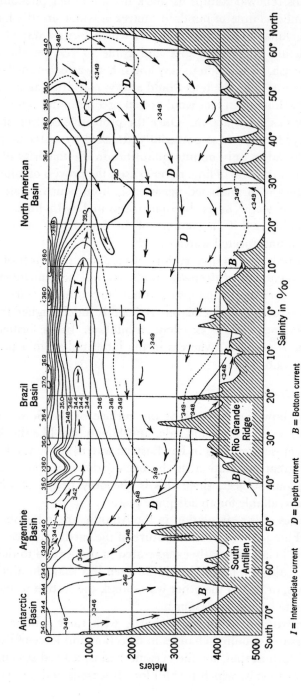

Fig. 39. Section (height exaggerated) through the Atlantic Ocean—on the American side—from Antarctica to Greenland. The currents are clearly perceptible by the distribution of the salt contents. (After Schott.)

I = Intermediate current *D* = Depth current *B* = Bottom current have seen, however, that, in contradistinction to the atmosphere, the seas are supplied with heat from above, and this enhances stability. Another important factor is the comparative incompressibility of water, owing to which the density is less variable than that of air. The small mass and heat capacity of the atmosphere and its varying transparency along with its great mobility, all contrive to make the air the plaything of the never-ending fluctuations from hot to cold. In the oceans, on the contrary, stable conditions prevail and on the whole the movements are, by and large, adapted to the average supply and transmission of heat, to average winds, average evaporation or precipitation and other agencies of propulsion. Any mean change brought about in the course of years will always be just balanced by the movement; circulation will nullify the effects of extraneous forces.

The superficial currents, which do not generally go down far enough to be perceptible in a vertical section (seldom reaching deeper than 300 feet), are usually less constant in speed and direction. We shall leave these out of consideration. In the upper 1000 to 2500 feet, currents occur with obvious up-and-down components and at three levels lower down there are important horizontal displacements of water. These are anything from hundreds to thousands of metres thick and occupy the breadth of the entire ocean. Though so much more massive than the surface currents, the movements are sluggish in the extreme, so that the term "current" is almost incongruous; "circulation" would be more apt.

The water displacements in the topmost layers consist predominantly in rising at the Equator, thanks to which the water there is kept relatively cool, and descent at moderate latitudes, where, therefore, relatively warm water disappears below. This convection is due on the one hand to the difference in density through warming and dilution by rain of the tropical water and, on the other, the somewhat lower temperature of the subtropical water which, moreover, becomes even heavier owing to considerable evaporation in these windy regions where there is scanty precipitation (Fig. 40). This difference maintains a constant movement, towards the Pole at the surface and towards the Equator at a depth of a few hundred yards.

The assumption that oceanic circulation *in toto* rested on this principle held sway for a century until a few years ago, when it was discovered that this so-called *thermohyaline* (heat and salt) circulation plays but a very minor part. The fact of powerful circulation down to the floor implies heat rising from below, which rules out the tropical sun as a major factor. Towards the Poles, the water is so cold that in a manner of speaking it might be called exposed deep-sea water, being part of the vast circulations through the dark, cold regions of the ocean. This is subject to the heat flow of the earth; hence a submarine source of heat is, in fact, operative, while, conversely, cooling takes place from above.

Below the superficial circulation mentioned, which reaches down 1000 feet in the Tropics, 2500 feet between latitudes 20° to 40° and is absent beyond 50°, is the domain of the true deep ocean and here the horizontal components of the movements predominate entirely. The uppermost of the three circulations consists of a South Atlantic intermediate current carrying cold water of poor salinity from the Antarctic under the waters of the central Atlantic Ocean which, though richer in salt, are nevertheless lighter on account of the high temperature; the current crosses the Equator and does

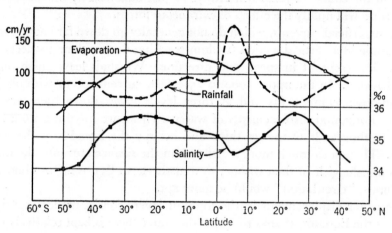

Fig. 40. Longitudinal graph of the Atlantic Ocean, showing the dependence of surface salinity upon rainfall and evaporation. (After Fleming and Revelle, in Trask.)

not die out till it reaches latitude 30° N. Its speed is estimated to be 3 miles per 24 hours. The development of its northern pendant between latitudes 60° and 40° N. is rudimentary.

Contrary to this intermediate current, the deep current is served almost entirely from the north. This circulation originates on the surface at latitude 60° N., in the neighbourhood of Greenland. There the water cools in winter to such an extent that it sinks to 7000–13,000 feet and then pursues its south-bound course horizontally. Such vertical movements could not possibly take place unless exceptional uniformity—hence a neutral or even labile equilibrium—prevailed in the water at high latitudes in winter.

Below 13,000 feet, the Atlantic Ocean is divided up into several basins. The Mid-Atlantic Ridge sharply separates a chain of basins on its east and west sides. In the south, on the African side, a prominent sill rises from the bed of the ocean, the Walvis Ridge, extending from Tristan da Cunha on the Mid-Atlantic Ridge to the west coast of southern Africa. This prevents the basins on the Africa-European side of the ocean from being properly ventilated. The only deeper break-through in the Mid-Atlantic Ridge is the Romanche Gap opposite Liberia. Fig. 41 shows how the bottom water is here carried from the Brazilian Basin and, flowing northwards and southwards, fills the eastern basins.

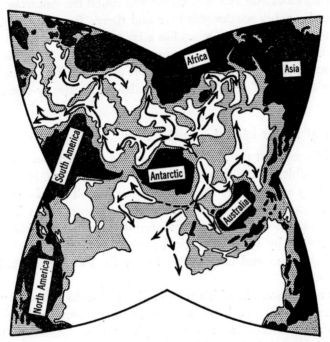

Fig. 41. Ramification of the Antarctic bottom water in the basins around the South Pole.

As our cross-section and the map show, the basins on the American side are ventilated mainly by the bottom current from Antarctic waters. This being the coldest and heaviest water in the ocean, it searches out the deepest places. The rate of circulation can be estimated at not more than 1 kilometre per 24 hours, which means that it would take the water a quarter of a century to travel from the surface to the farthest basins which it ultimately reaches. For all that, the amount of oxygen carried with it is enough to sustain animal life in all basins right down to the floor. Thus all the oxygen supplied to levels below 2500 feet is brought down from the cold superficial waters of the polar regions, for which reasons these are sometimes called the lungs of the ocean.

Actually, it is not only the Atlantic Ocean which derives its bottom water mainly from the Antarctic. The arrows in the map of the world reproduced in Fig. 41 show how the water of between $-1°$ C. and $+1°$ C. follows winding paths as it travels over the ocean bed towards the deep depressions of all the southern oceans. In several places it penetrates beyond the Equator, for the water goes farther, in less well-defined streams, than is shown by the arrows. Most of it descends in the south-western tip of the Atlantic Ocean and then runs clockwise as a bottom current round the Antarctic Continent, sending out branches northwards here and there. Consequently, the water at the bottom of the Pacific Ocean has a far longer journey from the surface than has that of the Atlantic. This probably accounts for the fact that the oxygen content of the northern deep waters of the Pacific Ocean is so much lower than of those of the Atlantic and also for its steady decrease northwards.

The Effect of Waves upon the Earth's Crust

Internal forces pent up within the bowels of the earth are, almost exclusively, responsible for the shape of the oceanic basins; so, in discussing the oceans, we may regard those shapes as unalterable. This, however, does not apply to the coast and the floor of the shallower seas, where both abrasion and the deposition of sedimentary material very considerably modify the contours created by other geological forces. We shall therefore have to enquire what waves and currents do to the fixed and loose matter of the earth's crust.

There are three ways in which waves affect rocks: they smash up and wear down both solid rock and loose boulders as well as smaller fragments; they move loosened material from place to place; they churn up the smaller fragments, thus enabling sluggish currents to transport material they could otherwise not move.

We have had occasion to say something about the terrific force of storm waves. When large boulders are thus tossed and rolled about, they cannot fail to be worn down and must, some time or other, split up. The smaller the fragments become the more readily will they be swept up and flung to and fro, becoming steadily smaller and smoother as the corners are rubbed off. And indeed the most perfectly rounded and smoothed pebbles and cobbles are found on rocky beaches. Among these collections there will seldom be found a pure sphere, as this could only be produced from a cube of entirely homogeneous material, and that is a rare occurrence. If the initial fragment is oblong or happens not to be equally strong in all directions, a sphere can never be produced, however perfect the rounding-off may be; the shapes will

PLATE V

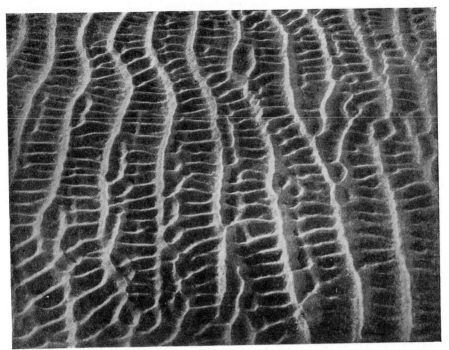

(a) "Warp and woof": asymmetrical current-pattern with the steep faces to the left (current coming from the right). Transversely to it, symmetrical wave-patterns. Sandy surface in tidal marshes. (*Photo Ehrhardt.*)

(b) Petrified ripple-marks in Carbonaceous sandstone, seen from above. The current, with apparently some wave-action, was from the left. Heiman's Quarry, South Limburg.

PLATE VI

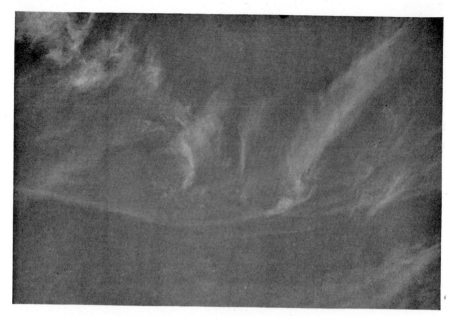

(a) Feathery cirrus clouds at a great height form long streaks across the sky.

(b) Altocumulus clouds high above a mass of cumulus.

always be oblong or flat. Fragments much larger than a football are rarely well rounded.

The never-ceasing action of the breakers not only polishes the broken-up rocks into shape; under local influences which vary its mode of action, it grades them according to size. Sand only will be deposited on one beach, shingle on another and boulders elsewhere. Whatever material is brought down by rivers and the wind into the sea is subject to the same forces as the rubble of littoral erosion.

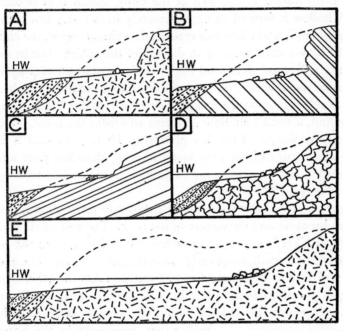

Fig. 42. Wave-cut notch in, and cliff formation of, various kinds of rock. A. Uniform strong rock. B. Beds sloping away from the sea. C. Beds inclining towards the sea. D. Friable rock. E. The same rock as in A., but with a broad platform of erosion.

The backwash of the breakers is constantly sucking material away from the beach but, being able to displace only the smaller fragments, leaves the larger masses behind. The farther seawards we go, the weaker becomes the action of the waves upon the deepening sea floor and, therefore, the material becomes progressively fine-grained. The finest of all, i.e. particles of clay, are at the mercy of even the faintest movements, which churn them up and carry some of them far out, even to the deep sea.

The imperishable parts of dead animals and plants, like tests, shells and pieces of bone, are likewise selected by wave action and mixed with the in-

F

organic products of decomposition. From these they differ, not only because they consist of lime, but also in that large fragments are able to settle in deep water, when the animal happened to die far out to sea. Thus tests of unicellular organisms a couple of millimetres across may easily settle on the ocean floor with clay of the finest texture. More generally, however, large heavy shells are deposited with gravel or coarse sand near the shore.

Breakers do not confine their attentions to detached fragments only, but attack solid rocks on the coastline with grim persistence, using boulders as battering rams hurled at the foot of the cliffs, which thus become undermined. A hollow is formed at approximately high-water level, known as a "wave-cut notch", and when this reaches the critical depth, the cliff tumbles down. The waves then proceed to dispose of the rubble, but in due course the rock face will stand clear, and the process can start all over again. There will be no wave-cut notch in very soft or friable coastal rock, because the face will crumble away as the gradient steepens. When the sea has eaten its way far inland, a broad, shallow platform will front the coast. Much of the wave energy is dissipated on this platform. Hence, the cliff is no longer exposed to the brunt of the attack; weathering then has time and opportunity to step in and transform the rocks into a mild incline lacking a wave-cut notch (Fig. 42, Plate IV, 2).

The rate at which the coast retreats depends predominantly upon the force of the breakers and the nature of the rock. The soft chalk forming the white cliffs of Kent is exposed to much wear and tear, with the result that landslides, big and small, frequently come tumbling down. The average loss of land is reckoned to be about 2 feet in a century. On the other hand, coasts consisting of granite, basalt, quartzite and similar hard, tough rocks have undergone no perceptible change within the memory of man. It is hard to realise that, repeatedly in the history of the earth's crust, vast areas of land have been planed down by the oceans to below sea-level. But the enormous spans of geological time have to be taken into account (Fig. 44).

Fig. 43. A bay partly enclosed by spits on the coast of Alaska. (After Johnson.)

Sandy shores present an entirely different picture. At a fair distance from the shore, along a line more or less parallel to the beach, heavy breakers in a storm raise the sand and pile it up into a sand-bar. Several rows of sand-bars may be built up, one behind the other, each corresponding to a different size of wave. Eventually, one of these will emerge above sea-level, forming a long, narrow strip of sand lying before the coast. This is called an offshore bar, while a spit has grown *laterally*. The enclosed water is a lagoon (Fig. 43), and this may change into a fresh-water or brackish basin, depending on the

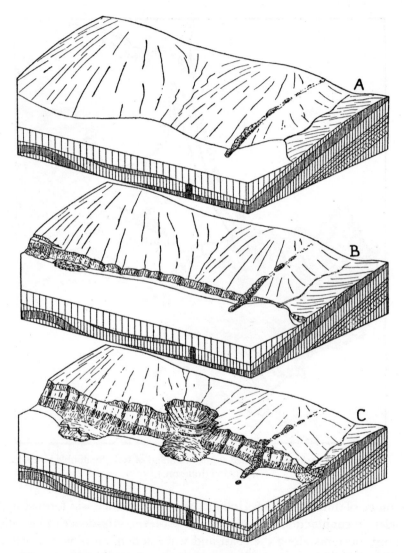

Fig. 44. Three stages in the erosion of a landscape which in A was suddenly inundated by the sea. In B erosion has begun. A high cliff has been formed in C with, on the left, hard strata laid bare, in the middle a minor landslip, while to the right volcanic rock offers greater resistance. On the extreme right, the river has cut down owing to the increased gradient at its mouth. (After v.d. Vlerk and Kuenen.)

degree of access of sea or river water. Once the offshore bar has been built up to an appreciable size and height, the wind can take hold of the drying sand and a dune landscape is gradually formed. Peat may form in the fresh-water lagoon, or clay may be deposited behind the protecting offshore bar.

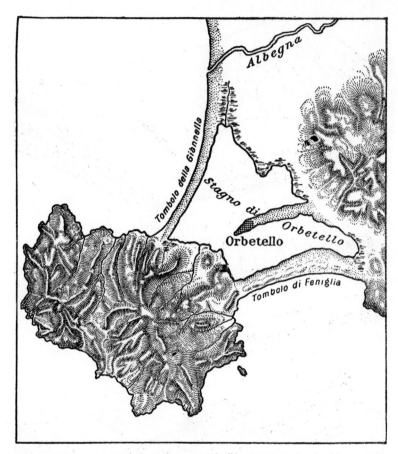

Fig. 45. Monte Argentario, tied to the mainland of Italy by double tombolo.
(After Johnson.)

The range of dunes to which Holland owes its existence was formed by both agencies, in conjunction with changes in sea-level, subsidence or elevation of the crust, currents along the coast and wave action, all of which play some part in breaking up or gradually expanding an area of this kind.

Closely allied to the spit is the *tombolo*, an arm of sand connecting an island with the coast. It may be either single or double, the double form enclosing a lagoon, as may be seen in Fig. 45.

The Effect of Currents upon the Earth's Crust

Marine currents resulting from drag by the wind or due to differences in density are very seldom swift enough to displace sand; nor do they tend to sweep the bottom sufficiently to churn up sediment. In exceptional cases, the smaller particles may be prevented from settling on the sill or outlet of a basin, as in the Bosphorus (Fig. 30).

It has been pointed out, however, that particles may be dislodged by wave action and then even the weakest currents can carry them along until the material is deposited on the bottom again.

The currents which have a more enduring effect upon the sea floor and sedimentation are due to the tides. As we have seen, it is precisely in shoal water, in the mouths of rivers, in narrow straits, over the sills of ocean basins, etc., that they attain to their maximum velocity. Even in straits more than 6000 feet deep between oceanic basins in the Far East, the tidal currents are so strong as to prevent the deposition of sedimentary material altogether. Loose fragments of coral, small stones and the like are the only "catch" fished up by dredging.

It is the tidal currents coming and going which have scoured the deep channels in the arms of the sea around the island of Walcheren and between the Frisian Islands strung between the Netherlands and Denmark. Here and there, these channels are 200 feet deep, a depth which will not be found anywhere else in the southern portion of the North Sea. The currents can only carry along the material they detach so long as they are running swiftly; as soon as the water enters the open sea—say, when the tide is running out— and its speed is greatly reduced, it drops its burden. In this way marine "deltas" are formed off tidal inlets as off the mouths of rivers; but, because the current supplying the sediment never rises above high-water level, a tidal delta shows no dry land or vegetation and is therefore marked only on sea charts. Double deltas are sometimes formed in gaps crossing offshore bars, one on the inside due to the flood, the other on the outside due to the ebb; the one sprouting, as it were, from the other (Fig. 46). The seaward delta is smaller, because the wash of the waves scatters much of the material and also because the greater depth demands a greater volume of accretion.

The smaller ramifications of the system of tidal channels draw a curious pattern on the tidal flats. Twice every twenty-four hours a large quantity of water flows in and then drains off again. Leaving the vast expanses of sand-banks and mud-flats, the water collects in numerous small, winding gullies which, uniting, discharge into a few large channels. Ultimately, they drain into the big waterways between the islands leading to the open sea.

After the turn of the tide, the water follows the reverse route and is therefore able to flow far more swiftly than would be possible over the surface of the shoals themselves. The principle is much the same as that of our own vascular system, by which blood flows with little friction through progressively smaller vessels, thus circulating rapidly to all parts of the body (Plate II, 2).

Sand Ripples

The variation in size and form of ripple-marks made by water in sand is almost endless. It is as though the waves and currents contrive, with the

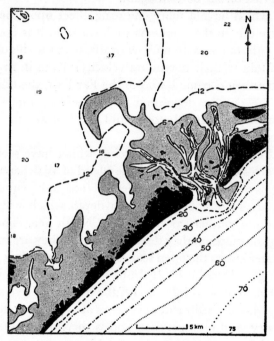

Fig. 46. Double tidal delta at Ocracoke Inlet crossing the offshore bar off the East Coast of the United States (depths in fathoms; fathom = 6 feet).

utmost ingenuity, to devise ever new patterns to cover huge expanses of sand. Some ripples are symmetrical, others asymmetrical in section. In the former group, the crests and troughs of the wave may be true images of each other, but sharp-edged crests between broad troughs are far more common. The asymmetric type also varies from barely aslant to ridges inclining at perhaps 35° on one side and only very slightly on the other.

There are also marked differences in a longitudinal direction. In rare cases, the individual ridges can be followed in lines dozens of times their width. Sometimes the lines of crests are sinuous, or are barely longer than the interspaces. Some ripples seem to be cut out sharply in the sand, while others are only just visible. Reticular patterns result when one system of ripples is intersected by another perpendicular to it. We then often find that the troughs are divided up into small basins by partitions, without any perceptible detriment to the ridges of the larger system.

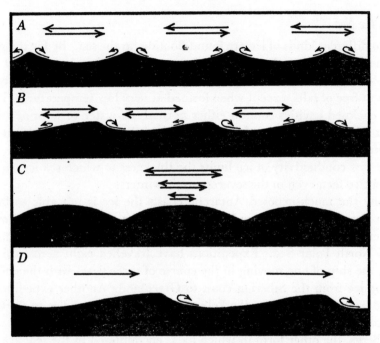

Fig. 47. Sections through ripple marks. Those formed by a current are asymmetrical (D), possibly due in part to wave action as well (B). Wave action alone produces symmetrical ripples with hollow troughs (A). If these are attacked while the water is draining off, the shape changes and rounded ridges may be formed (C).

The cause and mechanism of sand-ripple formation have been the subjects of much recorded and unrecorded speculation, but a convincing and conclusive solution of the problem is not yet forthcoming. Ordinary waves, breakers, flowing water, any or each of these in turn or combined may be the cause. Obviously important factors are the velocity of the water and the depth, the nature of the sand and the general slope of the bed. Finally, wind may quite well produce ripples on dry sand. The theory of water waves is difficult, and the mathematical problem of ripple formation still awaits solution. We shall not get very far until theoretical and field research have succeeded in correlating ripple shapes with their formative conditions.

Geology would likewise benefit by the solution of this problem. Very well-preserved ripples are often found in consolidated deposits of former periods, and geologists are eager to know under what conditions these were formed. This would indicate a great deal more about the life of the fossils enclosed in the deposits, about distribution of land and sea and about the climates of earlier ages.

Ice in the Sea

Two different kinds of ice are found floating on the sea. By far the greater volume is formed by the freezing of sea-water. This takes place at about 2° C. below zero and results in brittle, somewhat porous ice. The ice itself is almost free of salts, except when formed at very low temperatures. But the small enclosed cavities contain either normal sea-water or a brine of even higher salinity. In course of time, some of this brine tends to leak out of the ice. Hence potable water can be obtained by melting older sea ice.

The low conductivity of ice limits the thickness to which sea ice can grow to about 10 feet, even in the severest arctic winters.

Along the much-exposed Antarctic coasts the ice is not able to become fixed or to continue to grow beyond one winter season. The thickest and most extensive sheets of sea ice are therefore encountered in the more protected North Polar Sea. Expeditions have travelled right across this deep basin, the ship of one moving in the course of three years with the enclosing drifting ice from the Siberian coast to Greenland. Another expedition was landed from the air close to the Pole and drifted on a large floe to the Greenland coast, where it was rescued a year later.

Icebergs, the other form in which ice is encountered in the sea, are much more spectacular than sea ice, although their aggregate volume is far smaller. They are formed, not by the freezing of sea-water, but by glaciers flowing out into the sea. The ice, deriving from snow, is entirely fresh. Icebergs will be described later in connection with their parents, the glaciers.

III

Water in the Atmosphere

Atmospheric Humidity

The total amount of water in the atmosphere is comparatively small. Were it to condense on the earth, it would form, on an average, a layer no more than one inch thick. At any given moment, the atmosphere contains only a hundred-thousandth part of all terrestrial waters. The total amount of water on and in the solid crust of the continents—the fresh water of rivers and lakes and all the ground-water—amounting, as it does, to a good three per cent of the contents of the oceans, far exceeds the total quantity of atmospheric water. In fact, it is three thousand times as much.

For all that, since the water in the atmosphere constitutes the ascending section of the cycle, it is of prime importance. In the reservoirs of the oceans the water remains without change of level; in glaciers, lakes, rivers and as ground-water it is impelled by gravity to seek an ever-lower horizon (disregarding a temporary rise here and there in springs, which will be discussed later). It is in this descending section that geological activities are carried out; there it is that water forms the dynamic element in the landscape and that moisture serves the needs of vegetable and animal life. But solar energy, the source of power for all this activity, the fuel, as it were, that drives the engine, this can only be imparted to the water when it is raised through the atmosphere.

Evaporation and rising currents of air are capable of lifting water to thousands of feet and carrying it to the highest mountain peaks and to the centre of the vastest continent.

Water in the atmosphere fulfils another function, entirely different, no less important, but considerably less conspicuous; for, while it lets through from above most of the heat of the sun's rays, it holds up and absorbs the counter-radiation emanating from the earth, so that it cannot escape into outer space. This action maintains the temperature of the earth's surface at a much higher level than would otherwise be the case. It is, indeed, true to say that were it not for the fact that water vapour in the atmosphere acts like the glass in our garden frames, neither liquid water nor life could subsist on this earth. We shall see presently why this is.

There is not, of course, an unlimited amount of water vapour in the air. If a glass bell is placed over a saucer of water, the water evaporates until the humidity of the air attains a certain degree, when the air is said to be saturated with water vapour. If the air under the bell is heated, more of the water will evaporate, but when it cools down, vapour will condense on the glass and in the saucer. The water vapour, as a mass of gas, reacts independently: even if all the air were removed from the glass bell beforehand, exactly the same thing would happen. Now we find that the higher the temperature is, the larger the degree of vaporisation and the greater is the vapour-pressure, and that water vapour has a given maximum pressure at any particular temperature. If the pressure is less than this maximum, water evaporates from free surfaces, but once the maximum pressure for the prevailing temperature has been reached, evaporation stops, however much water may be present. At 30° C., 30 grams of water vapour can be absorbed in one cubic metre of air; but only one gram at −20° C. It follows that, at the very low temperature of 55° below zero which prevails in the upper layers of air, there can scarcely be any water vapour at all; the stratosphere is virtually a dry atmosphere. The further the air is from being saturated, the more rapidly will evaporation of available water take place.

In winter, when it is much colder outside than in a heated room, the air against the window-panes may be cooled to the point where it can no longer hold water vapour at the prevailing pressure. Condensation on the window-panes results and, if the temperature is low enough, frost-flowers are formed on the glass. These are crystal skeletons, i.e. crystals growing so fast that they have no time to develop beyond the outlines. In summer there is too little difference in temperature in and out of doors to blur the windows. This only happens, e.g., through the condensation of very small drops when a kettle is left boiling hard in the room; then the air becomes practically saturated even at the prevailing high temperature. When it is near freezing outside, the air can absorb very little moisture, so that as it enters the house it is practically dry. Once that same air has been warmed up by the fire or stove, and especially by radiators, it is capable of carrying a great deal of water vapour and sucks the room dry, a phenomenon very noticeable in such weather.

This at once suggests another aspect of the humidity of the air. There is a clear-cut distinction between the *absolute humidity* and the *relative humidity*. The former refers to the quantity of water vapour present per cubic metre, the latter to the *ratio* of the amount present to the possible maximum at the prevailing temperature. Thus at low temperature an insignificant absolute humidity will nevertheless be a high relative humidity, because the maximum quantity the air could hold is likewise very small. At a much higher temperature, that same amount of water vapour would constitute only low relative humidity, giving the impression of very dry air. What generally concerns us is the relative humidity, since on that depends whether there can be any further evaporation and how much cooling is needed to produce condensation. The point of cooling at which the air is completely saturated, so that condensation or dew must result from any further drop in temperature, is called the *dew point*.

It will be evident that the ever-changing conditions of temperature and evaporation cause continual variations in the absolute humidity. We might therefore describe the water vapour in the atmosphere as a species of individual gas of erratic and fluctuating density, which does not extend far above the earth because the temperature soon drops too low to allow it to subsist. Towards the Poles the water vapour becomes very rarefied for the same reason.

Water pursues its journey through the atmosphere in four stages, namely, the transition from fluid or solid to the vaporous form, or evaporation; then transportation mainly as vapour, followed by condensation to liquid or solid water, sometimes with further displacement; finally, its return from the atmosphere to the earth, known as precipitation.

Heating and Evaporation at the Earth's Surface

The rate of evaporation depends on several factors, viz., 1. The temperature of the water and the air. 2. The supply of heat, which is needed for evaporation. 3. The relative humidity of the air. 4. The rate at which adjacent air is replaced, because that is the rate at which the water vapour is carried away. 5. Atmospheric pressure. 6. Salinity of the water, because given like conditions the evaporation of sea-water is slower by about 6 per cent than that of fresh water. 7. The size of the vaporising surface, because the saturated air over a small area is carried away quicker and more completely than that of a large surface of water. The air above a lake is in general drier the smaller it is.

Liquid requires a great deal of heat to vaporise it, a fact abundantly illustrated, e.g., by the cooling effect of perspiration, or by a kettle on the hob. In the latter case, the water may come to the boil in a few minutes, but will take many times as long to boil away altogether. The heat of evaporation of water—that required to vaporise 1 gm. at normal pressure—is 540 calories, or 540 times as much as will raise it through one degree of temperature; and so it takes $5\frac{1}{2}$ times as much heat to boil away a quantity of water as to heat it from freezing to boiling point. Even more heat is required for evaporation at lower temperature. Seeing that heat looms so large in the picture, we obviously cannot discuss the evaporation of water in nature without taking the economy of heat into account.

For our purposes we may safely disregard the heat given off by the interior of the earth, as it is only just enough to cause a film of water one millimetre thick to evaporate in a year. It is only solar heat with which we are concerned.

Before we can tell how much heat the earth's surface receives from the sun, we must first find out how much per unit of time reaches the outer fringe of the atmosphere. This is ascertained by measuring, at various altitudes of the sun, the heat imparted to a black object with a dull surface, which may be assumed to absorb all the heat which impinges upon it. At various altitudes of the sun, the distances the rays must travel through the atmosphere vary; so it is possible to calculate by extrapolation how much heat would reach the earth if there were no atmosphere. The problem is complicated by the fact that the various colours of sunlight are absorbed in unequal measure by the atmosphere. After taking numerous measurements, it was computed that the heat radiated upon the outer margin of our atmosphere per minute, per square centimetre, amounts to 2 calories, subject to variations of 10 per cent through sunspots. This energy is partly in the form of visible light and partly of rays imperceptible to human eyes—the infra-red beyond the red end of the visible spectrum and the ultra-violet beyond the violet end.

With a clear sky and the sun high in the heavens, about half penetrates directly to the earth's surface. About 12 per cent is absorbed by the atmosphere, which it heats; another 38 per cent is scattered. It is predominantly the short blue and ultra-violet rays which are deflected on their path through the atmosphere; that is why the scattered light of a clear sky appears to be blue, and why the setting sun is able to send across to us only its longer red and yellow rays through the thick layers of air. Yet half the 38 per cent of light diffused still reaches the earth, as radiation from a clear sky; that is, one-fifth of the sun's rays penetrates the shade.

It follows that, given a clear sky and with the sun high, a total of about 70 per cent of solar radiation directly or indirectly reaches the earth's surface. As about a tenth of this is reflected straightway, in the same way as sunlight is seen to be reflected from the moon, only some 60 per cent of radiation from the sun is in fact converted into heat on the earth's surface. Matters are entirely different when the sky is overcast, as a thick bank of cloud reflects back quite three-quarters of the incident light and absorbs much of the penetrating light, with the result that not 60 per cent but nearer one-sixth part reaches the ground. Averaging all weathers over a long term the figure is probably something less than half. Less than another half is reflected back direct from the earth, from the clouds, and the atmosphere; while the balance is absorbed by the atmosphere and converted into heat.

Now, as the climate is not steadily getting warmer the heat coming from the sun is evidently not stored up (apart from chemically combined heat (coal, etc.), which is a negligibly small fraction). Conduction, evaporation and convection may displace heat, but it is only by radiation that the earth *as a whole* can rid itself of the energy received.

As we know, the nature of radiation depends on the temperature of the radiating body. A windowless anthracite stove like an Ideal boiler, will throw out perceptible warmth, but is invisible in a dark room and it is not until it is burning at red heat that the radiation can be not only felt but also seen. The higher the temperature, the stronger and whiter becomes the light emitted by an object, as the expression "white heat" implies. It is not, however, only a question of difference in cloour; it is also the quantity of light emitted which increases with rising temperature. The filament of a 100-watt bulb is very much smaller than the flame of a single wax candle, but it produces a hundred times more, as well as whiter, light.

Since every object—even a block of ice—radiates heat, the earth and the atmosphere must give off warmth everywhere; but, owing to the far lower temperature of the earth compared to that of the sun, the radiation is different, comprising only invisible rays beyond the red end of the spectrum. Now it happens that these are absorbed by the water vapour and carbon dioxide in the atmosphere far more than is visible light. Hence the moist atmosphere is very "opaque" to radiation from the earth. If the weather is bright and the air humid, only one-tenth of the earth's radiation is able to pass straight through the atmosphere and escape into space; in cloudy weather, less still. The atmosphere is, therefore, warmed by the earth's radiation; it also receives warmth by conduction from the heated surface of the earth and by condensation of water vapour which had evaporated from the earth. In its turn, the heated atmosphere radiates in all directions, some heat returning to the earth in the form of atmospheric counter-radiation, some being dissipated in space. So we see that, thanks to this small addition of water vapour, the atmosphere is able to intercept the radiation proceeding from the earth and the sea. If there were no water vapour in the atmosphere, the air, earth and sea would radiate sufficiently to throw back all solar radiation into space, at a very much lower temperature, and one subject to considerably greater variations.

Summing up, it may be said that over a long term three-eighths of solar radiation is reflected, partly as visible light, upon clouds, and one-eighth on the earth and the particles in the atmosphere. The remaining half of the energy received returns to space as invisible radiation, the quantity given off by the atmosphere being three times as much as that coming from the earth.

What particularly concerns us is the fact that the energy used for evaporation from the surface of the earth and sea together corresponds to only one-fifth of the solar radiation reaching the outer limit of the atmosphere; and the

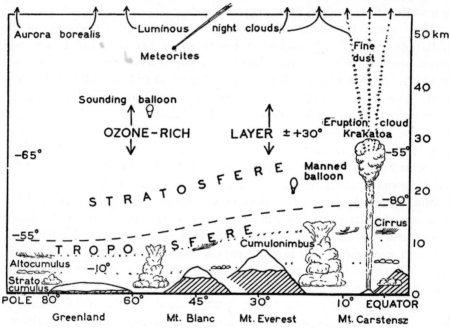

Fig. 48. The atmosphere. Thickness of bottom line represents the figure to true scale.

quantity passing by conduction from the earth to the air, thus serving for the direct heating of the lowest strata of the atmosphere, is only one-quarter of that.

It will now be apparent why the temperature of the air becomes progressively lower at increasing altitudes. For, as a considerable proportion of the heat is derived from the earth by conduction and convection or the condensation of water vapour, the highest temperature must naturally occur nearest to it. Moreover, the water-vapour atmosphere becomes thinner and thinner as we ascend; hence absorption and conversion to heat of the earth's radiation must also gradually decline, while the heat given out by condensation steadily decreases. At medium latitudes the temperature about six miles up is already −55°, and in the tropics, at 10 miles, it is −80°. This is the boundary between the *troposphere* and the *stratosphere*. The upper layer is virtually devoid of moisture because the vapour pressure at those low temperatures is in the neighbourhood of zero. The bottom layer contains the water vapour, one of the greatest single factors and visible aspects in that concatenation of vicissitudes we call *weather*. Conditions in the stratosphere (in which there are no clouds) are far more equable (Fig. 48).

The temperature at any point on earth is determined by a number of factors, such as (1) the supply of heat by direct radiation, (2) the supply by

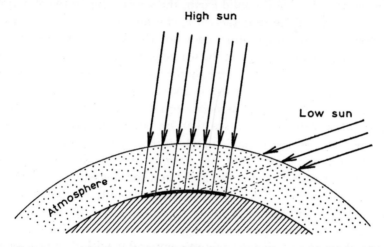

Fig. 49. Greater warmth when the sun is high because the beam of incident solar rays is broader and, in its shorter passage through the atmosphere, retains more strength.

diffused light, (3) the degree of atmospheric counter-radiation, (4) the loss of heat by radiation, (5) cooling through evaporation, (6) the transport of heat by convection towards it. It is therefore scarcely feasible to forecast what the temperature will be at any one place by calculation alone, and reliable figures can be obtained only by actual measurement. What we are able to do is to account in broad outline for the distribution of heat on the earth's surface. First of all, we have to remember that the more acute the angle at which the rays strike a plane, the less will be the warmth imparted to a given area (Fig. 49). Moreover, the rays have to pass through a progressively thicker layer of air, by which they are further weakened. This of course explains why the Equator, with the sun at its highest altitude, is hottest and the Poles coldest. For the same reason, the times of the day and year when radiation is most intense are at noon and midsummer, though we actually experience the highest temperatures an hour or two later in the day and about six weeks after the summer solstice. This is because the transmission of solar heat, though now declining, still exceeds loss by radiation, evaporation and conduction, so the temperature continues to rise. Eventually, however, the cumulative loss incident upon rising temperature surpasses the diminishing supply, and from that moment the temperature begins to fall. The lowest temperature is attained soon after the shortest day and at the end of the night, just as dawn is breaking, when heat-loss has furthest outstripped heat-gain.

There exists, moreover, a fundamental difference between the continents and the oceans. Unlike the solid earth, the sea is comparatively permeable to the other rays of the sun; therefore, the heat received is spread over a thick layer and the temperature does not rise in anything like the same degree, while also the mobility of the sea helps to dissipate it. Further, water requires more heat per unit volume than rock to increase its temperature by an equal amount; and the greater evaporation from the sea has a cooling effect. Hence, other conditions being equal, the *temperature* in summer or during the day will rise less at sea than on land. That is why it is usually cooler down by the coast than inland, especially if an onshore wind predominates. On the other hand, the *quantity* of heat absorbed by the sea, i.e. the amount stored up for the night and for the winter, is larger, notwithstanding the lower temperature. This accounts for the mild winter climates of the oceans and adjacent areas. For instance, the formerly named Zuider Zee, during the winter, used to give off approximately 15×10^{16} cal. of heat to the ambient air, an amount comparable with that provided by a train of coal-wagons 6000 miles long.

Evaporation is another factor in the levelling influence of the oceans on temperature, for it intensifies with heat. Accordlingy, most of the water vapour in the atmosphere derives from tropical seas which, owing to this evaporation, are far cooler than they would otherwise be. This vast amount of "latent" heat is stored in the vapour carried by the lower air and released again directly condensation takes place. The sea wind carries a large amount of this energy in the form of potential heat of condensation to other regions.

Then there are the marine currents, which also mitigate contrasts of temperature. Warm currents, like the Gulf Stream, carry, as we have seen, an enormous amount of heat to higher latitudes. The colder currents admittedly have the reverse effect, in that they tend to cool off adjacent areas, but, cold water being heavy, they are more than likely to sink fairly soon and thus cease to affect the surface.

The word "desert" connotes in our minds a region of intense aridity and

PLATE VII

(*a*) Fine-weather cumulus with horizontal base and towering mass.

(*b*) A misty September morning in the province of Drente, Netherlands. The microscopic droplets which later the sun evaporates form a thick morning haze, visible especially near the hay-wagon.

PLATE VIII

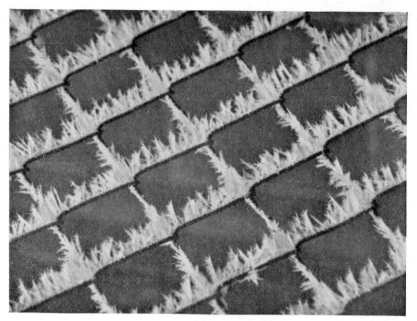

(*a*) Delicate crystals of hard rime, formed from mist and growing in one direction on a trellis of 5 cm. mesh.

(*b*) Frost-flowers inside a window about 3 ft. × 2 ft., taken at a time of fuel-shortage.

very high temperature, but is less evocative of the strong contrasts between day and night which prevail there. These are due to lack of water, for, as no heat is used up for evaporation, all of it is employed in raising the temperature, added to which, the absence of clouds exposes the whole region to the full brunt of solar radiation. Conversely, there is no protective water-vapour atmosphere to hold back outgoing radiation at night, and little heat is released by condensation to mitigate the fall of temperature. In this respect the Tropics, especially down by the coasts, are the exact opposite, as it is there that the water vapour has its maximum shielding effect, while the strong evaporation absorbs much of the circulating energy, which thus ceases to be available for temperature variations.

For meteorological purposes the temperature should be registered in the shade and in a place shielded from radiation; and, for the results to be comparable, the readings should always be taken at the same height above the ground, the international standard being 2 metres.

The highest temperatures registered are in deserts and exceed 50° C. (122° F.). This, of course, is many degrees above blood-heat and human life would be impossible at such places, were it not for the cooling of the skin by the rapid evaporation of perspiration. The lowest temperatures ever recorded were in Siberia, namely −70° C. (−94° F.). So these two extremes are farther apart than is boiling point from freezing point. The extremes of winter and summer in one and the same place are not as widely separated as these, but even so, the difference between the highest and lowest *average* temperature in Siberia is 50° C. On the Atlantic Ocean the corresponding figure is only 10° C.

Although the prevailing temperature on high single mountains is low, the variation in it tends to be moderate. Conditions are somewhat comparable to those in a captive balloon; the earth's influence being almost negligible, those factors usually responsible for marked changes do not come into play. Extensive plateaus are a very different matter; the expanse of solid rock is large enough to make its influence fully felt, causing variations within a wide range.

Like water, a covering of snow has its specific effect upon the ambient temperature. In the first place, snow reflects far more radiation than does any dark soil, yet emits just about the same amount, with the result that a much lower temperature prevails than on a surface not covered with snow. Through conduction, moreover, the air on the snow-covered ground becomes very cold. In summer, the great heat of liquefaction of snow absorbs a large proportion of solar heat and the temperature remains low until all the snow has melted. An east wind reaching Western Europe over a Central Europe

G

which chances to be under snow, is very much colder than it would be when it has passed uncovered land.

Our next point of enquiry is the relationship between temperature and humidity. Above the sea, the vapour pressure follows the temperature fairly closely, for the quantity of water evaporating is in direct ratio to the heat; and in winter it is the same on land. In the warm season, however, absolute humidity on land has a double maximum. In the morning, when the sun is beginning to warm the land and lower atmosphere, the vapour pressure

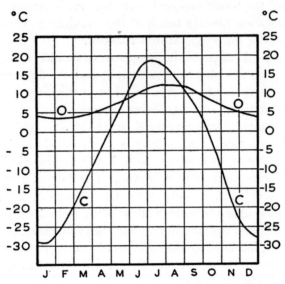

Fig. 50. Temperature chart of climate on mainland and at sea for a year. C, Average of 9 stations in Siberia. O, Average of 5 island stations in the Atlantic Ocean, all at approx. 60° N. latitude. (After Jong.)

increases; then there comes a drop while the heated air rises, giving place to colder, drier air from higher altitudes. Towards evening, convection of the air ceases and the vapour pressure begins to rise again, only to drop to its second minimum during the cold night.

The yearly movements follow the course of the temperature far more closely, because the humidity has more time to adapt itself to the gradually changing temperature.

The relative humidity generally tends to decrease when the temperature is rising, owing to insufficient supply of moisture to saturate the increasingly thirsty air. This applies in particular to the daily variations of temperature, which are comparatively rapid. It is only if constant sea-winds happen to co-operate that a peak of relative humidity sometimes coincides with the temperature maximum. Fig. 51 offers an eloquent example of this in the daily movements of temperature and humidity in Senegambia under the influence of wind blowing in from the sea.

For the earth as a whole, it is estimated that the water evaporating from the oceans every year amounts to 74 thousand cubic miles and from the continents, to 18, together therefore totalling 92 thousand cubic miles. This, then, is the stock, so to speak, from which our cycle has to draw for the further development of its activities.

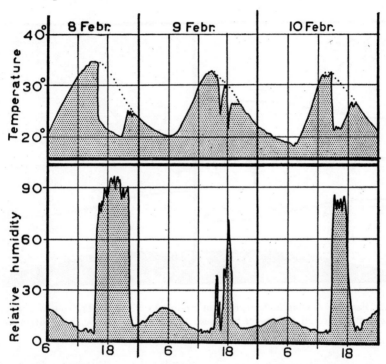

Fig. 51. Daily trend of temperature and humidity on the coast of Senegambia. The strong heat starts a sea-wind in the afternoon, which causes the relative humidity to soar suddenly.

Movement and Condensation of Water Vapour

It is necessary to distinguish between horizontal and vertical movements of the air, because the former seldom cause condensation of water vapour, whereas the latter generally do. Horizontal winds claim our attention inasmuch as they transport moisture from the sea to land, thus making our cycle an active geological agent. For, if it is to be active in this sense, water must be brought to high land in order to be able to drain off. Its potential energy can then be converted to kinetic energy and it can provide life on the continents with essential moisture. Besides, if the land no longer received moisture from the oceans, it would cease to provide opportunity for significant evaporation.

While it is true that vertical movements do not carry water vapour from the sea to the mainland, it is they which raise it above sea-level, hence increase its potential energy. Moreover, it is largely through cooling in the course of ascending movements that condensation occurs, and therefore, that the preliminaries to precipitation are set in motion.

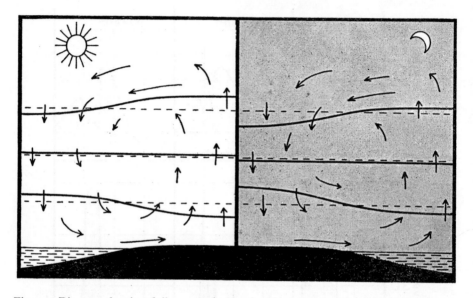

Fig. 52. Diagram showing daily reversal of land and sea winds. The dotted lines give the levels of initially equal barometer readings. The full lines show the position after the atmospheric currents have set in.

The horizontal and vertical movements of the air cannot be separated and will therefore be considered together. It is not uncommon for the air to ascend or descend obliquely and the two components of the movement are then indistinguishable manifestations of a single phenomenon.

Winds are initiated mainly by differential solar heating. Let us imagine an island lying in an area of calm. As soon as the sun rises (Fig. 52), the land becomes warmer than the surrounding sea; therefore, the lower layers of air above the island will be heated and must expand, forming a kind of mound of warm air. Just as water would do, the air at higher altitudes will flow down the sides of this mound, so that a belt will form all round, in which this flow is increasing the number of particles. A difference in pressure is thus generated, since there is less air above the island than at first, and more above the surrounding sea. Such a condition is unstable; the excess pressure will start off a wind in the lowest layers of air towards the land, i.e. what we call a sea-wind.

At night the process is reversed. The land, with the air resting on it, cools down more than the sea around it. This cooled air contracts, forming a "hollow" above the island, which has to be filled up with adjacent air. The column of air above the island thus becomes heavier than that above the sea and a land breeze now gently wafts seawards (Fig. 52).

The continental coasts are subject to the same influences, as illustrated in Fig. 51, but other factors usually predominate and a rhythmic alternation of land and sea winds is not clearly perceptible.

The same process takes place on a far larger scale and in slow motion where a whole continent becomes warm in summer and the winds blow in from the oceans, only to be replaced in the cold season by air currents going in the opposite direction towards the sea. These periodic winds are the well-known *monsoons*.

A room and an unheated corridor provide a model in miniature of this kind of exchange. If the door between them is left just ajar, it is easy to feel with one's hand or to show with a lighted match that the cold air down by the floor is streaming into the warm room, while higher up the warm air is escaping into the cold passage. Indeed, our ankles are the first to feel a draught through a chink in the door.

This interchange of air is seen on the largest scale between the Equator and the higher latitudes. Heat pours down with the maximum intensity on the Equator; hence the movement of air is upwards. There is little wind and barometric pressure is low, but high up it flows off laterally towards the Poles. Reaching subtropical regions, the stream of air, meanwhile cooled down, returns to the earth's surface, again in a zone of only minor horizontal air movements. Along the surface of the land, it is sucked back towards the Equator. The upper current—that is, the "anti-trade wind"—is, of course, imperceptible to us, but the surface winds in the opposite direction are the famous trade winds, the most constant winds we know (Fig. 53).

Nearer the Poles, the winds are far less constant, though westerlies predominate. In the Southern Hemisphere especially, where continental influences are less pronounced, these air currents in the "roaring forties" are only too well known to seamen. Closer still to the Poles, the dominating factor is the increasing cold, the salient features being high barometric pressures combined with a general downward trend in air movements. In these parts the air blows along the earth in the form of cold, north-east

winds and the places where they meet the warm winds coming in the opposite direction are the regions of the weather "fronts" and "depressions".

At medium latitudes we do not as a rule have the regular trade winds
and monsoons, but for all that, the wind always blows from areas of high
atmospheric pressure to pockets of low pressure. As, however, those areas
are continually shifting, breaking up and reforming, the winds are much
more changeable in character.

If we try, with the help of a chart of winds and barometric readings for a
given moment, to ascertain whether the air actually does move from regions

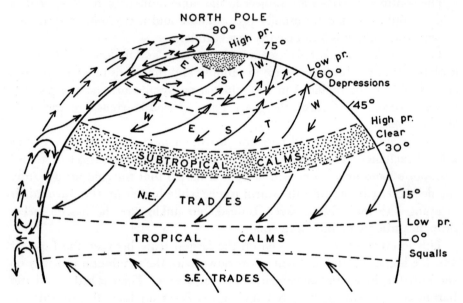

Fig. 53. Diagram showing terrestrial wind systems.

of high pressure to the depressions, the data at first sight do not appear to
confirm the theory. We must however allow for a demonstrable complication affecting all winds on this earth. On their absolute motion is superimposed an additional motion relative to the surface, owing to the earth's
rotation around its axis. Hence, any air current in the Northern Hemisphere
is deflected to the right, relatively to the surface, and, conversely, winds
in the Southern Hemisphere are deflected to the left. Air movements are,
moreover, modified by the spherical shape of the earth. The result is that in
the Northern Hemisphere air flowing out of a high pressure (anticyclonic) area
moves not radially but spirally outwards; while winds flowing in from high
to a low pressure (cyclonic) area tend to be directed first to right of its centre

before finally curving into it (Fig. 54). Exactly converse patterns are formed south of the Equator.

Tongues of cold heavy air often come down from arctic regions to moderate latitudes and "creep under" the milder light air (Fig. 55). The warm, dry air which is typical of areas of high atmospheric pressure is, on the other hand, often of subtropical origin. A very constant type of fine weather sometimes prevails in such areas of high barometric pressure with little or no

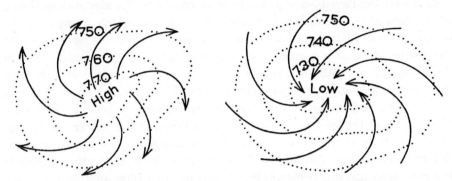

Fig. 54. Atmospheric pressure and wind systems around areas of high pressure (anticyclonic) and low pressure (cyclonic) in the Northern Hemisphere.

cloud. It is believed that these conditions are in large measure subject to the atmospheric pressure and winds in the stratosphere. Readers interested in the meteorological aspects of this matter and in weather forecasting are advised to refer to the more specialised literature.

What are known as *inversions* play an important part in vertical movements of air. It has already been pointed out that, generally speaking, the layers of air become colder with increasing distance from the ground. The air would therefore be heavier if the reduced pressure did not, on the contrary, involve a lower density. To discover whether the stratification is stable, we

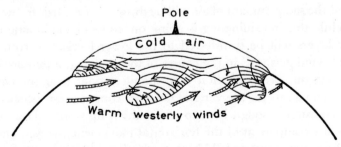

Fig. 55. Tongues of cold polar air travel southwards and insinuate themselves under the mild west winds at moderate latitudes.

have to perform an imaginary experiment by means of which a volume of air is caused to rise. If the resulting expansion brings about cooling exactly equal to the drop in temperature of the air all round the imaginary mass, the equilibrium is said to be neutral. Were the raised air to become colder than the layers into which it is introduced, it would also become heavier, and, if left to itself, would fall back, i.e. the stratification resumes its original condition after displacement—it is stable. When the distribution of temperature is such that the raised air is just a little warmer than its new surroundings, which means to say that it is lighter than the air which it reaches, the stratification is unstable. Now, when we speak of an *inversion*, we mean that the temperature as a certain height is reached suddenly rises, instead of dropping as it normally would. The cold, heavy air stays underneath, with the result that stratification is exceptionally stable; for, rising air cools down, as we know, and so the bottom layer would become even colder if it were lifted to above the level of the inversion. In this way the upward current of air in a thunderstorm will in many cases be stopped by an inversion layer. Sometimes the rising column can break through the first inversion, owing to the enormous upward pressure, but if the current strikes another inversion, it will seldom have enough power left to overcome this obstacle as well; the air above the second inversion layer is and remains lighter than the top of the thunder cloud. It is due chiefly to this phenomenon that the upper fringe of a thunderstorm often spreads somewhat in the form of an anvil (Fig. 58*b*).

The marked interaction between vertical and horizontal movements of air accounts for the fact that the wind so often drops in the evening, just as yachtsmen are preparing to set sail for home. At night, when the earth is cold, the cold and heavy air rests quietly on the ground; the wind in higher layers at some tens or hundreds of feet, encountering very little friction, skims unimpeded over this slow-moving lower mass. During the day, as the air in contact with the earth gradually warms up, rising currents will be formed and the same amount of air will be drawn downwards from the upper layers. While this intermingling is going on, some of the kinetic energy of the upper layers will be transferred to the lower levels. In common parlance, the "wind gets up" in the course of the morning, a manner of speech which betrays our preoccupation with manifestations near the earth's surface. As evening sets in, the vertical currents come to rest, because the sun no longer transmits enough heat to impel them upwards. Transfer downwards of some component of the horizontal movement ceases. The bottom layers of the atmosphere are held back by friction with the earth and become stationary. Then the upper wind regains its full force, though we are not

aware of it. All this may be enhanced or toned down by the effects of land-
and sea-wind; e.g. in clear weather a sea-wind will be checked in the evening by the cooling of the land, whereas a land-wind is stimulated by the
difference in temperature between the land and the sea.

Certain local winds have been given specific names. There is, for instance,
the Föhn wind of the Alps, a warm, dry, southerly wind which blows down
from the high passes along the valleys. It is developed somewhat in the
following fashion. When a south wind blowing against the Alpine chain has
to rise, cooling must often cause condensation of water vapour to heavy rain
or snowfalls against the southern slopes. That condensation releases a great
deal of warmth, and the air will therefore cool down only half as much as
it would at that height without condensation. Once this stream of air has
passed over the summits and flows down into the valleys on the other side,

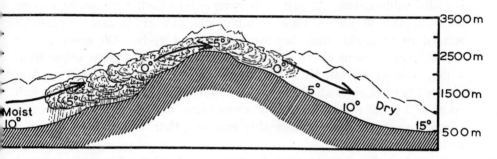

Fig. 56. The generation of the warm, dry Föhn wind from a moist wind which has passed
over a chain of mountains, shedding its moisture content on the way.

the compression will again tend to warm it. The process will not be precisely the reverse of what happened on the southern slope, because there has
been precipitation from the air. Only the small residue of moisture carried
along as clouds can now absorb heat of evaporation. Hence the heat of
compression is used almost in its entirety for elevation of temperature, which
is nearly twice as much as the cooling effected during the upward journey.
The air is consequently transformed into a dry, warm wind by the time it
reaches the northern foothills and it seems to the inhabitants as though they
feel the hot breath of the African desert on their faces. Actually, it is the same
air which drives the dwellers of the southern slopes indoors to seek refuge by
the fire from the cold and wet (Fig. 56).

Advancing whirlwinds eddying around a vertical axis are in a class apart.
They are called tornadoes in the United States, where they are comparatively
small, but particularly vicious. Owing to the immense centrifugal force,
there is a highly vacuous core in the axial line which sucks up water and all

manner of objects lying in its path. Typhoons, hurricanes and cyclones are of larger compass and occur usually at sea, especially along the eastern seaboards of Asia, America and Australia. Covering a larger area, these whirlwinds also last longer than tornadoes; as they advance along a certain path for days on end, shipping can be warned of their imminence and thus given time to seek refuge. When they eventually strike the coast, they die out, but not before raising huge waves, driving them inland and thus sometimes inflicting upon man one of those devastating catastrophes with which nature from time to time assails him.

Cloud Formation

Condensation of water vapour in the atmosphere produces minute drops of water. Ice crystals are formed if the temperature is below 0° C., and this is called sublimation. At first, it is immaterial whether the water vapour condenses into droplets of water or sublimates, as in either case the particles formed are so minute that they continue to float freely. The manifestation of condensation seen above, looking up at the sky, or as seen below from a mountain or aircraft, is called a cloud, but when the water- or ice-charged mass of air is all round us, we call it mist. The dalesman may well speak of a cloud round the peak of a mountain, but when the disappointed climber reaches it, he will justifiably complain that the mist robs him of a rewarding view.

It used to be thought that, because the droplets of water remained suspended, they must be bubbles, but that theory has long since been abandoned. They are globules varying from 0·005 to 0·5 mm. in diameter. We have *drizzle* when the drops have attained the comparatively large size of 0·1 to 0·5 mm., for by then they are becoming heavy enough to display a marked tendency to fall.

These drops may form as soon as the air contains more water vapour than could evaporate into it from a free surface of water at the prevailing temperature. This supersaturation with water vapour occurs either as the result of mixing or of cooling. If a current of warm, saturated air mingles with a mass of cold, likewise saturated air, the vapour content of the mixture will exceed the maximum pressure at the temperature which is now establishing itself. This seldom, however, causes more than a tenuous cloud or mist on the surface of the earth.

Otherwise all clouds are formed as the result of cooling to below the dew point. But clouds are not inevitably formed when this point is reached, owing to the phenomenon of super-cooling. Physicists have found that it is easier for molecules to escape from a convex liquid surface than from a flat one, and that the difference is in direct ratio to the curvature. Put in another way, a small droplet will be able to evaporate in a mass of air which, in relation to a flat surface of liquid, would be entirely saturated. Conversely, water cannot condense to a droplet until the pressure is higher than that required for precipitation in a flat water surface. Further, the smaller the drops are and, therefore, the more curved their surfaces, the greater will have to be the supersaturation compared to a flat surface. Supposing the cooling air contained no droplets at all; in that case, when precipitation is beginning, each centre of condensation can consist of only a few molecules at the initial moment of growth. The surface curvature of an embryonic droplet of this kind is so pronounced that very considerable super-saturation is needed to initiate condensation, and the saying "*Il n'y a que le premier pas qui coûte*" could not be better exemplified.

Condensation is, on the other hand, greatly facilitated by the presence in the air of small floating particles—say dust—provided they readily absorb moisture; for they are far larger than a molecule and, when covered with a film of water, they have from the outset a comparatively large radius of curvature and therefore require much less super-saturation. Hence the foreign particles, which appear to contaminate the atmosphere everywhere in varying degrees, act as "nuclei of condensation". There are multitudes of them—anything from hundreds to millions per cubic centimetre of air, with diameters varying from a hundred-thousandth to a millionth of a centimetre.

Normal dust appears to be comparatively inactive, but particles of salt, derived from evaporated spatters of sea-water, are ubiquitous as well. These are most apt to start off the formation of a droplet because, being hygroscopic, the salt attracts water. Their minuteness may be better appreciated when it is realised that, by the time they have formed the infinitesimal droplets in an ordinary mist by attracting water, the salt has been diluted down to a millionth part. It appears that electric charges of the nuclei further complicate the process.

The outstanding part played by nuclei of condensation may perhaps best be illustrated by the still notorious though now quite infrequent London fog. The smoke and soot from the chimneys of about one million private houses and many industrial plants make the atmosphere above the city so turbid that it effectively blankets the heat of the sun, keeping the temperature lower than on the surrounding hills. In addition, drops of sulphurous acid, likewise deriving from the chimneys, strongly stimulate condensation for, under the influence of daylight, these are transformed into sulphuric acid, which is far more hygroscopic and therefore promotes mist formation even in the face of rising temperature. These factors occasionally combine to produce very dense brown fogs, reducing visibility in the streets to practically nil and making it necessary to have all the lights on in the middle of the day. In the winter, the centre of a smoky city such as this is deprived of many hours of sunshine enjoyed by the suburbs.

In a cloud, the further cooling proceeds below the dew point, the greater will be the condensation of vapour; while if the temperature at which the latter begins is below 0°, ice crystals may be formed by sublimation. This, however, cannot take place without nuclei, usually very fine mineral dust. If these are lacking, condensation will occur—or continue, as the case may be—in the form of droplets, thus producing a so-called "super-cooled" cloud. As explained above, the droplets will need a very much lower temperature to begin to freeze. Even in the presence of suitable nuclei, however, sublimation rarely occurs until the temperature has dropped well below 0° C. If nuclei, though present, are few, both droplets and ice crystals are formed and we have a mixed cloud. Clouds consisting of ice crystals alone are usually very rarefied, because nuclei of sublimation are comparatively scanty, especially in the higher regions, where the prevailing temperature is below freezing point; besides, as has been seen, the available amount of water vapour at low temperatures is very small.

It may well be asked how the air comes to be cooled to below dew point. First of all, the temperature may be lowered considerably by nocturnal radiation. After a hot windless day, in particular, the lowest layers of the atmosphere will have absorbed a large amount of water vapour and, once the sun has set and the night sky is clear, intense radiation emanating from the earth will cause the temperature of the ground and of the contiguous layer of air to drop several degrees. This process may produce the familiar ground-frosts. With sufficiently high vapour pressure, condensation to ground-mists must inevitably occur. Ground-mist formed in this way is one of the most serious obstacles to flying. It is often slow to lift, because precipitation seldom comes from it; at most, it leaves a heavy dew. It bars passage to the rays of the sun, which are therefore unable to impart the necessary heat to induce evaporation of the droplets.

It is due to such conditions that, in winter, valleys and plains may be shrouded in heavy, cold air and it seems as though the thick blanket of cloud has banished the sun for ever, while those enjoying winter sports in the mountains are bathed in glorious sunshine. There is strong radiation from the upper part of the cloud, but the layers underneath remain cold under a continuous covering bank which holds down the melancholy, chill weather on the inhabitants of plain and valley.

Also, wherever warm and cold marine currents meet, the moist, warm air above the former cools off when it passes over the cold current. This is highly conducive to the development of mist. It is just such a rencounter which is responsible for the fogs prevalent around Newfoundland.

In the main, however, clouds are formed in a different way, namely by the ascent of moist air. Heat is not given off by the air to the surroundings, as in the cases we have been considering. The air is cooled as the result of an entirely different process. It was stated earlier that ascending air is exposed to diminishing pressure, expands and consequently cools, whereas descending air is compressed and therefore becomes warmer. This type of cooling is termed *dynamic cooling* by meteorologists and it is this which causes rainfall. It appears that the temperature drops by about $1°$ C. for every hundred metres of ascent, but if the temperature falls to below the dew point, involving condensation, a certain amount of counteracting heat of condensation is continually liberated. This balances half the dynamic cooling and the drop in temperature amounts in that case to only $\frac{1}{2}°$ C. for every hundred metres ascent.

Air is impelled upwards in a variety of ways. Ascent is said to be *forced* when a horizontal wind is deflected upwards by hilly or mountainous country. This is particularly notable when a moist sea-wind impinges upon coastal mountains, as in Scotland and Norway. A wetter climate yet, indeed one of the wettest in the world, is to be found in eastern India, where, again, the dominant factor is the forced ascent of a moist onshore wind. When wind impinges upon a tropical volcano, the air is driven perhaps a thousand metres upwards and must therefore cool down ten degrees or so. The air, moreover, contains a great deal of water vapour on account of the high initial temperature in the hot climate. It is not surprising to learn, therefore, that volcanoes in the tropics are exceedingly effective rain-makers.

In addition to high land, heavy, stable masses of air may form an obstacle causing forced ascent. The slow, continual climbing of air up this kind of obstacle is one of the most fertile sources of rainfall in the middle latitudes.

In contradistinction to this forced ascent, we have what is known as the *free ascent* of the air, when masses of air, heated by the sun, are made buoyant by their consequent expansion. Fine-weather cumuli and thunder-clouds belong to the condensation category of free ascent. Such a cloud only persists because the constant fall of water droplets formed by condensation is counteracted by an equivalent upward movement of vapour-laden air.

A very fine example of free ascent is afforded by the system of slope winds, occurring for instance on Indonesian volcanoes. When, in the course of the morning, the sun has sufficiently warmed the slopes of a volcano, air comes pouring in on all sides and rises along its flanks. Through the chilling effect of that upward movement, cumuli are formed, which can be seen slowly creeping up the slopes. At some distance from the summit, these clouds sheer away from the flanks, rise at first in a straight line and then, at a further height, spread out radially (Fig. 57). Precipitation from such clouds is not as heavy as that due to forced ascent.

Everyone has noticed that the bases of detached fleecy clouds sailing across the sky of a fine summer day are perfectly flat. Looking beyond at the horizon, where they seem to be packed closer together, it can be seen that all their bases lie in the same horizontal plane. That, of course, is not mere chance. If the air is rising somewhere, the dew point will, under the particular conditions, always be attained at a particular level and condensation

Fig. 57. Free ascent of air along the flanks of a volcano and the formation of a plume of clouds (cross-section).

will set in; under different circumstances, the dew-point level might well be different; but as long as the conditions do not change, the base of such clouds will always be precisely there. By contrast, the upper part is much more irregular in shape, indented here and bulging there. This upper part is formed where condensation ceases, and the ascending force is defeated by dynamic cooling. Its shape is irregular because the dimensions of the ascending current and other incidentals have a strong influence and the cloud is, as a rule, passing through succeeding phases of development.

During the day, the temperature will rise; so generally the flat bases of these clouds will likewise gradually shift to a higher level. We shall see later on that the degree of cloud-cover also follows a daily cycle.

In regions of low barometric pressure, the depressions of evil repute, air pours in from all sides, while there is a concurrent, constant ascent in the centre. It will be evident that these must become areas of rain. High-pressure regions, on the other hand, spell fine weather, because the air, constantly descending and spreading out all round, has no tendency to shed its water vapour.

Figure 55 shows the relation of some of the phenomena just discussed to weather in many parts of the temperate zones. We saw in Fig. 55 that sometimes a cold mass of air comes down into these zones from the Pole. If the development of one of these tongues is traced, it is found to display a marked west–east component of motion and an asymmetrical shape, with a steep side in front and a gentle slope at the back. Thus the warm air is rapidly pushed upwards by the oncoming cold front. Any boundary between warm and cold air is called a "front" by meteorologists and nowadays fronts loom large in weather forecasts. Now, the cold front with which we are dealing must, by this abrupt raising of the local air, chill it very considerably, bringing brief spells of heavy rain, of typical showers, in fact.

At the back of the tongue, the cold air is shifted forwards by the winds of the warm front coming in from behind, and the cold, moreover, is mitigated by mingling. When, as generally happens, a warm current of air runs up the gentle slope of the rear of the cold wedge, the upper stream will gradually expand and cool. That is why the passing of the cold front with its showers tends to be followed first by fair weather and then by a period of soft but persistent rain.

Labile equilibrium often prevails in the warm air before the cold front rolls up. The warm air has been strongly heated at the earth's surface, especially in hot, sunny weather, and in the course of the day has become lighter than the layers at a higher level. At the slightest provocation—e.g. a thin wedge of cold air—this labile equilibrium is broken up, causing the overheated air to rise. Once begun, this ascent continues up to high altitudes. There is marked condensation from the cooling air, enormous masses of cloud pile up and rise to many thousands of metres above the hot landscape; typical thunder-clouds loom up and finally discharge the abundant accumulation of condensing water in those violent thunderstorms in which hot summer days are prone to culminate. The hail which often accompanies them witnesses to the immense height to which the vapour has been carried before sublimation to ice took place. Thunderstorms of this kind usually die out at night because no more overheated air is formed to keep the upward impulse going.

One of the commonest causes of rain is the association of ascending air with depressions. In the medium latitudes, these tend to develop at the approximately west–east boundary between cold northern and warm southern masses of air. The cold air lies in a sharply-pointed wedge under the warm air. A wave trough develops, sloping slightly southwards, meeting the earth's surface in the form of a V with the open end facing south (Fig. 58a).

This wave-form is propagated rapidly eastwards, because this is the main direction of winds in these latitudes, one limb producing an eastern front, where warm air displaces cold, while the other is the western front, where

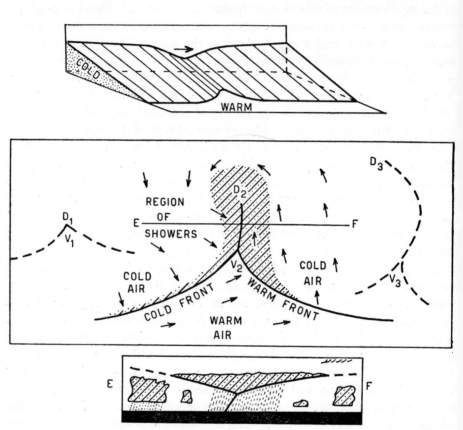

Fig. 58a. Wedge of cold air with a central trough, viewed (above) in perspective. A later stage is shown underneath in plan and section. D_1–D_3 successive positions of centre of depression, V_1–V_3 of meeting point of the fronts. Arrows denote direction of wind.

cold air supplants warm air. Low pressure—hence a depression—with strong winds circling round it, develops in the space between the two limbs. During the eastward movement, the cold front at the rear overtakes the warm front, squeezing the warm air in between upwards. This upthrust and those along the fronts produce the rain which falls in narrow strips along the fronts and with a wider range in the depression. In addition to this, there is an extensive region behind the cold front and the depression where showers occur.

Fig. 58*b* shows a slightly different situation where a cold tongue of air (see Fig. 55) travels eastward, with rain on the eastern side caused by the forced ascent of air, and on the western side caused by warm air flowing up the slope of the cold tongue.

Cloud Types

From the time man began to use his powers of reasoning, he observed the clouds and by degrees began to associate various phenomena with certain types of cloud. It does not require much perspicacity to notice that rain is liable to fall from dark clouds and that there is an evident relationship between thunder and cumuli. But a miller depending on a windmill has learnt to predict the direction and strength of the wind from the shape of the clouds and most countrymen have only to raise their eyes to the sky to tell with fair certainty whether rain is imminent or not. There existed no scientific classification of the types of cloud, however, until, in 1803, an Englishman correlated their shapes, physical properties (i.e. composition), height, and so on. His classification was so comprehensive and sound that it still stands, almost unchanged, notwithstanding the immense progress made by modern meteorology in its analyses of cloud formation. The modern system of cloud definition, although considerably more detailed, is based on the original principle. As the various types of cloud are not clear-cut, the descriptive names assigned to them were unavoidably apt to be somewhat arbitrary. It was therefore decided to

Fig. 58*b*. A cold tongue of air travelling from left to right. Cold front with thunderstorm; warm front with persistent rain. In between, sunny weather with cumuli.

H

establish an international nomenclature, providing all observers with a universal "cloud language" by which they could make themselves unambiguously understood. Artificial lines of demarcation of this sort have to be drawn for all natural phenomena which merge into each other. For instance, without a prearranged terminology no two people could agree as to exactly where the yellow strip of a rainbow merges into the orange or green.

We can classify clouds in the first place as: 1. *Individual clouds.* 2. *Stratified clouds*, sometimes subdivided into streaky or flaky. 3. *Blankets.* Then we may differentiate high, medium, low, and of great vertical extent. In this way we arrive at 4 families and 10 genera.

FAMILY A. HIGH CLOUDS, usually 6000 to 13,000 metres, consisting of small solid or hollow columnar ice crystals.

1. *Cirrus* (from tendril or fringe). Detached tufts or bands of delicate fluffy or streaky fabric, the so-called feathery clouds, without shadows. They are always pure white, except at sundown (or sunrise), when they are often tinged pink when the lower-lying clouds have already become (or are still) grey. The fibrous structure is due to the arrangement of the crystals in lines of flow, although the streaks need not necessarily lie in line with the wind (Plate VI, 1). It is not uncommon to see bands of cirrus cloud across the sky, seeming to radiate from a common origin. Actually, such bands are parallel and only *appear* to converge as the result of perspective, as do the parallel rays of the sun.

2. *Cirro-cumulus* (cumulus = pile). To this class belong those fleecy clouds which, colloquially, form a mackerel sky. They are small rounded masses or flakes of cloud without shadows, arranged in groups or lines, sometimes like ripples.

The appearance of a mackerel sky or other rhythmical shapes of cloud has been effectively accounted for by showing that friction occurs if one layer of air sweeps over another, transforming the boundary plane between them into an undulating interface. The air passing along these waves is being constantly forced to expand and is then compressed again. If the air is just saturated with water vapour, condensation will occur as it expands, and evaporation when it is compressed. If it is the top layer which is involved, clouds will therefore be formed in the rising sector, while a clear sky will develop in the descending portion. The small variations in air pressure following each other in rapid succession when a set of cirro-cumuli are passing overhead have, in fact, been registered on the ground. The period, i.e. the speed at which cirro-cumuli sail past, varies from two to four minutes. Corrugation also occurs with some of the other genera of cloud (Plate VI, 2).

3. *Cirro-stratus* (stratus = layer). A thin sheet of whitish cloud, varying in density, sometimes imparting a slightly pale appearance to the sky, at others covering it with a milky haze, which scarcely obstructs the passage of the sun's rays, but often produces a beautiful halo round sun or moon. These haloes are only faintly tinted, but are made conspicuous by the darker hue of the sky within the circle than outside it. If cirro-stratus covers large expanses of sky, it is fairly certain that umbrellas and mackintoshes will be needed in the next twenty-four hours.

FAMILY B. MODERATELY HIGH CLOUDS, from 2000 to 6000 metres, liable to contain massive small discs of ice in addition to water droplets.

4. *Alto-cumulus* (altus = high). Thick, rounded masses, or strips of clouds, sometimes contiguous, with shaded (hence darker) portions, arranged in groups or lines. The thin edges are often iridescent, or have the sheen of mother-of-pearl.

5. *Alto-stratus.* A thin to dense veil of cloud, grey to bluish in colour, often of fibrous structure, through which the sun is sometimes only just visible or penetrates only patches. There is no halo. There are transitions to cirro-stratus, but also to nimbo-stratus, and this explains why rain sometimes falls from it.

FAMILY C. LOW CLOUDS occurring below 2000 metres, which may contain star-shaped crystals or flakes of ice in addition to drops of water.

6. *Strato-cumulus.* Strips or rounded masses of cloud, often completely covering the sky in waves and consisting of fairly large elements. They are seen predominantly in winter, a dirty grey in colour and with irregular borders. Sometimes, instead of blanketing the sky altogether, they show patches of blue sky here and there, or a higher bank of clouds. They are called mammato-cumulus if they have rounded protuberances on their lower surfaces. This genus often develops from cumuli in the evening and, not infrequently, a nimbo-stratus is formed from it if the cloud cover becomes even more evenly spread and streaks of rain detach themselves from it.

7. *Stratus.* An unbroken, flat sheet of cloud, rather like mist, but not reaching down to the ground. When its under-surface is ragged, it is called fracto-stratus and it sometimes sheds drizzle. Now and again more relief may become discernible, the stratus then tends to break up and show patches of blue sky.

8. *Nimbo-stratus* (nimbus = rain cloud). A low-hanging, shapeless bank of cloud, an even dark grey in colour, from which steady rain or snow may fall. This, however, by no means invariably reaches the ground, and may evaporate again on the way, nevertheless imparting a distinctly damp appearance to this genus. It is often difficult to distinguish this from the

preceding genus. Frequently it is formed from a descending, thickening layer of alto-stratus with fracto-stratus beneath it.

FAMILY D. CLOUDS WHICH DEVELOP VERTICALLY, occurring anywhere between 500 metres and the cirrus level many thousands of metres higher.

9. *Cumulus.* Thick piled-up clouds, the upper surface of which is dome-shaped with semi-circular protuberances while the base is generally horizontal. They occur as a rule at a height of about 1000 metres. When light falls upon them from the side, they stand out in strong relief, but, seen against the sun, they are dark with light margins. Their contours are well defined and, fair-weather clouds as they are, it is upon them that the cherubs are reputed to frolic (Plate VII, 1).

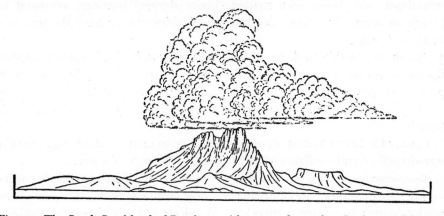

Fig. 59. The South Sea island of Borabora with a cap of cumulus cloud created by up-draughts induced by the sun. (After Davis.)

Cumuli are formed in updraughts in an otherwise clear sky. As has been stated, the horizontal base is situated at the place where these updraughts reach the dew point (Fig. 59). If these clouds reach any considerable altitude, they are covered on top by a thin veil of cirrus-like texture.

10. *Cumulo-nimbus.* These clouds are even more markedly vertical in their structure than cumuli, rising in great masses like towers or mountains to as much as 9000 metres. These are the true thunder-clouds, but in point of fact the pure type of cumulo-nimbus should exhibit a fibrous structure at the top. Gliders have reported vertical currents of air in this cloud type of 10 to 20 metres per second and some have succeeded in gliding to a height of 9000 metres in the updraughts. The top enters the region of ice formation, with the result that the outlines at the top are somewhat blurred. If this upper part comes up against an inversion which it is unable to pierce, it flattens out and the typical anvil shape is formed.

The base of the cumulo-nimbus cloud is reminiscent of nimbo-stratus and usually rain, hail or snow falls from it in short, sharp showers. They have been styled "cloud factories", because other types of cloud sometimes issue from them: e.g. cirrus may develop from the top part, or a mass of alto-cumulus may detach itself.

Specialists elaborate the classification of clouds by subdividing the genera into a number of varieties according to typical properties and shapes. There are, in addition, certain nebular manifestations, such as "luminous noc-turnal clouds", the nature of which is not as yet fully understood, but they have little to do with precipitation and the cycle. In passing, however, we should mention those artificial cumuli which rise up from serious con-flagrations.

There is one type in a class all by itself, which might well be regarded as the eleventh genus, viz., *eruption clouds*. Every volcanic eruption produces some kind of cloud, but these are almost as various as normal clouds. Their density and darkness are in direct proportion to the amount of volcanic ash hurled into the air. Their dimensions and altitude depend not only on the quantity spewed out, but also on the nature of the eruption. The higher the pressure of the gases escaping with the lava, the greater the distance to which the eruption cloud is shot into the atmosphere. In the 1906 eruption of Vesuvius, the gases rose six miles and then spread into an extensive "cauli-flower cloud". The mighty explosions during the devastating eruption of the Krakatoa in 1883 flung the pitch-black masses of cloud to a height of 20 miles (see Fig. 48) and the finest dust reached an even greater altitude. In the catastrophe which befell Montagne Pelée in the West Indies in 1902, it was the heavy clouds of ash and burning hot gases which rolled *down* the flanks of the volcano which razed the town of St. Pierre, at its foot, to the ground.

Water vapour in varying amounts is an ingredient of all these types of eruption cloud, but we have no idea of the exact quantity. Heavy down-pours of rain are often associated with eruptions, from which some have inferred that volcanic gases contain a large percentage of water, an inference which is highly questionable. For there can be no doubt that the jet of gas escaping from the volcano carries ambient moist air with it as it rockets into the sky and that air naturally expands and cools (see Fig. 1). The resulting condensation is indubitably the principal factor causing precipita-tion during many eruptions.

What is the percentage of moisture in volcanic gases is likely to remain a moot point and we cannot, therefore, tell how much water sweats through by this means from the interior of the earth to its surface. Compared to the whole mass of the oceans, it must be a very small fraction.

The floods which accompanied the Kelud disaster of 1919 had a very different origin. This is a volcano in the eastern portion of Java with a crater lake, the contents of which overflow during every eruption. On this particular occasion, huge quantities of water suddenly cascaded down the slopes of the mountain, destroying the coffee plantations and covering the foot of the cone with a thick cake of mud. Scorching ash heated the water to boiling point and clouds of volcanic gases came sweeping down the slope to add horror to the calamity.

Comparing the amount of cloud relative to the visible surface of blue sky, we find that there is both a daily and yearly rhythm. Nocturnal radiation and cooling produce maximum cloud in the early morning hours towards sunrise. The warmth of the morning sun dispels much of it but, in the course of the afternoon, this same warmth, causing the ascent and dynamic cooling

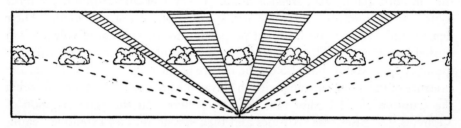

Fig. 60. Apparent piling-up of clouds towards the horizon. Visible blue sky is hatched in the figure.

of the atmosphere, again amasses cumulus clouds. As evening comes on, this vertical movement subsides and, by the time the sun has set, there is relatively little cloud left. Cloud cover is also seen to vary with the seasons.

It would be well to remember, however, that an observer looking at the whole vault of heaven within his view is bound to receive an exaggerated impression of the amount of cloud present. It is only immediately above our heads that we can gauge the exact percentage of cloud delineated against the blue sky. Farther off towards the horizon, the clouds appear to pile up, but this is due to their thickness, as will be clear from Fig. 60.

Dissolution of Clouds

Clouds not only form and gather; they also disperse and vanish, and clearly the two processes strike an approximate balance. We ourselves are seldom aware of the dissolving; to us it merely seems as though the clouds are passing overhead and are replaced by a clear blue sky. If we observe more attentively, however, we can sometimes see the clouds fading away or contracting.

This may be due to one of several processes. First of all, there may be precipitation from a cloud: the surplus drops of water or ice crystals fall out of
it and the saturated but clear air remains behind. Clouds and mist can
however dissolve without precipitation. If a fog bank absorbs solar heat or
receives heat radiated from the earth, the temperature may rise sufficiently
to vaporise all the droplets it contains and "the fog lifts", as we say. When
unsaturated air mingles with the margins of a cloud, the water droplets will
evaporate and the cloud will waste away from its periphery inwards.

Down-draughts are common destroyers of clouds. This movement involves compression, hence heating. The warmed air is able to contain more
water vapour and the elements of the cloud will therefore evaporate. We
came across an example of this process when we were considering the Föhn
wind.

Turbulence is of equal importance. A rising wind or the passage of air
over uneven territory intensifies intermingling and eddying. Turbulence
may also result from heating of the air by the earth's surface. It induces
mixing, by which dry air from without is introduced into the mass of a cloud,
which begins to expand. A layer of mist resting on the ground may be
transformed by the same process into low-lying cloud. As the average
humidity is decreased by this influx of drier air the drops begin to evaporate,
and the cloud or fog may dissolve entirely.

The majority of these processes represent side-paths, what we may call
"back-loops" from the cycle, since they do not carry water down from the
atmosphere to the earth but turn it back again into vapour. Precipitation
alone takes water a step forward on the road which we are following.

Forms of Precipitation

Although rain is the most common form of precipitation, the expression
includes snow, hail, dew, hoar-frost, rime and glazed frost. We shall consider these briefly one by one.

Dew is moisture deposited upon objects such as grass, pavement, etc.,
which have been chilled considerably, by nocturnal radiation in particular.
With no wind to stir the lowest layers of the atmosphere and a clear, star-lit
sky conducing to radiation, flat, horizontal objects will drop to a lower
temperature than the air. The air, in turn, is cooled by contact with them.
Sometimes this results in the formation of ground-mist, but as a rule the
water vapour precipitates upon the cold objects on passing the dew point.
Only a thin layer of air is involved in feeding the dew. The moisture thus
imparted to the soil is by no means all gain to it. In the first place, much of
it will evaporate in a short time; secondly, some moisture will first have

risen from the damp, warm soil; thirdly, an appreciable amount of the moisture deposited on grass and other plants does not derive from dew in the narrower sense at all, but is sweated outwards through the capillaries of the plants themselves.

The diurnal temperatures in the desert vary within a very wide range and, although the 24-hour average humidity of the air may be very low owing to the great heat during the day, dew is liable to be formed towards dawn, when the thermometer has dropped to nearly freezing point. The sun has only just to rise above the horizon, however, for the dew to evaporate in the twinkling of an eye, and the soil to become bone dry again.

Hoar Frost. Outside the Tropics, the dew point may be below 0° C. in the cold season. If, then, surfaces under a clear sky cool down to below freezing point owing to radiation, the water vapour will sublimate on them as a solid and the result will be a hoar frost. True hoar frost consists of very thin crystal skeletons deposited by immediately adjacent air, upon roofs, grass, a covering of snow, etc. Its characteristic feature is its crystalline structure, which makes it glisten in the sun when seen at close quarters.

A fundamentally different process is at work when mist is super-cooled and its minute droplets adhere to all manner of objects and freeze to crystal skeletons. White films of very light weight then grow in thickness up to a centimetre and more on one side—the windward—of such things as twigs, telephone wires and the like. This is, correctly speaking, *Hard Rime*, but colloquially is usually referred to as hoar frost. Sometimes it takes a dull, granular form, but often it consists of small crystal skeletons which sparkle in the sun, imparting brilliant splendour to the winter scene when the mist lifts (Plate VIII, 1).

Glazed Frost derives from another process again: when large drops fall upon ground chilled to below freezing point, they spread out into a thin, transparent crust of ice. It is this which makes roads and streets perilously slippery and occasionally encases all vegetation.

Hail consists of irregularly shaped or round pellets of ice, usually cloudy, very occasionally clear and sometimes made up of alternating films of clear and milky-white ice a few millimetres thick. Hailstones are usually less than a centimetre in diameter, but some giants have been picked up now and again of as much as ten inches and weighing more than eight pounds. Hail falls usually during a thunderstorm, never when there is a frost. A curious thing about hail is that its temperature is far below freezing point. Anyone caring to take the trouble to collect a mugful of hailstones during a shower and place a thermometer in it will see the mercury falling to far below 0° C., attesting to the immense altitudes to which the stones are carried by the strong updraughts in the cumulo-nimbus cloud from which they ultimately tumble down. In clouds of this kind, currents may rise at the rate of 10 to 20 metres per second, and in this way large chunks of ice can, literally, be blown sky-high. The non-transparent layers are produced by sublimation of crystal skeletons around an ice nucleus, whereas the clear layers are ascribed to the collecting of super-cooled drops, hence to a species of glazed frost formation.

Snowflakes consist of crystal skeletons. The fine, powdery snow which falls during severe frost is a collection of tiny discs of beautiful hexagonal structure. The thick flakes associated with less acutely cold days are built up of an irregular agglomeration of crystal skeletons. They arise through sublimation of water vapour at a moderately low temperature and substantial supersaturation of the vapour. Whereas the temperature of dry snow is generally below freezing point, that of the wet snow accompanying a thaw is zero. The latter type, indeed, consists of a mixture of ice and water which can only exist at the freezing point. Sometimes the water acts as an adhesive and cements several separate flakes into a large one. These seldom grow to more than 3 centimetres, but agglomerations of about 10 centimetres have been seen now and again.

It is very rare for snow to fall from a clear sky, but the fine, dry snow laid down in frosty weather is apt to be picked up by a high wind and driven off the ground, leaving bare patches. The driven snow piles up into mounds and ridges behind any barrier in its path. In dry, frosty weather, much dust tends to fly with the snow and soil it, forming a protective layer when the thaw sets in, and retarding the final disappearance of the slush.

Freshly fallen snow lies in a layer about ten times the thickness of the corresponding amount of water. Wet snow, however, is far more compact and coheres more closely on the ground. At the end of six months, the density of snow lying on the mountains already comes to one-half, that of the *Firn* or congealing snow of glacier basins is also as a rule from 0·4 to 0·5, while, once it has been converted to glacier ice, the density is as much as 0·8.

If the air is very cold, but only slightly supersaturated with *water vapour*, compact ice crystals are formed instead of the crystal skeletons with which we have been dealing so far. This combination is most commonly found at considerable altitudes and it appears that the feathery clouds of the cirrus type are composed of these minute columns and platelets. Such conditions seldom prevail close to the earth's surface and then only in a severe frost. Innumerable little sparkling needles then flutter in the air and are clearly visible when the sun shines. We shall be reverting to the subject of snow in the next chapter.

Friable grains of hail or pellets like snowballs about the size of a pea are called *Soft Hail*. On closer examination they are found to consist of snow crystals which have been encased and agglomerated by deposition of ice of the hard rime type. In showery weather, soft hail falls in short, sharp bursts and occurs most frequently in the springtime, often preceded or immediately succeeded by ordinary flaky snow.

Rain. Finally we come to rain, the most important form of precipitation. Rain likewise seldom falls from a clear sky, drops of normal size being usually heralded by the appearance of cloud. If the droplets in the cloud grow and become too heavy, they fall out of it and we say that it is "drizzling". The greater the height from which they fall, the larger do they generally become, because the quicker drops catch up and swallow the smaller ones. It appears, however, that big drops of rain depend for their formation upon the prior fall of ice crystals from above into a wet cloud, serving as centres around which the liquid water collects. This also accounts for the fact that the heaviest downpours tend to occur when the cloud reaches to the height where temperatures of $-10°$ C. prevail. That is alto-stratus, possibly merging into nimbo-stratus and cumulo-nimbus clouds at a lower level.

The growth referred to may take place in various ways. The droplets of rain may evaporate while at the same time the ice crystals, exerting a stronger attraction on the vapour, grow into larger snowflakes; or else the ice crystals if larger will fall at a faster rate than the water drops and catch them up, with the result that sometimes snowflakes are formed, sometimes soft hail, or even real hailstones. Updraughts may hold the particles in suspension, giving the grains of hail a chance to grow into sizeable stones. Once the flakes or grains have begun to fall, they reach progressively warmer layers, where they may melt and coalesce into large drops of rain. Evidently, therefore, a drop of rain has passed through many vicissitudes by the time we see it land (see Fig. 61).

Rain of an entirely different kind falls when a warm current of air glides slowly upwards along a wedge of cold air, as shown diagrammatically in Fig. 62. At A there is only drizzle, because the cloud cover is situated below the ice-line and cannot produce larger drops. At B the cloud cover reaches a higher level and the drops are therefore bigger. On the left, precipitation can be seen to leave the cloud as snow, which does not turn to rain until it has fallen below the $0°$ level. At C, a shroud of falling snow is suspended from the high cloud cover, the snow evaporating before it can turn to rain. Finally, at D there is only a cover of cirrus cloud to warn observers that bad weather is on the way.

The percentage of liquid water in a cloud is always comparatively small, the maximum in a very dark cloud being approximately 1/3 gram per cubic foot, and it is safe to say that a cloud invariably contains far more vaporous than condensed water. There is also a physical limit to the size of the drops, namely 1/6 inch in diameter, for, although larger drops are constantly being formed, they disintegrate while falling through the air. Drops in a single shower may be of either uniform or of very varied sizes.

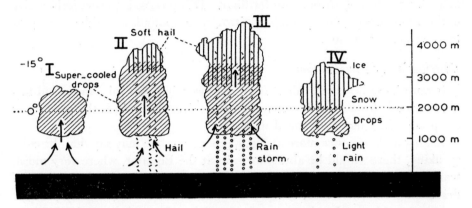

Fig. 61. Successive stages in the development of a cumulus cloud and the precipitation falling from it.

The falling of raindrops has been the subject of close study and it has been established that velocity and diameter are closely associated. Droplets of 1/100 of an inch in diameter fall 1 inch per second; the largest drops attain to 25 feet per second. Hence an upward current of air exceeding 25 feet per second prevents any rain from reaching the earth. It has already been stated that gliders have proved the existence of far higher speeds of ascent in clouds.

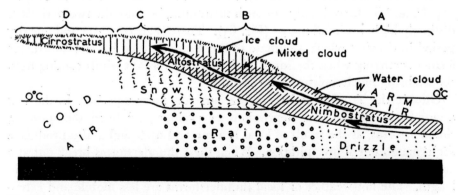

Fig. 62. Precipitation caused by the gradual rising of a warm above a cold mass of air.

Although rain is distilled water and might as such be expected to be particularly pure, it is nevertheless contaminated in a variety of ways during its descent. Apart from much dust, all sorts of dissolved substances have been identified in rain, e.g. carbonic acid, ammonia, nitrates and nitric acid. Some of these result from electric discharges acting on the nitrogen in the atmosphere and are, therefore, in a way, the products of a natural manufacturing process of nitrogenous fertiliser. This process is particularly active in the Tropics, where ten pounds of nitrogen compounds are added each year to every acre of the soil.

Distribution of Precipitation

It must have become evident from the foregoing that rain and cloud formation result from roughly the same causes, but that rain is the product of the process in a more advanced stage.

Taking a glance once more at Fig. 53, page 102, we may say that, broadly speaking, there should be abundant rain at the Equator, where very moist, warm air tends to rise. Outside the Tropics, however, in the regions of descending currents of air, compression and heating will normally produce a dry atmosphere. Farther towards the Poles, depressions at the fronts of cold and warm air cause precipitation in quantity. At the Poles themselves there is little precipitation, owing to the downward movement of air and the small moisture content of the cold atmosphere.

We can now proceed to consider a few details.

There are two wet periods within the Tropics, at each passage of the sun through the zenith, hence when it is producing most heat. It is then, too, that the upward movement of the air reaches its maximum, giving a peak in the rain chart (Fig. 63). The region where this double rainy season develops is situated between latitudes 10° N. and 10° S. From there to the Tropics (23° N. and S.) there is only one such maximum, because the two periods of distinctly higher rainfall merge (Fig. 63). There is also one wet and one dry period in districts where a climate of the monsoon type has developed, the former occurring when the sun is high and the constant winds coming from the sea bring much moisture with them.

Outside the Tropics we have rising currents, more especially in the vast atmospheric vortices, the depressions or cyclones, while in the summer, thunderstorms, as the result of local heating and updraught, also produce a slight maximum of precipitation. When these thunderstorms break out at a cold front, they are liable to occur along a strip several hundreds of miles in length. The hot-weather or local thunderstorms are less mobile and extensive, for which very reason they are liable to remain active for a protracted

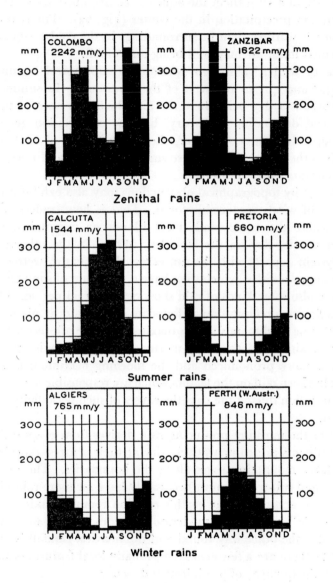

Fig. 63. Examples of varying distribution of precipitation during the year.
(After Jong.)

period in the same locality. Also, for days on end isolated showers may develop without any general break in the weather.

The oceans, and with them the adjacent coasts, outside the Tropics have their maximum precipitation in the winter (Fig. 63). The reason is clear: since the sea is warmer than its surroundings in the cold season, the ascent of the warmed moist air may well bring on rainfall.

An area of winter rains also develops in subtropical regions between latitudes 30° and 40° to the west of the continents. In summer at these latitudes there is a dry belt where the air which had risen at the Equator descends; and descending air is dry, because compression generates heat (see Fig. 53). In winter, however, the whole system of circulation shifts towards the other hemisphere where summer prevails and normal cyclonic rain is precipitated within this belt.

Rain caused by topographical obstructions may also exhibit a periodicity due to that of winds responsible for it. That is how trade-rains are precipitated where the trade winds meet islands or mountains, while it is more than usually dry on the lee-sides. When, in the other season, the cyclonic system departs with the sun across the Equator, wetter days may visit those same lee-sides, which then have a modicum of summer rain.

There are also some kinds of rain showing a diurnal period. On the seaboard, maximum precipitation is found to occur late at night, while the continental type of climate shows a maximum in the afternoon and a small secondary maximum in the early morning. In the Tropics the afternoon maximum is more pronounced and the morning maximum is very slight. After what has been said on the factors which are responsible for the variations in cloud formation during the day, the causes of such periodicity can readily be deduced.

As most of the moisture producing rain derives from evaporation at sea, the big continents are comparatively dry at their centres, especially where there are large mountain ranges along the boundaries. The east coasts in the Tropics and sub-tropics must necessarily have far more rainfall than the west coasts, on account of the earth's rotation round its axis and the consequent "trade" winds. In moderate latitudes, where west winds predominate, it is the other way round and the heaviest rainfall is on the west coasts. Thus there are a few general and many local features of the climate upon which the quantity of precipitation depends.

Before considering some of the statistics, the methods for measuring precipitation should be examined. A rain gauge is a vessel insulated against heat to prevent evaporation and placed out of doors to collect falling rain or snow. At regular intervals the contents are decanted into a graduated, narrow collecting vessel and the number of cubic centimetres is read. There also exist automatically registering gauges providing continuous readings of rainfall, a very welcome facility for showing how much rain has fallen in a short time, say ten minutes or half an hour.

Even such a small obstacle in the path of the wind somewhat constricts its course and momentarily speeds it up, so that rain or snow particles are apt to be swung past the rain gauge and to be dropped some little distance behind it. Eddies of air around it have a similar effect, accentuated in proportion to the strength of the wind. In a blizzard 40 per cent to 50 per cent of the snowfall may evade registration in this way. This also explains why high-placed rain gauges record less precipitation than those set up at a lower level—from which it was long held, erroneously, that precipitation diminished at increasing altitude. Unless a rain gauge is effectively shielded from the wind, its readings must inevitably give short measure.

Confining ourselves for the moment to Europe in a search for regions of high rainfall, Styehead Pass in the English Lake district is found to be the wettest place, with 170 inches per year. Though rarely registering more than half the record of Styehead Pass, the west coasts of Scotland, Norway and Portugal also have high figures. The only other places with comparable rainfall are on the west coast of Montenegro. If, however, we go outside Europe, especially in tropical regions, we shall find climates which, for wetness, far surpass those we have cited. The annual average measured at the south-west foot of the Kamerung Peak is 420 inches, while Padang, Sumatra, records 180 inches. Cherrapunji in Assam registers 430 inches, while Mount Waialeale (5800 feet, Hawaii Islands) holds the world's record with no less than 480 inches a year. The rainiest area of its size is undoubtedly Indonesia.

There is not a place on this globe which has no rain at all, for showers occur very sporadically, and sometimes with intervals of several decades, in even the driest deserts. When such showers do visit patches of these arid regions, they usually fall with a vengeance. The parched soil avidly sucks up this torrential rain and only very gradually yields it up again. Apparently the seeds of various desert plants are widely disseminated and some are lying in wait where the rain falls. These begin to sprout after the downpour, so that fairly luxuriant vegetation springs out of the ground as by magic. Slowly but surely all the moisture is consumed and one plant after the other wilts and dies, until finally even the toughest of them is defeated. This process may continue for months, or even years, and that is why travellers in the desert sometimes come across patches of vegetation in various stages of desiccation. The conclusion that the deserts of our world are drying out and that our age has been preceded by a wetter period may be true but the evidence is faulty. We now know that the manifestation is merely the protracted aftermath of widely separated local downpours.

The average rainfall for the whole of the solid earth is estimated to be 28 inches a year. The total amount falling in one year on all continents and islands is 25,000 cubic miles, while about three times that amount of precipitation falls into the oceans. It would take the Rhine no less than 5000 years to drain off all the water falling on land in the course of twelve months. But as less than half the quantity is in fact brought down to the sea by rivers, the balance evidently evaporates.

Before leaving the subject of water in the atmosphere, let us take a glance at the quantities of precipitation within shorter periods. The world's day maximum was registered in Cherrapunji, mentioned above, where no less than 41 inches of rain fell on 14th June 1876—nearly double the world average for a whole year—and 113 inches from 12th to 16th June, about four times the yearly figure for Britain. At Baguio in the Philippines, 47 inches were collected between 14th and 15th June 1911. On the Kii Peninsula in Japan, 36 inches were registered on 19th August 1889. All these very high figures were reported by meteorological stations situated on the slopes of hills or mountains.

At Porto Bello, Panama, 2½ inches fell in 5 minutes on 29th November 1911; at Galveston, Texas, 4 inches in 14 minutes on 4th June 1871; 1 inch at Tournai in Belgium in 6 minutes on 10th July 1889; and at Palmetto, Nevada, 9 inches in 60 minutes in August 1890.

It will be clear from these figures that tropical showers of rain do not much exceed in violence the cloudbursts which occur in our own latitudes, but that the downpour is liable to be more prolonged.

In view of the large quantity of rain which may fall out of the sky during a few minutes, it is interesting to know that, on a damp summer day in Europe, the entire height of the atmosphere cannot contain more water than would form a 1½-inch layer of water. Seeing that in a single hour several times this amount may deluge one particular spot, we have to assume that air is sucked in laterally during the torrent, drops its moisture while rising and escapes sideways at a high altitude. There is no other plausible explanation which would account for the known maximum downpours. Indeed, this fits in very well with what we know of the usual cause of precipitation, namely, an upward current of air which is cooled to below the dew point by expansion.

PLATE IX

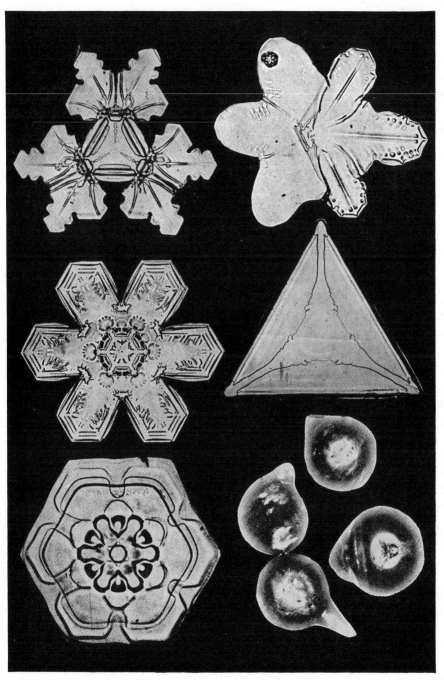

Snow crystals and hailstones. Even Nature occasionally has aberrations. (*Photo Bentley.*)

PLATE X

Variations on a hexagonal theme. (*Photo Bentley.*)

IV

Water in the Solid State

Most of the water vapour condensing in the atmosphere is sublimated to snow. Admittedly, this as a rule thaws and turns into raindrops before it reaches the ground, but none the less a substantial percentage of all precipitation comes to rest on the continents in one or other form of solid ice, thus following the longest route of the cycle. In this chapter we shall be concerned with the fate of that precipitation which falls as snow, until it has thawed and has been swallowed up in streams or in ground-water.

Snow Lying on the Ground

The simplest case we have to deal with is that of snow melting as soon as it touches down, which it very often does in spring and autumn. The ground is then several degrees above freezing point and the wet snow itself is just about to melt into water. It is only where the snow amasses in somewhat larger bulk that the great heat of fusion required uses up all that is immediately available and a little time elapses before the necessary calories can be supplied from a remoter distance.

With the temperature practically down to freezing point, the snow may lie, particularly if it contains no free water, and a thicker layer will be formed. As stated in the preceding chapter, snow in the atmosphere is composed of crystals of various shapes and precipitation

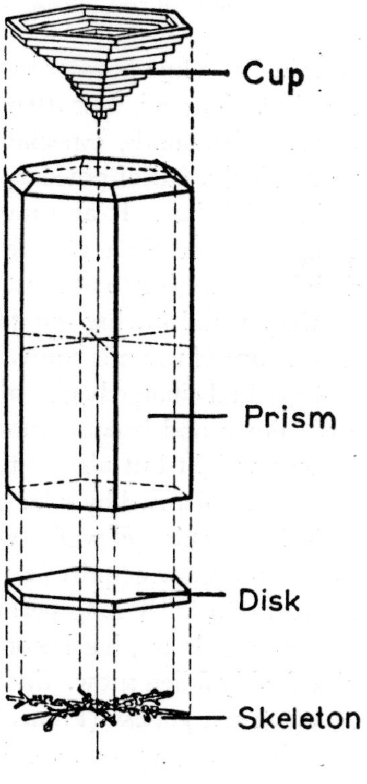

Fig. 64. Various forms of ice crystals, all built up on the hexagon. (After Paulcke.)

usually takes the form of openwork hexagonal discs and flakes composed of a few crystals, the latter sometimes mixed with droplets of water.

Large flakes of snow are more apt to fall when there is no wind and when atmospheric temperatures are in the neighbourhood of freezing point. Once they have alighted, these angular crystals interlock firmly and nothing short of a storm wind can separate them and sweep them off the ground. The fine, powdery snow which falls in a hard frost, usually accompanied by a high wind, is utterly different in appearance.

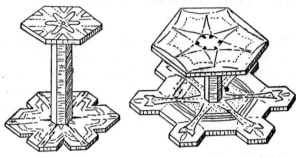

Fig. 65. Snow crystals in the form of rodlets with disks at each end (greatly magnified).

The delicate lacework structure can be seen in a few flakes falling on the sleeve of a dark coat and, if examined through a magnifying glass, the elegant variations on a hexagonal theme are a sight worth seeing (Plates IX, X). Larger flakes and fresh snow blown off the ground can also be atomised to a fine powder by the force of the wind, but the particles are then formless. The wind scatters fine, powdery snow and stacks it in uneven layers and mounds, especially under the lee of any obstacle. Among high mountains, a fall of powdery snow will often happen in calm weather—the Swiss *Wildschnee*. It accumulates in a very light mass, its specific gravity being no more than 1/50 to 1/100; hence a layer, say, half a metre thick shrinks on melting to at most one centimetre of water. Ordinary flaky snow on the ground having one-tenth the density of water, the precipitation in millimetres of water is equivalent to the same number of centimetres of snow.

A gradual change begins almost immediately. Slowly but surely the flakes settle down and become more compact, owing not only to compression by its own weight but also to the fact that the surface undergoes a "setting" process, accelerated by solar heat or direct thawing. The lacework structures shrivel to droplets of water, which in turn freeze into globules of ice at night, so that the snow acquires a much coarser and more granular structure. At the end of a fairly long period of frost it is obvious to sight and touch that the snow, as it lies, has become sandy and friable compared with the kneadable freshly fallen snow. Snow a couple of months old, known in the Alps as *Firn* (German) or *névé* (French), may be found to consist of loose accumulations of grains of ice, a product quite different from what came down.

Other changes are liable to take place. Under the strong rays of the sun a thin, transparent crust of ice may be spread out over the snowfield. The melted drops on the surface flow between the topmost ice crystals and the interstices in this mosaic are gradually filled up, until a crust is formed some millimetres thick, resting very lightly on the substratum of snow. This "Firn mirror" is very glaring when seen against the light. It forms an extremely slippery base for fresh snow to fall upon, which, accordingly, needs little provocation to slide off such slopes.

The processes responsible for the formation of hoar frost in fresh snow are highly interesting. Sublimation from the atmosphere forming hexagonal ice crystals sets in the moment the snow comes to rest on the ground. If humidity is supplied predominantly by the atmosphere, it will be the surface layer of snow which becomes crystalline in this way and may even visibly grow outwards in thickness. Even from a distance, a cover of snow thus changed has a crystalline, sugar-like appearance. The freshly-formed hoar crystals are found to be goblet-shaped (Fig. 64, at top), or to consist of hollow prisms and pedunculate platelets. If it continues to freeze hard, however, evaporation and sublimation will also proceed within the mass of snow. The solid, hexagonal, usually cup-shaped newcomers thrive at the expense of the crystal skeletons of the snow, which are consumed. This signifies a concentration of material for each crystal and the snow thus changed is therefore of looser structure. As these more solid ice crystals do not cake together as easily as do the delicate snow-crystal flowers, the new product is less kneadable; on the other hand, it is exceedingly mobile, almost like dry sand.

Snow-drifts of a kind which the Swiss call *Wächten* are formed along ridges. They resemble the crests of breakers curling towards the steeper slope and result from the anchorage of snowflakes swept over the ridge by a strong wind. The canopy thus formed by degrees curls downwards under its own weight. Successive accumulations in the course of the winter complicate its structure (Fig. 66).

Avalanches

Unless it melts at once, snow in flat country remains lying where it falls. Evaporation causes loss from the start, but the bulk as a rule awaits the thaw and then trickles down towards the ground-water, or maybe runs off the surface. The same processes take place in mountain country, of course, but they are complicated by a further factor, which for several reasons claims our attention, viz., the falling of *avalanches*.

Any snow-slip worthy of mention might be called an avalanche. In mountainous country a slope of 20° is considered to be the smallest angle at which snow is liable to slide, but it will as a rule remain stationary on materially steeper gradients, unless conditions particularly favour its movement.

Avalanches can be differentiated into several types according to the kind of snow which initiates the movement. The appearance of an avalanche depends primarily upon the quantity of loose snow flurrying upwards. If there is little and the declivity is moderate, all the sliding takes place along the ground and the fragments can be seen tumbling and slipping or swirling like a mass of dry sand. If, however, a great deal of powdered snow on a

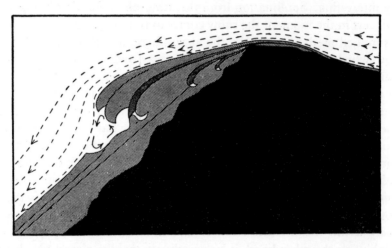

Fig. 66. Vertical section through an old *Wächte* of gradual growth, showing stream-lines of the wind. Looser snow lightly shaded; consolidated snow dark.

steep slope is carried along, it will be tossed up into a thick cloud hiding all other movement from view. The snow-cloud then sweeps down at terrific speed and, with hurricane force, snaps off stalwart trees in its path like so much matchwood, pulls down houses and even flings live cattle high into the air.

It was a long time before the nature of these snow-slips, known as *Staub-lawinen* (=dust avalanches), was properly understood. Some declared that the advancing snow propelled air in front of it, while others were of opinion that somehow air was attenuated behind the avalanche and that the wind, following in its wake, swept past the avalanche when it had come to a stand-still. It is now known that an entirely different mechanism is at work, though the suggested attenuation and densifying of the air play a subsidiary part.

As soon as a large amount of loose snow swirls up in a dense cloud, a snow-air mixture is evolved of very high specific gravity, easily attaining to ten times that of the surrounding clear atmosphere. In principle, the mechanism is the same as that of turbidity currents mentioned in an earlier chapter. The snow-cloud sweeps down the available slope with irresistible force and terrifying speed, far exceeding that of the fiercest hurricane. Velocities of 200 miles an hour are claimed for some of these blasts. When it reaches the valley floor, the avalanche may press on, frequently crossing to the farther side of the valley and climbing hundreds of yards up the slopes,

Fig. 67. Upper margin of a *Schneebrett* (floe avalanche). (From a photograph.)

blasting everything it passes in its onrush. Finally, the snow settles but, compared to the huge cloud, it often dwindles in bulk almost to vanishing point.

It is not only by their tempestuous onslaught that "dust-avalanches" inflict so much damage; anyone overtaken by such a cataclysm must inevitably inhale large quantities of snow-dust which instantly melts and the unfortunate victim is asphyxiated. It is very much the same thing as drowning.

As soon as some degree of cohesion has been established, however, between the snow crystals on the ground, only larger aggregations can begin to slip and thus initiate the movement of the avalanche. If the slope is steep and long, fragmentation and atomisation of the slabs of snow progress until the dust type of avalanche is evolved. Wherever the snow cover is well hardened and consolidated, the sliding and subsequently tumbling movement of the large aggregations continues to be the main feature. This accounts for *Schneebretter*, which might be translated as "floe avalanches".

What, it may well be asked, could cause a rigid mass of this kind to start moving at all? A likely cause is the development, as described above, of little solid cup-shaped crystals under the layer of indurated snow; for, as it will be remembered, this kind of snow is exceedingly mobile and will therefore act like a ball-bearing under a thick pack of snow, causing the superimposed material to start slipping.

In addition to the avalanches we have been describing, the initial movement of which is due to dry, powdered snow, there are wet avalanches resulting from thaw and rain. It is now the melt-water which is the lubricant and the movement is purely one of sliding. This slipping may be very gradual, causing the snow at the nose of the moving mass to fold and wrinkle, and then it comes to a standstill. But generally it accelerates, and clumps of material break away and begin to roll. Just as children are able to make an immense snowball by rolling as soon as the thawing snow binds well, so the wet snow wraps itself round the rolling fragments, swelling them to gigantic spherical boulders. Collisions and bumping over the ground eventually disintegrate them, yet fragments six feet in diameter are often found at the foot of the slope where the wet avalanche comes to rest. There is much checking of progress among the balls themselves, in that the front of one is revolving in a contrary direction to the rear of any other which it overtakes. As these conditions do not favour powdery snow, there is no trace of a snow-cloud. These *wet avalanches* are sometimes called *ground-avalanches*, because they generally comprise all the snow right down to the solid ground and are then soiled and dirty masses discoloured by earth, débris and grass sods.

This latter type of avalanche occurs more especially in the spring and develops mainly along permanent slides, which, scoured afresh every year, are characteristic. Hence they do not take the natives unaware. Though by far the most massive, they are the least malignant, because they are familiar to the inhabitants, who know how to avoid them. It is only after an exceptionally heavy fall of snow that they may break their normal bounds and swallow up inhabited areas. There are, certainly, some notorious ground avalanches which year after year bury some stretches of main roads and railway lines, causing considerable material damage, but they rarely involve casualties. By contrast, dry avalanches may sweep down from any steep slope, here, there and everywhere, dealing destruction in places never before in human memory threatened.

The wet type of avalanche commonly develops gradually. From time to time in the winter, minor snow-slips take place until all hollows have been filled up and unevennesses smoothed out. In this way a natural bob-sleigh track is formed, along which the wet and heavy springtime avalanche is able to slide, almost without let or hindrance, right down to the bottom of the main valley, at a speed sometimes not far short of 200 miles an hour.

It is notable that the mountaineers often give specific names to these tough customers. Sometimes they are called after the ravines in which they occur, e.g. the *Rieslahner*; or sometimes a feature is called after an avalanche, e.g. the *Gamslahner Graben* and the *Breitlauibach* (Lahn=Laui=Avalanche).

A *starting niche*, a track, and a *cone of deposition* are distinguishable in the

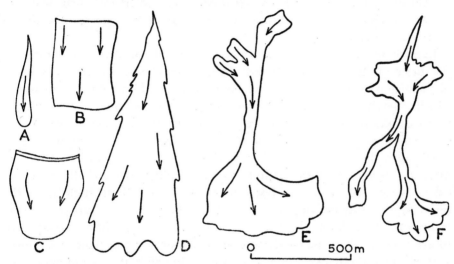

Fig. 68. Mapped avalanches of various shapes. A and B = dust avalanches, C = floe avalanche, D = wet avalanche on mountain slope, E and F = wet avalanches along stream beds. Scale in metres.

majority of avalanches. It will be seen later that a mountain stream comprises corresponding parts, while a glacier also consists of a collecting, drainage and melting region. These divisions in typical wet avalanches show up clearly when mapped, as in Fig. 68. Sometimes two starting niches or two cones of deposition merge into more complicated shapes or, alternatively, the depositing snow may split into diverging tongues (Plate XI, 1).

Avalanches range in size from a ball of snow rolling off a stone to snow-slips many kilometres wide, several kilometres in length and exceeding a million cubic metres in volume.

In the event of an enormous snow delta coming to lie athwart a river bed, the water is at first dammed up. It nevertheless soon manages to start trickling under the pile, and to melt out a tunnel, thus clearing a passage for the water stored in the temporary reservoir. Roads and railway tracks are, of course, just as likely to be blocked. If the mound of snow is too thick to be removed, the usual practice is to dig a tunnel through it and leave the work of clearance to the spring thaw.

In Switzerland alone there are nearly 10,000 regularly recurring avalanches, covering half the area of the country. Apart from the toll they take of human lives, what an economic burden this must mean! In notorious avalanche years like 1689, 1935 and 1951, scores of people are killed. There was a front in the Tyrolese Alps during the First World War where, on 16th December 1916 alone, more than 6000 Austrian soldiers met their deaths in gigantic avalanches, notwithstanding the many safety measures taken to avert such a catastrophe.

Every effort has naturally been made to fend off, or at any rate mitigate, the destruction and ever-present danger threatened by the avalanche phenomenon in mountain country. As early as the Middle Ages, some woods which offered protection to settlements against avalanches were placed under public protection and felling was forbidden. Hamlets were located under the shelter of bosses on the slopes and later pointed bows were built on to individual buildings on the side facing the slope, with the idea of driving a wedge into a snow-slip so that it should divide and slip along the sides. In the second half of last century, walls were built high up in the Swiss Alps, across the slopes, to hold back the snow and thus protect the railway tracks at least. The more recent devices are putting arterial roads under tunnels along menaced sections and bombarding dangerous slopes with mortars to provoke a premature snow-slip before the accumulation has had time to grow to catastrophic dimensions.

It need hardly be said that the steeper and smoother a mountain slope is, the more likely is it to be the site of an avalanche. A skier with a gift for map-reading, a trained eye and proper experience will be able to recognise dangerous spots and keep clear of them. The leader on an excursion should know what kind of incline is to be avoided in a thaw and where freshly fallen powdery snow is piled so high in the lee of ridges and crests that it may slip away at any moment. Much then depends on the substratum, for a smooth surface of *Firn* is far more liable to shake off its covering of snow than is a soft pack of flaky snow. In a thaw, grass forms a very slippery substratum, but boulders or wooded slopes retain their snow cover effectively.

Given propitious general conditions as to situation and nature of the snow, any minor disturbance may start off an avalanche. If a pile of snow is on the point of moving, a loud report, the careless kicking on to it of a small amount of snow, the cracking of the topmost gelated layer by a ski, the snapping of a *Wächte*—any of these trifling mechanical disturbances may unleash an avalanche. In this respect, too, therefore, a skier should know where and under what circumstances he is endangering his own life or the lives of his associates.

Finally, there is one more type of avalanche, namely the ice-avalanche, which has as good a right to be classed with glaciers. Whenever a glacier slips over a step in its bed high and steep enough to destroy its internal cohesion, masses of ice roll down at intervals, and this is called an ice-avalanche. Again, if covered with snow, the fall will be accompanied by a dust avalanche.

There are two ways in which this type of avalanche may be catastrophic. In the form of a gigantic avalanche, the Giétroz Glacier fell to the bottom of the Val de Bagnos in 1818, where the pulverised fragments formed a dam of ice and, behind it, a barrier lake filled up with 800 million cubic feet of water. Then the dam burst and this enormous volume of water cascaded down the valley. In one hour and a half the whole contents of the lake had gushed along the 12-mile road to Martigny and cleaned out the floor of the valley, spreading destruction as far, even, as the Rhône Valley.

Some years ago the Altels Glacier in the Bernese Oberland dealt a more immediately disastrous blow. When the ice-avalanche broke away, 150 million cubic feet of ice were smashed to pieces and ground to dust. The avalanche had gathered such enormous momentum that, even after having crossed over the 400-foot-wide valley, the cloud of ice hurtled against the opposite slope with such force that later the corpses of cattle swept along with it were found flattened against the side of the mountain 1300 feet above the floor of the valley.

The Snow-line

The word snow-line is used to denote the dividing line above which the amount of solid precipitation is greater than the amount of water removed in the course of the year by evaporation or melting. In polar regions, this line lies at or near sea-level, becoming higher the nearer we get to the Equator and reaching the altitude of nearly 15,000 feet in the snow-capped mountains of New Guinea. It is, however, not only a question of geographical latitude, but also of the quantity of precipitation. The drier the climate, the higher the snow-line. In Central Asia it reaches, locally, some 18,000 feet.

An attempt to trace the snow-line in any one particular district, like the Alps, will show that it by no means holds to a constant level. On the cold northern slopes it drops to far below the average and on the sunny southern sides it is well above it. Then again, precipitation is more abundant on the western slopes than on the eastern ones, and therefore they have a lower snow-line. In the Tropics, snow melts more profusely on the eastern than on the western slopes because there is more cloud in the afternoons. It will be found, too, on close examination that snow lies in uneven thicknesses on a slope; there is a patchy zone in summer between that part perpetually covered and that which is bared annually. Conditions, moreover, vary from year to year; sometimes less than the average precipitation will happen to coincide with a hot summer and melt away, while at another time there may be abundant snowfall in the same place, followed by a cold, wet summer unable to dispose of it all.

The snow-line is, therefore, merely an approximate demarcation. Thus in the Northern Alps it is at about 8000 feet, whereas more centrally it is at 9000 feet or thereabouts.

Now if more solid precipitation falls above the snow-line than the local atmosphere is able to cope with, the surplus is removed by other processes, one of which, as we have seen, is the avalanche. Whether regularly every year, or erratically now here, now there, avalanches perform the task of carrying surplus snow off all the steeper slopes and landing it where there is enough warmth left over to melt it.

From Snow to Glacier Ice

Snow, however, does not come to lie only on those steeper slopes, but also in less precarious places, where avalanches cannot occur. There the yearly surplus remains and accumulates. But this cannot go on for ever, otherwise the mountains would eventually be buried. Nature has another agent for the removal of this glut and that is the slow-moving glacier which carries precipitation from the regions of perpetual snow to lower, warmer areas, where melting sets the water free to find its way to the sea. Glaciers are assisted in this work by those avalanches which begin above the snow-line and deposit their burdens below it. Many avalanches from high altitudes, however, cannot carry their snow beyond a valley where it is still too cold for melting and the glaciers then effect further transportation.

Glaciers can be divided into a gathering ground, the *Firn-basin*, and a melting region. In the former, above the snow-line, the accumulated snow changes to ice, which slides very slowly to beyond the *Firn-line*, below which loss occurs through melting.

The Firn-fields are perpetually covered with snow, which can never be more than one year old because every winter a fresh covering is laid down upon the residues of previous seasons. Hence, although the snow may be old in summer and this type of old, granular snow is therefore called "Firn-snow", there is no visible trace of true ice anywhere. Below the snow-line, all the precipitation of the preceding winter melts in the summer and then older material is exposed; this proves to be blue glacier-ice.

We shall consider somewhat more closely the gradual transition from snow to ice. Firn-snow is granular and consists of globules of ice, each of which is built up of one ice crystal. The interstices are filled with air and it is the reflection of light coming from the sky which causes, as in any powder of only slightly pigmented material, the white colour.

Now, two changes take place while, as time goes on, fresh layers are being deposited on the Firn-snow. First of all, the increasing pressure expels the incorporated air and further consolidation to compact ice is brought about by melting water dripping from above.
The deeper one digs down into a Firn-basin, the bluer, heavier and more transparent does the snow become until, some scores of feet below the surface, one comes upon ice containing only a few air bubbles. This change is also reflected by the gradual increase in specific gravity. That of freshly fallen snow is roughly 0·1, that of granular Firn-snow 0·3 to 0·5, and when it is three years old (when, that is, it is covered by two years' deposits) 0·6; after 10 years 0·7; while the specific gravity of glacier ice is about 0·9.

Fig. 69. Granular structure of glacier ice (half actual size).

Meanwhile, however, a second change will have taken place in the Firn-snow and the globules will have grown to the pea-size grains of glacier ice. During their journey towards and along the tongue of the glacier, the grains increase in size and, therefore, decrease in number. This is due to two processes. First, contiguous grains occasionally coalesce into a single individual. As long as two neighbouring grains are in crystallographically different positions, they continue as two separate entities, but from the moment the flowing movements of the ice happen to place them in exactly similar positions, they become welded into a single crystal. Then there is the other process—actually the principal one—by which the larger grains in the glacier tongue grow at the expense of the smaller ones, because the latter have slightly inferior force of crystallisation. It is the larger grains which always profit by every melting or evaporation and regelation. At the extremity of a long glacier, the grains are the size of a man's fist. When melting, the dovetailed grains can be seen detaching themselves and they are clearly visible in a clean cut through glacier ice (Fig. 69).

The Movement of the Ice

It is, surely, a most remarkable fact that ice, a solid, should be able to flow and is thus capable of carrying precipitation from high mountains down slopes so gentle that loose, light snow would rest quietly and immovably upon it. Indeed, until comparatively recently, a glacier was thought to be a rigid, inert mass and the fact that it advances, however slowly, had not been realised. At the beginning of the last century, some, more curious than others about the workings of nature, began to watch glaciers more attentively and they were followed by scientists, who took the matter up methodically. As the result of their study the conviction gained ground that glaciers creep down their valleys at the rate of some tens of yards per year.

The flow of a glacier shows much resemblance to that of a liquid, in that the velocity in the middle is several times that at the margins, while there is also gradual deceleration downwards from the surface. This is naturally accounted for by friction against the bed. Now, these being movements of the various parts of the ice mass relative to each other, they are, in effect, a species of flow. In addition, however, the layer in direct contact with the bottom and sides of the glacier valley also shifts forward, and this must be a sliding movement. Wherever the shape of the valley forces the glacier to follow a curve, the main flow swings towards the side of the outer bend, in exactly the same way as with a river. Like water, the speed of flow increases over steeper stretches of the channel and, given sufficient acceleration, the ice tends to break up into lumps, which again is comparable with the turbulence induced by rapids. This is called an *ice-fall*. On inclines steeper than these, all cohesion is destroyed and *ice-avalanches* are formed, thus simulating waterfalls. If the ice does not melt away on arriving at the foot of such a fall, it consolidates again to a perfectly compact mass and pursues its course, as though nothing had happened, in the form of what is known as a *regenerated glacier*.

Where there is a confluence of two glacier tongues of equal size from neighbouring valleys, the movement of the component parts is forthwith adapted to the new combination. The tongues coalesce and the join between the two component parts is completely sealed. Although made up of ice which had hitherto been retarded by contact with the side-walls, this seam, being at the centre of the new tongue, at once acquires the quickest movement.

Matters are somewhat different when a small side-arm discharges itself into the valley of a large, main tongue (Figs. 70, 72). The branch then comes to lie *upon* the main tongue, but sinks into it so far that the surfaces become level. Fig. 72 shows clearly how the confluent in the foreground, coming from the left, occupies a far wider section of the thicker main glacier than its modest volume would seem to warrant. It can be seen by the striations

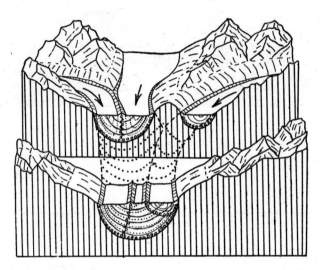

Fig. 70. The confluence and juxtaposition of two equal glacier tongues, which are then joined by a smaller tongue, from the right. This lies on top of the main stream but spreads over a disproportionately large part of the surface area. Note the changes in stratification.

due to rock-waste that not only is the main glacier pushed to one side, but a substantial part of it vanishes under the encroaching tributary.

If the tributary should flow more slowly than the supporting glacier, it will stretch and disintegrate into chunks of ice (Fig. 71); but that seldom occurs. Conversely, the confluent may happen to flow so rapidly that it spreads across the main stream, covering it almost altogether, or at any rate forming a mound for a short time on the broad back. Commonly, rapid flow of this kind is transitory and a more normal confluence is soon re-established.

The less obvious laws of glacier flow have been studied in various ways. In 1874 two rows of coloured stones were laid on the Rhône Glacier, and these were surveyed regularly. The result shown on the map in Fig. 73 is quite revealing, showing plainly the wide central strip moving at comparatively great speed and the abrupt transition to the sides which advance slowly.

Fig. 71. End of the tongue of the Western Chamshen Glacier (Karakorum). Having come in from the right, an overlapping tongue of white ice, cloven into pyramids, rests upon a tongue of dirty, stratified ice which it has pushed slightly to one side. (From a photograph.)

Fig. 72. Lower Fedtschenko Glacier (Pamirs, the largest in the world), looking downstream and showing medial moraines. The tributary, joining the main stream from the left, elbows out and overruns a considerable portion (*a*) of the main stream. (From a photograph.)

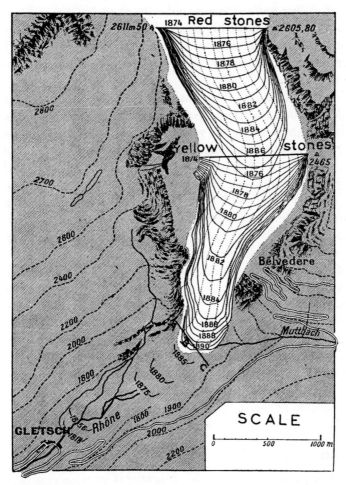

Fig. 73. Differential motion of glacier surfaces illustrated by the successive position of rows of coloured stones placed on the Rhône Glacier in 1874. Note the retreat of the glacier since 1818. Successive cross-sections through Line A B C are shown in Fig. 98. (After Robin.)

A slightly different method is to drive stakes into the ice and watch these through field glasses from the bank.

The rate of flow—by which, for the sake of simplicity, we mean the highest speed attained—varies with every glacier according to the place where it is measured. The smallest movements are found in the Firn-basin, the highest figures are where the tongue begins, and there is a gradual slowing-down towards the extremity, where many glaciers creep along at a very slow pace. The Great Aletsch Glacier in the Alps advances 20 inches a day at the

Firn-line, 16 inches halfway down and only 10 inches per 24 hours two kilometres from the end. In the big arctic glaciers, which discharge into the sea
and there break off into icebergs, it is at the lower end that the highest
speeds are measured, naturally enough, since there is barely any friction to
hold them in check.

The disparities in speed are greater still between the glaciers themselves.
The steeper the bed and the larger the stream, the more rapid is the flow.
In the Alps, the movement per year of the moderate-sized tongues is in the
neighbourhood of 150 feet, hence something like the hour-hand of a watch;
that of the larger ones is about 300 feet. The Hintereisferner, which is six
miles long (surface area only five square miles), moves at the rate of no more
than 150 feet per year; the Rhône Glacier, likewise six miles long, with a
surface area of nine square miles, flows at an average of 300 feet per year;
the Great Aletsch Glacier, that 15-mile giant among the Alpine glaciers
(45 square miles), reaches as much as 550 feet. Some of the enormous
glaciers of Central Asia, 40 miles long and with surface areas of 400 square
miles, advance no less than 2500 feet per year. The speed, however, with
which the gigantic tongues of ice slip from Central Greenland to the sea is
of an entirely different order of magnitude, amounting, as it does, to 80
feet a day, or five miles a year, a speed comparable, therefore, with the scurry
of the second-hand of a wrist-watch.

One surprising fact that has been discovered, but as yet by no means
satisfactorily explained, is that the speed of one and the same glacier varies
very considerably at times. We shall revert to this matter when we discuss
the variations in length of glaciers.

Why do Glaciers Advance?

The following are the mechanical properties of ice which enable the glacier
to move. First of all, ice is fairly *plastic* at the melting point. If a column of
ice is firmly compressed in a cylinder with a lateral orifice, a roll of ice
emerges from the hole, like oil-paint squeezed out of a tube. The main
agency at work here is the property inherent in many kinds of minerals
enabling the opposing sides of certain crystallographic planes to glide without loss of mechanical cohesion (known as *translation*). As ice possesses this
property in a high degree, the component grains of the glacier are divided
into slices, as it were, which are able to slip past each other for a short
distance without prejudice to the strength and cohesion of the ice crystal.
When a larger mass of material, composed of variously orientated crystals,
undergoes this process, it becomes subject to plastic deformation very similar
to the flow of a fluid.

PLATE XI

(*a*) Octopus-arms of a great ground-avalanche spread out over the plain. (*Photo Eugster, from Flaig.*)

(*b*) Air view of Kong Johan Bre glacier, Spitzbergen, taken from 3,500 metres. It spreads out seaward in a vast moving plate; the steep "calving" edge is clearly seen.

PLATE XII

A

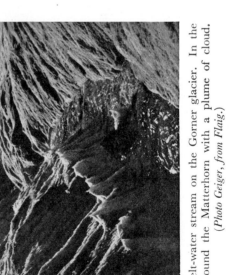

(*a*) Melt-water stream on the Gorner glacier. In the background the Matterhorn with a plume of cloud. (*Photo Geiger, from Flaig.*)

(*b*) The earth too can flow! Ice Age happenings originated these formations. View with A at foot; depth about 3 ft. Havelte Airfield, Drente, Netherlands.

Ice, moreover, exhibits the property of *regelation*, by virtue of which, if two pieces are so placed that they touch each other, they will, even without any pressure, stick together and freeze to a single unit. Furthermore, ice melts *under pressure*, when it gives a little, so to speak, for water is more compact than ice. In the process, heat has to be absorbed (the heat of fusion); consequently, the water formed and the immediate surroundings drop to below 0°. If the pressure causing the ice to melt is uneven, the resulting water will be forced to one side and thus evade the pressure but, having been cooled to below freezing point in the preceding process of melting, it immediately freezes again.

It is also assumed that the grains in a glacier have scope for a certain amount of relative *rotation*. It appears that weak solutions of salt lie on the planes of the grains, having separated out while freezing was going on, and these very likely assist any gliding tendency. The gradual deformation and growth of the glacier grains repeatedly provide some opportunity for relative displacement and this implies an important form of plasticity of the tongue of the glacier, and therefore, its ability to flow. Strong opposition will, on the other hand, be offered to this tendency by the interlocked crystals.

The soaked, plastic mass of clay on the bed of the glacier, called the *ground-moraine*, undoubtedly acts as a lubricant, helping the glacier to travel onward.

Bearing in mind that a glacier consists of a plastic material, which moreover melts under pressure and is squeezed away, only to freeze to a solid again immediately, that the tongue of ice rests on plastic clay and that tensions may be somewhat relaxed by internal rotation of, and displacements amongst, the grains, the phenomenon of glacier flow becomes slightly less mysterious. The question as to which of these factors plays a dominant part may be left to the specialists to fight out amongst themselves.

There are one or two facts, however, which we cannot ignore altogether. When a glacier-tongue is examined carefully, it will be seen that there are a number of sharply cut cracks along the edges at the end and perhaps in the middle. It looks as though the glacier had been split up into thin slabs parallel to the trough-shaped bed. At the lower end they curve upwards, becoming spoon-shaped.

According to some schools of thought, the glacier travels largely in short, intermittent slips along these sliding planes. It is held that the tensions in the ice increase until a sliding plane cracks open, being lubricated by a film of water formed in the process. When the movement has come to a standstill, the sides are cemented together again by regelation.

K

Although the existence of the sliding planes testifies to the actual occurrence of this forward movement by fits and starts, there can be little doubt that it plays a very minor rôle in the general advance of the glacier.

Equally compatible with plastic flow, involving movement—however slight—of all parts relative to their surroundings, a process by which the ice is thoroughly kneaded, is the splitting and healing again of crevices in glaciers, a very common occurrence which we shall consider presently. It is not as easy to see how this phenomenon could be accounted for by the hypothesis of the local shifting of large, rigid slabs, each retaining its unmodified shape. Moreover, the mechanical properties of ice touched on above concord better with the theory of plastic flow. The adherents of the latter view regard the sliding planes as a secondary phenomenon of minor importance which, in a quantitative sense, is a negligible factor in the movement of the glacier. They maintain that it is only on the surface of a glacier that the ice is to some extent brittle and can crack as well as flow. Some dozens of metres lower down, pressure is already so great that the ice has become highly plastic and yields through flow alone both to pressure and tensile stresses. There can, therefore, be neither sliding planes nor cracks down there.

They advance the following strong argument in support of their view. Enclosed dirt, air bubbles and the like often impart a form of stratification to the ice. Photographs taken from the air sometimes show this stratification at the lower end of a glacier lying in folds, or even in intricate crumples. Ice situated at depth farther up the tongue becomes exposed by the melting of superincumbent ice when it has travelled down to the end of the glacier. Although the plastic deformation can never be observed in action, because it takes place under a thick layer of ice, it is in this way that the result comes to light.

Glacier Crevasses

While ice possesses the mechanical properties we have been discussing, it is also brittle under tensile stress. Consequently, rents must inevitably be formed in a glacier-tongue wherever flow involves stretching. The quicker flow of the central portions must obviously bring oblique tensile forces to bear all along the edges of the tongue. Imagining strip I in Fig. 74 as stretching straight across the tongue, it will evidently, after some time, assume the shape and position II, the square ABCD having meanwhile changed to A'B'C'D' and the elongation in the direction D'B' by then being quite substantial. The result will be a fissure perpendicular to this direction, widening in proportion to the increasing length of D'B' entailed by the flow. In a few days the fissure will be an inch wide and at the end of some months there may be a gaping rent 60 feet wide and more than 300 feet deep. Melting causes gradual deformation and rounding of the margins.

This widening does not go on indefinitely, however, for, while the mass is advancing, the fissure swings round by virtue of the inner portion travelling at a quicker pace. As soon as the fissure has rotated beyond the perpendicular position relative to the side, it will undergo a pinching process until it has closed up. For the concomitant of elongation in the direction D'B' is pressure in the direction of the shortening axis A'C', and it is this pressure

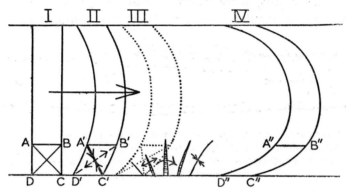

Fig. 74. Diagrammatic representation of the formation and closure of marginal cracks in a glacier tongue. The rate of flow of the margin relative to the centre is in reality far slower than here suggested.

which eventually closes the crack. People have fallen to their deaths down these crevasses and when the ice melts, bodies recovered may be found to be flattened.

Although these crevasses may be very deep, they appear rarely, if ever, to extend down to the bed of the glacier. Not only are there smaller differences in rate of flow in the depths, with consequently weaker stresses, but the pressure of the heavy burden of ice causes the ice to react plastically and stretch rather than to crack.

Marginal crevasses are not as common as the theory of the process would lead one to expect and are often largely limited to narrowings in the glacier valley (see Fig. 75).

A different type of crevasse is formed in a longitudinal direction when a glacier reaches a wider part of its bed. The expansion in width causes transverse stretching—which, in turn, causes the longitudinal cleavages. The end of the tongue may also be a region of stretch because, although the thin lobe of ice is melting away, it nevertheless continues to cover the full width of the valley (Fig. 75).

Where a glacier has become attenuated towards its terminal, a sizeable protuberance in the bed will raise the ice, cracking the tongue open on the surface. In extreme cases, such as that illustrated in Fig. 76, it may lead to an actual discontinuity and the rocky hillock will be exposed.

Allied to this is the complicated system of rents formed when a glacier passes over a sudden change of slope in the rock floor, i.e. an ice-fall. There is scarcely a glacier tongue which does not pass over at least one such step and the rugged, savage pattern of the deeply scarred surface adds in no small measure to the beauty of the glacier landscape. Where there is a mild downward step, a regular system of transverse, conspicuous fissures is

Fig. 75. Crevasses in a glacier tongue. An ice-fall at V gives rise to compressional undulations at G. Longitudinal crevasses appear where the bed widens and marginal crevasses are predominant when it narrows. At the tip of the tongue radial crevasses form and an ice cave is shown at P.

formed, testifying to the accelerated movement as gravity acquires more hold over the sluggish flow and tears the rigid ice apart. The downward bend over the edge of the step must also assist in stretching the surface. At the converse bend at the bottom of the fall, the crevices are squeezed together again. The small transverse wave-crests on the surface bear witness to the compression at the lower end of the fall (Fig. 77).

If the drop in the valley bed is steeper and higher relative to the thickness of the glacier, cleavage will intensify, the number and depth of the crevasses will increase and the pattern will become progressively haphazard. The slabs into which the transverse crevasses cut up the ice are warped in a downstream direction owing to the greater speed at the centre. This produces tensile stress in the slabs and causes them, in turn, to disintegrate into prisms. The broken-up surface of a sizeable ice-fall presents a bewildering maze of blocks and pinnacles, crevices and holes through which it is difficult to pick one's way. The melting of the margins helps to diversify these weird patterns which, in the French Alps, are called *séracs*. Now and again the pinnacles topple over and dash to pieces on the glacier tongue at the bottom of the fall. Finally, if the step in the valley floor is higher and steeper still, the crevasses reach to the rock-bed and the glacier leaps down the bare, steep slopes as one of those periodical ice-avalanches which were described earlier.

The plastic and re-freezing ice adapts itself in a remarkable manner to the space available. No better illustration could be devised than that which rewards close scrutiny of the glacier tongue below an ice-fall. Just as the

Fig. 76. The Travignolo Glacier (Dolomites) rent asunder where it passes over a rocky knoll, revealing stratification of the ice. (From a photograph.)

foaming, turbulent waters of a river soon reunite below a rapid into a smooth-running stream, so too do the fissures in the ice close completely and swiftly below the ice-fall. Despite the facts that the edges have long ceased to fit on account of melting, that the fragments have partly slipped past each other and that the ice-blocks which were flung down are no longer in position, the surface of the glacier is rapidly regenerated and ironed out to an intact and continuous surface. There is not a trace left of the recent

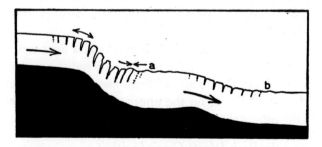

Fig. 77. Vertical section through a high and a low ice-fall over steps in the valley floor of a glacier. Compressional undulations occur at *a* and *b*.

rending and fragmentation and the savage outline of the sérracs. Even the shattered ice at the bottom of the track of an ice-avalanche is soon re-knit into a normal, massive glacier tongue.

Some change has none the less taken place at the surface of the glacier in the ice-fall, notably in the distribution of dirt and detritus. When the tongue splits open and the sharp edges of the slabs of ice melt, the material on top rolls into the clefts and is thus concentrated in a number of strips right across the glacier. The dirt which is held captive in the closed cracks is soon liberated again when the top layer of ice melts. This is how regular bands of dirt are formed on the tongue below an ice-fall. Remembering the displacement of the rows of coloured stones on the Rhône Glacier, we shall not be surprised to hear that these bands curve in a downstream direction, bending more and more as time goes on.

The *Bergschrund* crevasse up in the Firn-basin is in quite a different class from the crevasses dealt with in the preceding paragraphs. The thin margins of the Firn-field against the steep surrounding mountain flanks are frozen solid to the rock-bed and do not move, largely on account of their light weight. The thicker central portion of the Firn-ice may reach melting temperature on its lower surface and is therefore not frozen to the bed; hence this part is able to flow towards the valley. The gradual removal of these central parts of the Firn-field from the margins at a higher level sets up tensile stresses resulting in a deep fissure, sometimes several yards wide, right through the whole mass of snow and ice to the bed. This is the notorious *Bergschrund*, a very common feature in Firn-fields, the bane of mountain-climbers, who, hoping to find a short cut across the gently sloping Firn-snow, are abruptly confronted with an impassable, gaping fissure, which bars their way to the surrounding slopes (see Fig. 92, right).

In winter, these yawning gaps are bridged by snowfall or are filled up by avalanches, but in summer the arch or filling collapses and the old gulf reappears. Thus, for years on end the *Bergschrund*, though actually developing all the time, appears to be a fixed landmark between stationary snow-field and moving glacier.

During the First World War, whole barracks and forts were hewn out of the glaciers on the Austro-Italian front. This offered the geologists a unique opportunity of studying the nature of these fissures and they obtained convincing evidence that the ice on the upper side of the cleft remains stationary, frozen to the mountain wall.

The Glacier and the Rock Waste Carried with it

Glaciers not only transport the surplus precipitation from the upper regions of mountains, but also rock waste and detritus falling upon them and scraped from the floor. All this mineral matter displaced by a glacier is called *moraine material*.

The high, steep flanks of bare rock projecting above the glacier and upon which the snow can find no anchorage, are constantly undergoing weathering. It is predominantly the varying of temperature around freezing point, again and again causing the water in clefts and hollows to freeze and expand, which is responsible for the gradual loosening of fragments, which one fine morning in a thaw roll down the slope, as Alpine climbers experience to their cost. These blocks and stones go bounding down until they reach the glacier in the valley. Here they pile up into *surface moraines*, more precisely *lateral moraines*, because they lie along or near the sides of the glacier.

Medial moraines, so called because they lie like a band on the central part of the glacier tongue, are formed where two glacier tongues coalesce and the two adjacent lateral moraines unite (Fig. 70).

The surface moraines above the Firn-line are being continually buried under fresh accumulations of snow. This line can be established by reason of the fact that in autumn the dark bands of rock waste disappear below the Firn-snow above it. This is an astonishing thing to see, particularly in the case of the medial moraines, which suddenly come to light in the centre of the ice-stream "out of the blue" as it were. But if we look higher up, we are bound to come upon the confluence to which the medial moraine owes its existence.

In addition to these surface moraines, there are *ground moraines* and the *englacial* type. The material of the former derives from the floor of the glacier and from the blocks which have rolled down crevasses and reached the sole of the glacier—the *Bergschrund*, more especially, offers easy passage to detritus. There are innumerable gutters in the steep snowfields above this crevasse, cut by tumbling blocks, and most of these grooves end abruptly at its edge. Apparently only a few of the blocks manage to jump across and land on the glacier.

Once the material reaches the bottom, the burden of ice and friction pulverise it to very fine rock-flour, in which all unground fragments of stone become embedded like currants in dough. The resulting ground moraine consists of a typical combination of semi-rounded pebbles in a tough clay, such as is to be found nowhere else in nature. It is easily recognised and wherever it occurs bears irrefutable witness to the presence of a glacier at the time of its formation. If the ground moraine originated in an earlier geological period, it is called till or boulder clay. This product is of common occurrence in northern countries and is evidence of the existence of large glaciers there during the Ice Age. Such evidence is enhanced if the till rests on a polished and striated rock-bed, as, for instance, in South Africa, where it was found to derive from an ancient geological period which must have had an entirely different climate.

Like the rock-bed, many of the pebbles in the ground moraine are striated and semi-polished. One pebble will be worn off all round, another will have one or two flat facets. The striations in the bed may be as much as an inch deep and continuous for 10 yards. But, in addition to being scratched, the rock-bed and loose fragments acquire a dull lustre imparted by the polishing loam.

It is not only the scratching and polishing of the rock-bed which reveal the agency of the glacier, but the shapes, which are specific. The ice will not tolerate sharp edges or points; it continues to rub and abrade until all irregularities have been planed down and the surface is smooth or knobbly.

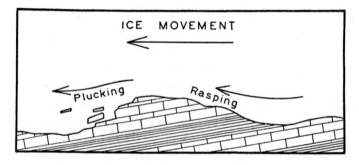

Fig. 78. Types of erosion on the bed of a glacier.

In the Alpine valleys, which were filled with thick tongues of ice during the Ice Age, the typical, rounded shapes of the valley walls and knolls of rock, projecting above later river deposits, are still conspicuous. Seen at a distance in wet weather, the round humps on the grass-grown slopes look like the greyish backs of outsize sheep, for which reason the French call them *roches moutonnées*.

Sometimes mounds and other protuberances on a glacier bed suffer what is called plucking. The glacier rounds off the obstacle on its higher side, while exerting suction on the lee-side. Aided by the loosening of joints, wherever alternate melting and freezing of ice have been insidiously undermining the structure, the glacier will from time to time pluck out large blocks from the lower part of the protuberance, carry them forward and ultimately absorb them in its ground moraine (Fig. 78).

Englacial moraines are situated in the interior of the glacier and comprise all fragments which have fallen down crevasses without reaching the floor. Continuous englacial moraines form where tongues coalesce. The seam of the united ice-streams lies under the medial moraine formed from their two ground moraines, which are compressed along this seam (Figs. 70, 86). As the united tongues are attacked from above by melting, this englacial moraine comes to the surface by stages and thus reinforces the medial moraine with ground-moraine material, i.e. boulder clay. The intermingling of various kinds of moraine is inferred from the mixed composition, although the original surface moraine, not having been through the mill, contains neither loam nor striated and rounded blocks.

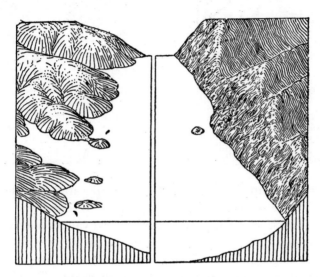

Fig. 79. The shores of a lake formed by the submergence of a normal river valley (left) compared with those of a lake formed in an abandoned glacier valley. (After Davis.)

Glaciers as Landscape Architects

Most of the mountain scenery visited by tourists was buried deep under mighty glaciers during the Ice Age. Their traces are still clearly visible, and their action has changed the contours of the mountains entirely. One has but to compare the morphology of the Alps or the mountains of Scotland and Canada with Indonesian or Central African mountains to realise what glaciation has done to the former. Anticipating Chapter VI, it may be stated here that, in unglaciated regions, the walls of river valleys in their mountain courses have a practically constant angle of inclination and the valley floors tend to be very narrow. In cross-section they are, therefore, V-shaped. The valley system ramifies in a regular manner and confluences are without any marked differences in level. Hence waterfalls and rapids are comparatively rare, as is also the damming of lakes. As the sub-division of the drainage system continues all the way upstream, the tiny tributaries are separated merely by narrow ridges. In lower hilly country the shapes are more rounded, the valleys are wider, often with a flat floor over which the big rivers follow a winding course.

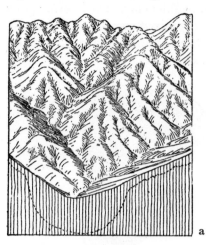 

a   b

A glaciated landscape is entirely different in appearance. The valleys are more in the nature of troughs, U-shaped in cross-section and without the lesser bends. The spurs between the small lateral valleys have been cleared away and the walls of the trough abraded until they become very steep (Fig. 79). The longitudinal profile has become far more irregular. Knobbly slopes and flat basins, often containing lakes, alternate. The glaciers in the

c

lateral valleys were thinner than in the main one and as the respective surfaces were on the same level, the floors underwent less deepening. This is how the hanging side valleys came into existence, as illustrated in Fig. 80. At the same time, all the peaks and ridges which protruded above the ice were weathered by frost and chiselled to sharp points and crests.

Fig. 80. Morphological changes in a river valley by glacial action. Note hanging tributary valleys, in the third stage, after the ice has vanished. (After Davis.)

Why, it may be asked, should glacier valleys be so different? First of all, the glacier tongue may be compared to a rigid rasp which files down all projections and unevennesses in its path. Plastic though ice may be, it cannot possibly undulate over all the divides between the side valleys of a river system (see Fig. 79, left). The tongue comes to rest mainly on these projections, which therefore bear the brunt of its attack. Temporarily, the inlets and channels are in the lee and therefore suffer no erosion. On the other hand, variations in the power of resistance of the different kinds of rock composing the bed will produce humps and indentations as the glacier shears over them (Fig. 81).

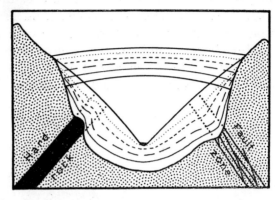

Fig. 81. Development of a U-shaped glacial valley from a normal V-shaped river valley.

Secondly, because its movement is so much slower, the glacier's cross-section is thousands of times that of a river in the same valley. Not being restricted in its erosion to the depths of the valley, it scours the sides up to considerable heights. The valley walls therefore retreat, and, as Fig. 81 shows, the result is a wide U-shaped trough. Moreover, the ice in the narrow bottom of the original valley is held in check and thus loses much of its erosive power. Hence the deepest part is shielded from abrasion and there is scope for lateral expansion. In other words, the effect of the constant friction will make for maximum smoothness and evenness of the glacier bed and there will, therefore, be a definite tendency towards the formation of a regular U-shaped trough.

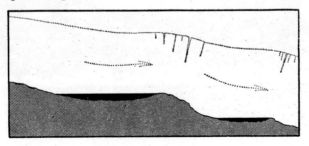

Fig. 82. Logitudinal section of glacial valley. Obstacles which today cause lakes to form would offer little hindrance to the flow of a thick glacier.

The rigidity of a glacier enables its sole to slide up slopes, and such is its thickness that it can take quite sizeable inequalities in its stride. An ice-stream 3000 feet thick can easily pass over a sill 300 feet high without notice-able let or hindrance, where a comparable river would be only a few feet deep and would be dammed up to a lake of substantial proportions behind so high a barrier. The innumerable lakes in recently glaciated mountain ranges demonstrate this difference; ever since the ice melted away, the water has been busy smoothing out these inequalities as fast as it can (Fig. 82).

A curious product of glacial erosion is the *tind*, an isolated mountain shaped like a sugar-loaf found especially in Norway; it is one of the most

Fig. 83. Circular "sugar-loaf" mountain (*tind*) formed by glacial erosion. Lofoten Islands. (After Hobbs.)

striking and impressive of all mountain forms. A small, beautifully modelled specimen is shown in Fig. 83. A far commoner landscape form produced by glacial erosion is the *corrie* or *cirque*, a deep recess hollowed out of the flank of a mountain. A stage in which the original shapes of the mountains are still recognisable is to be found in Wales (Fig. 84). When the corries (also called *combes* in the Lake District) have grown to the extent of intersecting each

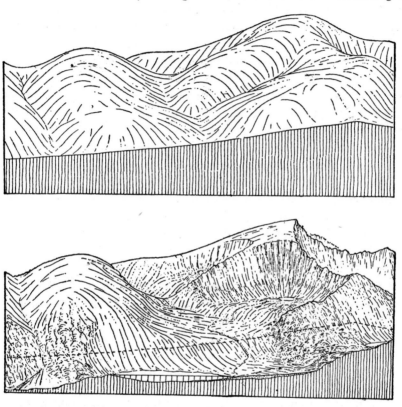

Fig. 84. Presumed pre-glacial configuration around Snowdon in North Wales compared with present-day topography. The large corries, valley-sills, hanging side-valleys, etc., were all caused by glaciers during the Ice Age. (After Davis.)

other, only sharp ridges and peaks remain, leaving no hint of the configuration prior to the glaciation. Large Alpine districts are in that stage at the present time.

There is as yet no satisfactory explanation of the formation of corries. Frost weathering at the bottom of the *Bergschrund* is presumed to be the dominant agent. It has been corroborated by direct observation that the temperature there does fluctuate around freezing point. The rocks are alternately soaked with melt-water and exposed to frost, when the water freezes and expands. The blocks thus loosened are carried off by the glacier, with the result that fresh rock surfaces are laid bare to this cavalier treatment. The ultimate effect, presumably, is the hollowing out of the upper parts of mountain sides by the glacier (Fig. 84).

We have seen that, if the ice in a glacial valley melts and a river takes over the glacier's task, a lake is formed behind the barriers left. Other lakes are situated behind a natural dam in the form of a terminal moraine. It is, in fact, to the action of glaciers in the great Ice Age that the Alpine country owes its numerous lovely lakes and tarns (Figs. 101, 102).

The ability of the glaciers of the Ice Age to scour with sufficient rapidity to mark so strikingly the Alpine landscape in so short a geological period has been called into question. Measurements of glacial erosion show roughly an inch in five years and, for larger ones, an inch in two years. For the huge Alpine glaciers of the Ice Age, therefore, the suggested figure of three years per inch equivalent to three feet per century is a conservative estimate and, as the Great Ice Age included four glaciations of several tens of millennia, the valleys could easily have been scoured out some 3000 to 6000 feet. It is not fanciful, therefore, to credit the glaciers of the Ice Age with the ability to alter radically the architectural style of mountain country.

Rock Waste and Melting

The rock waste on a glacier tongue affects melting in no mean degree. Ice allows solar heat to penetrate to some depth and reflects much of it, too. Hence it distributes the energy through a thick layer, which can therefore rise only slightly in temperature. A small flake of rock, on the other hand, is heated powerfully and will consequently melt out a small hole in the ice on which it rests. Sunk a couple of feet below the surface, the small "screen" still receives enough rays through the ice to descend a little farther. The upright tube thus hollowed out is filled with melt-water, which, however, gradually leaks into the porous glacier ice. By morning all the tubes are empty but, owing to the thaw, fresh water is formed in daytime and they are also filled by melt-water deriving from the surface of the glacier (Fig. 85).

With a *thick* block of rock the process is reversed. Like the chip, it is strongly heated on top, but rock is such a poor conductor of heat that the ice beneath is, on the contrary, shielded effectively and does not melt. Every day the sun melts a film of the adjacent ice, but under the rock a pedestal remains intact and a so-called *glacier table* is formed. The rocky toadstool protrudes higher and higher above its surroundings until equilibrium is menaced by slight undermining on the sunward side of the pedestal. The top of the glacier table slides off in that direction and the process can start all over again (Fig. 85). This may occur with the same block once a year; less often for larger boulders and two or three times a year for the smaller ones.

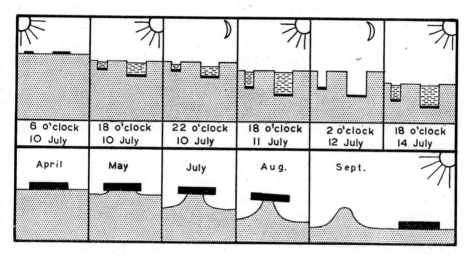

6 o'clock 10 July	18 o'clock 10 July	22 o'clock 10 July	18 o'clock 11 July	2 o'clock 12 July	18 o'clock 14 July
April	May	July	Aug.	Sept.	

Fig. 85. Diagram of the formation of melt-holes and of a glacier table.

Similarly, the moraines protect the underlying ice and thus develop a steep slope towards the melting surfaces (Fig. 86). Hence their material tends to scatter on the glacier until it paves it in a uniform layer, while the medial moraine takes the form of a steep longitudinal ridge. Alpine moraine ridges,

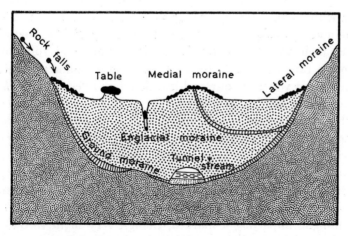

Fig. 86. Typical cross-section of a glacier tongue.

at the end of the tongue, may rise to 150 feet above the general surface. On trying to climb these massive banks, the unwary will find them treacherous, for they consist of only a thin skin of stepping-stones perched precariously on a steep barrier of slippery ice.

Downstream, boulders, gravel and other detritus collect in ever-increasing quantities on the tongue and, as melting bares more and more englacial moraine, all this material is spread more uniformly over the surface. The lower end of many an Alpine glacier is virtually hidden under a cloak of moraine. Some of the very long Asiatic glaciers, like the Fedschenko, owe the last few miles of their existence to a rich moraine cover which maintains their resistance to the sun's rays.

The lower end of a glacier passing through a period of retreat and limited movement is an unsightly flat cake, in which the tourist will at best obtain a mere glimpse of that blue glacier ice which enthusiasts had described to him in such glowing terms. But in phases of advance, when the tongue is flowing rapidly and the débris is sliding off the markedly cambered back, it is a grand sight indeed and the intense blue of the ice scintillates in all its glory. Unfortunately the glacier world all over the globe has been declining for many decades now and it is an exception rather than the rule for an Alpine glacier to present that resplendent picture which, in the 1850s, was to be seen everywhere in the fast-advancing tongues.

The Deposited Detritus

The moraine material carried down by the glacier has to be deposited somewhere. To some extent this is effected in the ground moraine, but this seldom grows to any appreciable thickness and, once the bed has been smoothed with loam, any surplus is pushed along with the ice. Most of the rock-flour and a considerable portion of the finely divided material eventually find their way to the turbid glacier stream and run out beyond the mountain range or else to the first lake they encounter. The fine clay makes the glacier water opaque and it is therefore referred to as *glacier-milk*. In summer, when melting is at the height, a glacier stream is recognisable by its turbidity and, at quite a distance downstream from its confluence with a clear stream, the two kinds of water may often be seen hurrying onwards, side by side. Another common sight is that of a long, white plume of glacier-milk beyond the mouth of a stream, contrasting with the greenish-blue waters in one of the Swiss lakes. By degrees this stream is submerged in the lake, because it is cold, and therefore, heavy. Ultimately the two kinds of water mingle, imparting a marked, though very slight, turbidity to the lake. The lovely iridescent blue of the Alpine lakes is due to the same optical effect of dilute suspensions as the colour of soap-suds and watered milk. The active agent, in addition to algae, is the washed-in rock-flour.

When a glacier tongue is retreating, an inconspicuous sprinkling of detritus is left behind on the valley floor, but if it remains the same length for a considerable time, so much is deposited that a barrier of moraine material piles up. This mound is reinforced if the tongue is liberally fed with ice and begins to advance. Fresh supplies of moraine and of deposits ploughed up from the bed in front of the glacier are built up to a high,

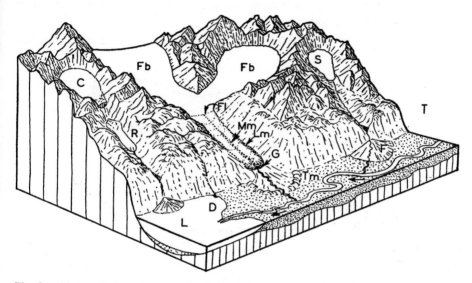

Fig. 87. Alpine glaciers. C = corrie glacier. R = regenerated glacier. S = slope glacier. L = lake. Fb = Firn-basin. Fl = Firn-line. Mm = medial moraine. Lm = lateral moraine. G = ice cave. Tm = terminal moraine. D = delta. F = alluvial fan. T = trough valley.

crescentic wall. This is called a *terminal moraine*. If the glacier should then happen to enter one of its retreating phases, the terminal moraine stands as a landmark of the furthermost point of the previous advance. Sometimes ridges are added on, running up the valley and laid down direct from the lateral moraines. They are, therefore, of a different type from the lateral moraines lying on the moving ice, from which they are clearly distinguishable by their massive structure and the absence of interior ice. (See Fig. 101.)

Since the Great Ice Age, Alpine glaciers reached their highest positions in the seventeenth century, and in about 1820 and 1850. The moraines of one of these periods can be recognised on approaching many of them. If a

L

later moraine overtakes and passes beyond an older one, the latter is apt to be annihilated (Fig. 88).

The Melting of a Glacier Tongue

Solar heat, of course, is an exceedingly energetic melting agent, particularly in the mountains, where the atmosphere is so clear that the sun's rays are able to pour down in almost unabated strength. It needs but one hot and sunny summer's day to melt down a four-inch layer of the glacier tongue. With an overcast sky, even if it rains, the glacier stream does not carry away anything like as much water.

The dark mountain sides also receive warmth, which they in turn transmit

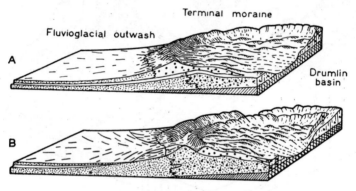

Fig. 88. Formation of terminal moraines in lowlands. A the glacier has advanced over, B retreated from a preceding terminal moraine. Drumlins are small mounds of ground moraine.

to the margins of the glacier tongue (particularly the northerly one, in our hemisphere) causing them to melt more rapidly. In Central Asia it is liable to become so warm along the wall that small valleys develop on the margin of the glacier, with luxuriant vegetation far above the normal borderline for the flora.

Turning to Fig. 73 again, one can note that it was only the stones at the centre which reached the tip of the tongue. The others were gradually pushed to the sides, and ended up in the lateral moraines. In a way, this is comparable to the manner in which englacial moraines are brought to the surface. Hence the tip of the glacier tongue must consist of ice which was formed at the rear of the Firn-basin near the *Bergschrund* and advanced centrally close along the bed. Whatever was added to the side of the median line, or in the Firn-basin at a lower level than the *Bergschrund*, will have melted before reaching the end of the tongue.

Provided the temperature of the air be above 0° C., melting goes on even when the sky is overcast. The windier it then is, the more air will there be sweeping along the glacier and transmitting heat for the melting. In windless weather, the heavy, cooled air coming from the glacier will form a current down the valley and be clearly perceptible many miles from the ice front. A warm counter-flow ascends over the top of the cold current, replenishing the air at a higher level over the glacier and in this way circulation is set in motion and abets the process of melting.

Rain is another accessory and, thanks to the great heat capacity of water, tepid rain converts an appreciable proportion of ice into water. There is, furthermore, the formation of dew. On coming into contact with the cold surface of ice, the air is chilled and, if the dew point is above 0° (i.e. if the air, on cooling, becomes saturated with water vapour before it drops to 0°), dew condenses on the glacier, thereby liberating a very substantial amount of heat which attacks the ice to excellent purpose. An immediate result is that the air is dried and this desiccating atmosphere, in conjunction with the low temperature, acts as a preservative of organic matter. Thus dead animals are mummified on the glacier and it is due to the same influence that meat can be preserved in good condition for a long time on a glacier tongue. Pronounced evaporation from the surface of the glacier is a simultaneous concomitant; indeed, in the dry climate of the Asiatic highlands, evaporation is one of the most voracious consumers of glaciers.

Internal melting takes place under the influence of warm air and meltwater entering through clefts and channels from outside. In addition to these exterior agents, however, there are two others, viz., the earth's heat and the friction set up by the sliding movement of the glacier. The earth's heat is only a weak source of energy, emitting only just enough to reduce a half-inch layer of ice to water in a year. It will be obvious that the glacier must undergo friction of two kinds, namely with its bed and internal friction during the transformations continually involved in its flow. Potential energy is thus converted to heat, for the ice falls, as it were, from the Firnfield at a high level down the valley towards the end of the tongue. Even in a small glacier, this contribution is twice that of the earth's heat and it is about ten times as much in, for instance, the Aletsch Glacier.

The effectiveness of these two sources of heat is evident from the fact that the glacier stream continues to flow in winter. Even though the whole glacier is exposed to severe cold for months on end and is without doubt progressively frozen from above, the glacier stream never "dries up" entirely. Drainage does, admittedly, diminish to only a small percentage of the aestival amount (5 per cent for the Rhône Glacier), but friction and the earth's heat continue to play their part and there is always at least a trickle of melt-water issuing from the snout.

This winter drainage has a peculiar result. At the melting end of the great ice streams in the plains of Spitsbergen the outflowing water freezes in winter while picking its way between the abundant moraines and fluvio-glacial deposits. Thick slabs of ice are built up *in situ* in stream beds, after which they are often buried under substantial beds of sand and gravel. They are then so effectively insulated that they do not melt away in summer, taking root more or less permanently in the subsoil.

Similar processes took place on a large scale at the margins of the ice-sheet in northern Europe during the glacial period. Long after the great retreat, blocks of winter ice lay buried in the ground, as also slabs lopped off the glacier. Thousands of years elapsed before these fragments of fossil ice had disappeared. When this happened, the covering layers gradually caved in, leaving an irregular surface, and the landscape was dotted with numerous shallow lakes which later bogged up.

Let us now follow the melting of a glacier tongue on a hot summer day when the sun is shining. The temperature on the glacier is 0° at dawn and there is not a puddle of water to be seen anywhere. The melt-holes are dry and there is no running water in the melt-channels. But no sooner has the sun risen than melting begins and the interstices fill with water. It will not be long before the growing volume of water can no longer find harbourage in these, and has to pursue its course on the surface. The minute rills unite into streamlets and the melting action enables the water to cut out a shallow channel along which it winds downwards on the gentle slope of the tongue. As a rule, however, the stream does not get very far before it is brought up short by a cleft, into which the melt-water pours. Down below it comes upon some sort of tunnel melted out of the ice and through this pursues its further course. Not long after, a final downward leap will bring it to the bed of the glacier and thence onward it travels over and in the ground moraine. Finally, all the streamlets unite under the ice, reaching the nose of the glacier and the open air again as a single stream (Plate XII, 1).

In hot summer weather there is a constant murmur and the sound of plashing on the glacier tongue; but at night, surface melting comes to a complete standstill. The rills run dry, the waterfalls become silent and there is not a sound to be heard on the glacier. The discharge at its mouth diminishes as all clefts in the ice empty out and the melt-holes drain dry.

The melting of a glacier tongue increases from the Firn-line downwards. Although the quantity of protective débris grows, in most instances the force of the melting factors at the lower levels outweighs the effect of this defence. It is mainly the higher temperature which is responsible. We may take as an example the mean rate of melting on the Rhône Glacier, which is only 3 feet a year at 9000 feet above sea-level, but as much as 36 feet at 5500 feet near the end of the tongue.

The irregular surface resulting from the melting process with its stream bed, glacier tables, etc., combined with the development of fissures and séracs, is largely effaced by snow during the winter. This naturally accumulates in hollows and when it melts away in summer, the protruding humps and ridges of ice will be the first to be etched off the face of the glacier.

Finally, much of the melting of glaciers takes the form of disintegration into icebergs. The annual precipitation upon Greenland amounts to 200 cubic miles, of which only 20 per cent melts *in situ*. The remaining 160 cubic miles are carried down every year to the sea and are eventually disposed of in warmer latitudes (Plate XI, 2).

Various Types of Glaciers

Those so far described have, in the main, been glaciers of the kind found in the Alps. The types which exist in various parts of the world fall into two broad classes, viz., land-ice and mountain glaciers.

Land-ice is an ice-sheet which covers the whole landscape with a continuous Firn-field, except, perhaps, for a few peaks. It lies like a slightly convex shield over the inequalities of the ground underneath, sloping gently away from the raised flat centre, in all directions. The necessary conditions for the formation of an ice-sheet are an arctic climate, abundant precipitation and fairly flat ground. If the Firn-line is at sea-level, or only just above it, the ice will remain covered with snow, reaching the sea in an almost unbroken front.

Like a large, more or less floating crust, the glacier front surrounds huge areas of the Antarctic Continent, where it forms the celebrated *ice barrier*. This may rear itself vertically, out of the sea, a few yards in one place and anything up to 100 yards in others, and must certainly reach three or four times that depth downwards. A completely flat, featureless plain, a hundred miles wide or more, stretches between the barrier and the land proper. The landward side of this cake of ice is fed by a few glacier tongues, but it is in the main preserved by the abundant precipitation and snowdrift, the upper part being therefore built up of an enormous pack of Firn-snow. The ice-sheet spreads very, very slowly towards the sea; it takes a grain of ice approximately 1000 years to travel from the mainland to the outer border. Wave action and tide tear off gigantic ice-floes from this floating margin of land-

ice and these drift away as porous, white icebergs. There are tabular icebergs on record as large as some of the Swiss lakes (see Fig. 2).

Those are the prevailing conditions in the Antarctic. If the snow-line is
at a somewhat higher level, as in Greenland, glacier tongues, uncontaminated
by snow, ooze out of the Firn-cap and transport the ice to the sea (Fig. 89).
The icebergs formed there consist of blue glacier ice instead of white snow.

In Greenland, *calving* usually takes place in fjords, where huge, fast-
flowing glaciers spread a large, floating tongue over the water. If the tip of
such a tongue is held just too high or just too low at the time of calving, an

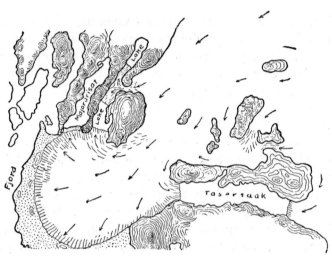

Fig. 89. The Friederickshaab glacier tongue formed from the land ice of Greenland. Note
lakes formed by ice barrier. (After Hobbs.)

enormous block of ice which was not in floating equilibrium suddenly
becomes detached, either plunging with terrific violence into the depths, or
rising up from them. Majestically, but with irresistible force, it revolves and
oscillates until it at last finds a state of equilibrium. The turmoil in the
fjord waters is indescribable and the shores may be subjected to the battering of catastrophic tidal waves. The tongue of a glacier may be eroded near
the surface of the water to such an extent that at some depth below sea-level
the ice juts out like a promontory to a considerable distance. Icebergs may
then suddenly and treacherously rise above the water a good way ahead of
the front of the glacier.

Calving does not cease altogether in winter. The individual icebergs
formed are frozen into firmly coherent units and a whole school of them may
lie imprisoned, awaiting release in the springtime, when they break away and

roam the wide oceans, driven by currents and the wind to warmer climates until they ultimately waste away. The enclosed moraine material is dropped upon the ocean floor many miles from its place of origin. In the process of melting, the submerged base suffers most, and more than one daring adventurer attempting to "board" an iceberg has come to grief when the ice monster, to all intents and purposes so stable, suddenly shuddered and turned turtle in one of those recurrent readjustments necessary to regain its balance.

On an average, a large glacier calves one good-sized iceberg a day and it is estimated that Greenland parts with something between 10,000 and 15,000 icebergs a year. Whereas the Greenland icebergs almost invariably dissolve completely before they are two years old, the immense Antarctic icebergs may roam the seas for a dozen years before they are consumed altogether.

On a clear night, an iceberg can be seen from a ship 10 miles away, but in foggy weather a collision is almost inevitable even in daytime unless the ship is equipped with radar. To protect shipping from this menace, the International Ice Patrol has been instituted for the North Atlantic Ocean to keep constant watch and to give due warning of iceberg-infested areas. The maximum height of Greenland icebergs recorded by this Patrol is 250 feet, and the maximum length 2000 feet.

The normal small-scale maps of polar regions are quite inadequate to convey the dimensions of these immense sheets of ice. It is hard to realise that Greenland has four times the surface area of France, while the South Pole mainland is one and a half times as large as Europe. No less than a tenth of the whole mainland is covered by ice, so that if that enormous expanse were to melt and run into the sea, it would raise the level by as much as 150 feet. This implies that a country like the Netherlands is only habitable so long as the world climate remains cold. Should it ever "improve" to an appreciable extent, all low lands would be doomed irrevocably and would founder!

The northern parts of North America and Europe were also covered by an ice-sheet during the glacial period, but plains, instead of the sea, surrounded the glaciated mountain ranges. At the periphery, where the ice-sheet became thinner by degrees through melting, it broke up into separate lobes.

As opposed to ice-sheets we have, as has been stated, *mountain* or *valley glaciers*. These develop in mountain country of such high relief that the peaks stick out above the Firn and ice and the tongues advance down valleys. The configuration of the mountains determines the shapes of the glaciers. The *Alpine type* consists of a Firn-basin with a girdle of steep peaks, little if at

Fig. 90. Firn-basin of the Argentière Glacier in the Mont Blanc region. (From an aerial photograph.)

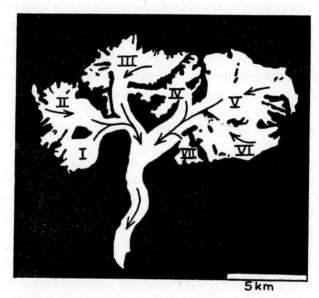

Fig. 91. Mer-de-Glace, near Mont Blanc. Type of Alpine glacier with one tongue originating from seven Firn-basins, some of which are sub-divided.

all snow-capped, so that the various glaciers are clearly partitioned. At the lowest point the ice flows in a single tongue downwards through a steep valley (Fig. 87). When several individual Firn-basins merge, or more than one tongue invades a common valley, where they coalesce into a single stream, we speak of *composite glaciers* (Figs. 90 and 91).

Sometimes a small Firn-field is able to subsist in a niche hewn out of a great mountain flank, from which it leaks in a more or less distinct tongue, though there is no clear-cut dividing line between the two elements. More often

Fig. 92. Corrie glaciers in cirques with *Bergschrund*. Mischabel Hörner, near Zermatt. (From a photograph.)

than not, an ice-avalanche constitutes the lower boundary of these *corrie glaciers* (Fig. 92). The appearance of somewhat deeper hollows in a mountain slope is reminiscent of an arm-chair (Fig. 93). These forms can evidently only be produced by the erosive action of a glacier, for they occur only in regions which were glaciated in the Ice Age or still harbour glaciers.

Valley glaciers of the Alpine type are very numerous, because so many small tongues are liable to develop as soon as the mountain peaks project above the snow-line. In the Alps alone 2000 glaciers of this type have been counted.

In the mountain ranges of Central Asia, such as the Karakorum, Himalayas and Kuenlun, the relief is so tremendously high and steep that it

Fig. 93. Bies Glacier on the Wallis Weisshorn (4572 metres) between the Matterhorn and the Rhône Valley. A single Firn-basin in a corrie with a divided tongue ending in ice-falls. During glacier growth, these falls threaten to engulf the hamlet of Randa.

precludes the development of Firn-fields. Direct precipitation and avalanches feed the glacier which, in fact, consists only of one enormous tongue wholly or largely covered with Firn. The gigantic extent of these glaciers may comprise a network of valleys. For example, the Chocho Glacier, more than 25 miles in length, consists of the confluence of upwards of 60 ice-tongues emerging from separate valleys (Fig. 94).

The *Spitzbergen type* is the opposite extreme. The relief is moderate and the snow-line is low in relation to the valley floors, with the result that a considerable length of the glacier is flanked by Firn-fields. Along the whole of this length, therefore, supplementary Firn coming from both sides feeds the glacier. In this way very large tongues eventually reach the coast, terminating in calving fronts at the fjord-heads (Plate XI, 2).

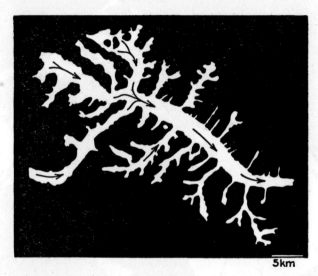

5km

Fig. 94. The Chocho Glacier, Muztagh Himalaya. A glacier of Central Asia without Firn-basins, composed of more than 60 tongues. Scale 1 : 600,000. (1 in. = 9½ miles.)

Scandinavia provides an intermediate form between land-ice and valley-glacier which can be regarded as a type in its own right. Whereas several Firn-fields may feed one tongue of the Alpine type of glacier, and land-ice comprises one immense Firn-field, which only at its termination shows some degree of splitting up into lobes, the Scandinavian Firn-plateau supplies a number of glacier tongues which radiate in all directions (Fig. 95). The existence of such glaciers depends on the presence of a large plateau above the snow-line, upon which a coherent Firn-cap is formed, and a sufficient slope for the tongues to advance.

The last distinctive type is that known as the *piedmont glacier*. This develops wherever a glacier tongue issues upon a plain with a sufficient supply of ice to keep it from melting away directly (Fig. 96). At the present time these conditions prevail on the littoral of polar regions, notably Alaska and Tierra

del Fuego, where the coastal plains are too flat to drain the ice off. It therefore piles up to a large cake which fans out under its own weight.

A good example of a piedmont type is the gigantic Malaspina Glacier of
Alaska (Fig. 95). Its movement is so slow and the extensive moraines
creeping imperceptibly along in the coastal plains cover such vast distances,
that a large forest of sizeable trees is growing on this lazily advancing

Fig. 95. Four glaciers drawn to same scale. 1. Morteratsch Glacier near Pontresina.
2. Batura Glacier in the Karakorum. 3. Malaspina Glacier in Alaska. 4. Justedals
Bräen in Norway. Scale 1 : 1,000,000. (1 in. = 16 miles.)

assembly belt. One can travel for many miles without being aware that one
is on a moving moraine until suddenly confronted with a small tarn en-
circled by perpendicular walls. The banks are found to consist of ice, and
the apparently firm, wooded ground to be no more than a thin layer of soil
on the same chilly foundation.

Piedmont glaciers had a more important part to play in the glacial ages.
All around several mountains, enormously swollen valley glaciers entered the
plain and there piled up to piedmont glaciers, as, for instance, at the northern
margin of the Alps. In the nineteenth century the Rhône Glacier formed a

Fig. 96. Sultan–Chhushku Glacier in the Karakorum terminating in a small piedmont glacier in the main valley. (From a photograph.)

Fig. 97. The Rhône Glacier in 1849 showing at its maximum the swollen tongue forming at its base a kind of piedmont glacier. (From a daguerreotype.) A cross-section through A B C is shown in Fig. 98 and a map of the area in Fig. 73.

kind of piedmont glacier on a small scale, where the tongue of the steep ice-fall entered the spacious main valley with its wide, flat floor (Fig. 97).

The Thickness of a Glacier

With a glacier in retreat, this can be found by first measuring accurately a line straight across the tongue. Then, when the ice uncovers the valley floor, the lower periphery can be measured, providing a complete cross-section. This was successfully done on the Rhône Glacier and Fig. 98 reproduces one of the cross-sections obtained. We see the slightly arched and cracked surface of 1874 and the successive stages of diminution until the final and complete retreat of the tongue. A far higher level of ice was deduced from the moraines of about 1850. This referred to the piedmont

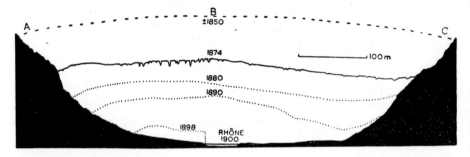

Fig. 98. Successive cross-sections through the dwindling tongue of Rhône Glacier. The first line is approximate, but others were measured exactly. (Cf. Figs. 97 and 73.)

glacier mentioned above. The tremendous shrinkage will be obvious. The swiftly flowing stream of water, with a cross-section perhaps 1/100,000 of that of the ice it has replaced, scours out a small, narrow cleft.

The method followed to discover the height to which the ice smoothed the sides of the valleys in the Ice Age is much the same in principle, though unavoidably less exact. The thickness estimated for the great glacier which followed the Inn Valley is no less than 5000 feet, which is $1\frac{1}{2}$ times the probable thickness of the present giant glaciers of Central Asia.

Another way in which the cross-section can be found is by drilling through the ice right down to rock-bed at several points. By combining the results, the ground relief under any part can be fairly accurately constructed and it is neither necessary to await the fortuitous dwindling of the glacier, nor to confine the site of drilling to a place near the end of the tongue. But the cost and difficulties involved are formidable.

In recent years the echo-sounding principle has been adapted to ice. The explosion of a charge of dynamite on the glacier produces a vibration which the ice conducts to the rock-bed, whence it is reflected back to receiving apparatus standing on the ice at a certain distance. From the interval of time between the explosion and the reception of the echo can be calculated the distance travelled and, therefore, the thickness of the ice. Although this test is technically difficult, it has already been successfully applied to a few glaciers, including the Hintereisferner (Austria), where drillings had been earlier performed. Upon comparison the two methods were found to produce virtually the same figures. The thickness of the Great Aletsch Glacier,

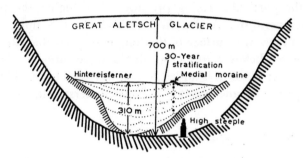

Fig. 99. Vertical sections through the Great Aletsch Glacier (22 km. long) and the Hintereisferner (9 km. long) at approximately maximum thickness, that is at the névé or Firn-line.

the largest Alpine ice-stream, was determined in the same way at approximately the Firn-line. Figure 99 represents the result together with a section of the Hintereisferner established by drillings. The fact, however, that a glacier is thin in comparison to its length will be evident from Fig. 100.

Attempts have also been made to discover the thickness of the land-ice in Greenland by echo-sounding. The resulting evidence is not altogether reliable, for one reason because the velocity of sound in ice under great pressure at depth is not accurately known. There can be no doubt, however, that it must be of the order of 6000 feet, which at the same time implies that the rock-bed in the centre of Greenland can be no more than a few hundred feet above sea-level and that the enormous piled-up sheet of

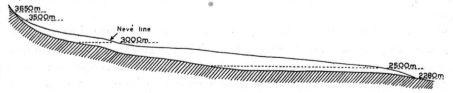

Fig. 100. Longitudinal section of the Hintereisferner. Scale 1 : 80,000. (1 in. = 1¼ miles.)

ice is predominantly responsible for the vast height at the surface. In Antarctica thicknesses up to 8000 feet have been ascertained.

Measurements of the thickness in Firn-basins have shown that snow and ice together are always somewhere between 150 and 250 feet. There is then apparently sufficient pressure for the formation and drainage of ice. With increased precipitation, it is the rate of flow rather than the thickness which increases; hence the Firn-basin remains filled to about the same level.

Drilling provided an opportunity of taking the temperature at all depths in the glacier and it was everywhere found to amount to the melting temperature at the particular ruling pressure. The higher the pressure, the lower is this temperature. As the effect of this factor is minute, however, the temperature at the lower surface of the tongue of a sizeable Alpine glacier is only half a degree below zero. Thus all the ice is already at the point of fusion, so whatever warmth is added goes towards melting. This, of course, is a valuable piece of knowledge for a proper understanding of the causes of glacier flow.

Length Variations in Glaciers

The configuration of a glacier is by no means permanent. Its length and thickness, being dependent upon many varying climatic factors, are constantly changing. It might be supposed that a glacier would undergo an annual change by lengthening in winter and shrinking in summer. Curiously enough, it does not, or only in a very minor degree. First of all, the flow of the tongue slows down considerably in winter and the tip even becomes virtually stationary. As forward pressure, though reduced, still continues, the end of the tongue swells as though more and more ice were being packed into a large bag. This increase in thickness may attain to several yards. Apparently the low temperature makes the margin of the glacier rigid and the outer surface does in fact become a kind of skin. In summer, more profuse melting consumes the ice as it advances again and reduces the tongue to exactly its former thickness, but it has not the power to shorten the length of the glacier.

Hence glacier variations are not due to the normal course of the seasons, but to deviations from the average in the various factors which govern its dimensions.

Increased precipitation in one or several winters must increase the pressure and therefore accelerate the flow. The thickening is propagated like a wave downstream and the extra snowfall is manifested a couple of seasons later by swelling at the tip. This propagation may be 20 to 150 times as quick as the movement of the ice itself, and is comparable with a wave pressing forward in a canal through the almost still water. As the thickening also accelerates the flow of the ice, it is not only a question of a thicker layer of ice that has to be melted at the termination of the tongue, but also of a mass of material thrusting forward at gathering speed. With melting at the ordinary rate, this extra supply of ice cannot be disposed of and the glacier is forced to move forward. This forward movement is, therefore, generally very rapid, whereas the retreat usually takes many times longer to accomplish.

The sudden accretions of the Vernagtferner in Tyrol, which have occurred several times, provide a well-known example of the foregoing. The valley is so steep that the glacier has been known to flow at as much as 12 metres per twenty-four hours! That is 30 to 40 times the normal speed. The glacier breaks up into fragments, some of which slide in front of the main mass on its downward course. In a year or so the insignificant tongue of ice has grown to the dimensions of a respectable glacier which issues from its tributary valley and spreads across the main valley. Behind this ice barrier, the stream in the main valley is dammed up and grows to a lake, sometimes a mile in length and as much as three hundred feet in depth, bearing the name "Rofnersee". Occasionally this lake finds means of egress, either by melting out a tunnel under the glacier or, by sheer pressure, breaking down the whole wall of ice. Disastrous floods being the inevitable result of the latter alternative, attempts, not always successful, have been made to drain the lake artificially before it is too late.

More commonly, however, the supply from the Firn-basin immediately decreases again to normal proportions and a period of retreat begins until, after the passage of several years, the Vernagt Glacier has been reduced to its original modest size.

Low temperature must retard melting and therefore cause the glacier to grow, but the process is so gradual that it is scarcely feasible to trace the trends of temperature in the variations which the glacier undergoes.

Conversely, if precipitation is well below normal or the temperature is above the average, a glacier tongue begins to shrink. The influence of both factors is spread over a number of years, because no wave is raised and the thinner tongue leads a waning but shielded existence under the accumulating moraine.

It is evident, then, that the life of a glacier is punctuated by alternating brief periods of strong growth and long ones of gradual decadence, sometimes continuing for decades. It is a very rare occurrence for a glacier to retain the same length for any considerable time, as it necessitates a highly improbable equilibrium between the many contributing factors.

M

Normally, the variations in temperature and precipitation will be comparable for all glaciers of a particular mountain chain; indeed, often even for the whole globe. For this reason, a few periods of conspicuous glacier growth stand out very clearly. The three chief periods for the Alps have already been mentioned, viz., round about 1640, 1820, and 1850, and about the same time glacier growth seems to have prevailed in other regions as well. The periods of lesser growth are not so clearly distinguishable, possibly being due rather to local conditions and thus not having world-wide significance.

Needless to say, the world growth and shrinkage of glaciers cannot synchronise exactly. Even supposing that all the factors exerted equal influence everywhere, a long, slow-moving tongue would react later than a short, fast-flowing one. Moreover, the covering of detritus is not the same in any two cases; nor is the position of the Firn-basin; one valley may be more exposed to warm air, or sun, or rain, than another; and so on. The Mer de Glace, reached its maximum at the beginning of the last century, eight years later than the average in the Alps, but in the middle of the century the same ice-stream had come to its extreme limit a little in advance of the average time.

It may be taken as a general rule that the steeper and shorter an ice-tongue is, the quicker and stronger is its reaction to increased precipitation. The shape of some Firn-basins is such that they are able to retain more than the normal store without appreciably increasing the feed to the tongue. Steep basins, e.g. corrie glaciers, by contrast, will be quite unable to hoard an excess of Firn material and are therefore compelled to pass the surplus on at once. Such considerations explain why neighbouring glaciers, alike in size and direction, are liable to react very differently to changed conditions.

The Glacial Epoch

Quite apart from the perpetual fluctuations to which glaciers are subject, as we have seen, and which appear to be inherent in the nature of the contributory factors, the geological history of our earth has witnessed rhythmic changes on a far vaster scale. The climate during the major part of the geological past was predominantly so mild that subtropical plants were able to subsist right up to the polar regions and there was little trace of the climatic belts which now control the distribution of fauna and flora on the earth's surface. But this bland state of affairs was punctuated by recurrent, comparatively brief periods during which existing glaciers swelled progressively and new ones covered ever lower mountains farther and farther from the Poles, until ultimately quite large tracts of the mainland were buried under vast ice-sheets. This was one of the *glaciations*, or *ice-ages*, when plants and animals had either to adapt themselves to the new rigours, or else had to retreat to near the Equator, where the climate apparently continued unchanged. Some classes, unable to change their habits, perished in the arctic climate of the medium latitudes.

As far as we are able to tell, the earlier ice-ages were always divided into

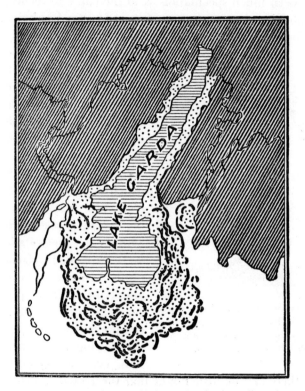

Fig. 101. Lake Garda, formed by the terminal moraine in the valley of an Ice-Age glacier; a typical piedmont example. (After Hobbs.)

several periods of intense cold by *interglacial periods* with a prevailing warm, uniform climate extending to just short of the Poles. Tropical animals like the hippopotamus then migrated as far north as North-West Europe. Actually, we are still living under the sway of the last glacial epoch and we have no guarantee that ice will not again begin to spread, making half the Northern Hemisphere uninhabitable for human beings.

It is now known that there have been at least six glacial periods in the earth's history with intervals between each of approximately two hundred million to two hundred and fifty million years. The last, the Quaternary, is the one known as "The Ice Age", which has left its traces all over the globe. (Figs. 101, 102.) It was divided into four main periods of glaciation and three interglacial periods. The penultimate ice age prevailed from the Middle Carboniferous to the Lower Permian Periods, shortly after the time when coal was formed.

There has been much speculation as to the cause of recurrent periods of glaciation, though no suggestion put forward so far has been unanimously accepted. There are some who hold that the explanation cannot be a general drop in temperature, as this could only bring about a greater expansion of glaciers if precipitation increased at the same time. The latter, however, would depend on intensified evaporation and where would the necessary heat come from under the postulated condition of reduced temperature? It is this which has led to the paradoxical suggestion that the temperature, on the contrary, rose during an ice age with greater precipitation, and therefore expanded glaciation as the result. In view, however, of the abundant evidence provided by the vegetable and animal kingdom of the prevalence of a lower temperature during the last period of glaciation, even in regions remote from the glaciers, there can be little doubt that the growth of glaciers was due to lower temperature.

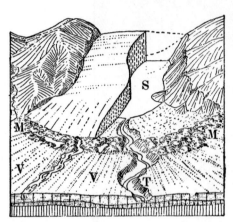

Fig. 102. Formation of a lake in a glacier trough, to explain Fig. 101. S = lake; M = Moraine; T = Incised drainage stream; V = Glacial outwash plain. (After Davis.)

Some scientists are inclined to attribute the formation of ice-sheets predominantly to local changes, such as the altered course of the Gulf Stream, producing a colder climate in a circumscribed area. Others, again, postulate a different orientation of the earth's axis, with Scandinavia, for instance, containing the North Pole. This school is opposed by supporters of the theory of a general cause, which they think to find in terrestrial or cosmic factors. The former would comprise weakening of solar radiation owing to an abundance of matter and carbon dioxide in the atmosphere resulting from very violent volcanic eruptions. The cosmic causes might include changes in the radiation of the sun, the passage of clouds of cosmic matter across the whole solar system, thus filtering radiation; changes in the shape of the ecliptic or the position of the earth's axis in relation to it.

In this way more than four dozen hypotheses have already been formulated; but as there is something, if not a great deal, to be said against every one of them, the causes of the glacial periods continue to be an enigma.

V

Water in the Ground

Earlier Views on its Origins

Nowadays the water supply to cities and towns and even the majority of villages is so efficient that we take it as a matter of course that we can get all the water we need, and more, by merely turning a tap. The urban population, more especially, has thereby lost contact with nature; we devote even less thought to the origins of ground-water than did our forefathers. Wells or pumps, and enforced economy, made them at any rate keenly aware of the indispensability of water in the ground and they knew by experience that nature does not surrender its treasures for nothing. Now that the water boards look after our water supply for us, we no longer realise how water has to be tracked down to its underground hiding-places, brought to the surface, then collected and cleansed. It is no longer brought home to us that by no means all water is suitable for direct consumption, nor that, short of distillation, much of it can never be made fit for use.

Nearly all the water of rivers was ground-water first and the discharge of the streams cannot be properly understood without some knowledge of what happens underground. Vegetation is also largely dependent on ground-water for nutrition. Hence if any one phase of our cycle has a more direct bearing on the life of mankind than another, it is this of water in the ground.

The ancient civilisations flourished for the most part in dry climates, viz., Egypt, Persia, Palestine. For the most part, no permanent settlement could be established unless there were a river or natural spring nearby. Very early, therefore, they began to dig wells and even constructed complicated subterranean canals to make sure of a steady supply of water. There are many allusions in the Old Testament to the digging or use of water-wells and the indispensability of water in daily life. It was once said that Genesis 26 reads almost like a report on water-supply. Ancient Athens was likewise largely dependent upon sunk wells.

Compared to their techniques of water-finding, the ancients had very primitive ideas about the origins of ground-water. Even Plato propounded a "theory of ground-water", according to which all underground waters united in a single big torrent hurrying towards the Tartarus, where it was again divided up into small streams and springs and thus returned to the earth's surface. Aristotle showed his genius by proclaiming that the cold atmosphere of clouds may cause air to condense to water, and that deep down in the earth the same may happen. Although we have learned to distinguish water vapour from air, the theory persists with very little modification. The only point of contention is the amount of ground-water formed by condensation from the air in the ground, but the reality of the process is not called into question.

Vitruvius was no less inspired when, a century before our era, he hit upon the idea that rain and the water coming from melting snow penetrate into the ground, whence, on meeting resistance, they seek an exit in the form of springs.

Most seventeenth-century scholars still believed that ground-water had penetrated underground from the sea, being convinced that rain-water is not able to trickle any appreciable distance down. They let their imaginations run riot in efforts to "explain" how that same sea-water sheds its salinity and is raised to great heights above the sea. According to one view, the latter occurs because the curvature of the earth places the centre of gravity of the ocean far higher than that of the land, so that the water is merely finding its own level. As late as 1827, when geology had attained a fairly high scientific standing, a scholar declared that mineral water was formed deep down in the earth by the suction of air and other gases as the result of a kind of respiratory process of the earth. Following in the footsteps of his seventeenth-century forerunners, he viewed the globe as an organism, which was supposed to produce ground-water in the course of its physiological processes.

For the past century it has been generally assumed that ground-water is fed chiefly by penetrating precipitation. That a theory, like many other things, may be the plaything of time is exemplified by the fate of Aristotle's ideas. After having lain in limbo for a long time, these were retrieved just short of a century ago and refurbished in modern garb; but shortly afterwards this condensation theory was once again thrown on the rubbish heap on the plea that it conflicted with natural laws. As we have seen, however, it was resuscitated a few decades ago and acknowledged to possess some degree of validity.

Water in the Subsoil

Microscopic cracks and larger clefts occur in all solid rock, and in damp climates they are as a rule filled with water to just below the surface. It is only in deserts that voids are dry to greater depth. Very much lower down, that is to say several miles below the surface, the rock is so firmly compressed that pores and cracks close up and the water is ejected as from a squeezed sponge.

Although this moisture too is ground-water, it is easier to visualise sub-surface hydrology in loose sandy and clayey soils. Let us consider a vast expanse of sand in a low-lying, damp district. On sinking a well into this, the ground is found to become progressively moister until water eventually runs into the bottom of the well and remains standing there at a steady level, which is called the *ground-water level*. Suppose we sink a number of such wells and imagine all the water levels connected by a flat or undulating surface, the result will be the *ground-water table* or *phreatic surface*. Everywhere between the grains below this surface there exists water which escapes if an outlet is provided, but the water, which is responsible for the moisture of the soil above this surface, cannot ooze out by its own power, being, as it is, held between the granules of the soil by a force known as *capillarity*.

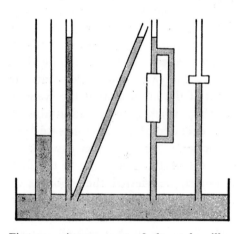

Fig. 103. Arrangement of glass tubes illustrating capillarity of water.

The suction that retains the water in this way is illustrated by blotting paper, in which the minute voids between the fibres suck up the wet ink from writing or blots, by capillarity. But a clearer idea of the nature of this force may be obtained by standing a thin glass tube in a basin of water. It will then be seen that the water inside the tube is raised above the level in the basin, especially if the inside of the tube has first been moistened. And the narrower the tube is, the higher will be the level to which the water is raised.

In a glass tube of 1 mm. diameter, water rises one foot, but if the diameter is one-tenth of a millimetre, the ascent is no less than ten feet.

Water in an irregularly bounded hollow will always try to creep into the smallest nooks and crannies; and it is for this reason that a sponge can draw up and retain water (Fig. 103).

Reverting to our sandy soil, we can visualise the structure if we think of a heap of gravel very much reduced in size. The grains are of irregular shape

and varying sizes. Everywhere between the grains there are small inter-
connected voids, the whole mass being perforated, as it were, by an exceedingly irregular system of minute tubes. All these ducts have a tendency to
suck up the ground-water from the reservoir below the ground-water surface
by capillarity. Suction continues in each duct until the capillary force is in
equilibrium with the weight of the column of water which has been raised

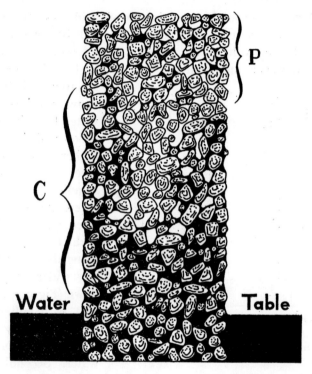

Fig. 104. Representing zones of capillary water in a column of sand. C = capillary zone;
P = pendulate water.

above the phreatic surface. If the ducts in the ground were arranged like a
system of glass tubes all of the same diameter, the water would be drawn up
to the same height in all of them. Actually they vary, not only in diameter,
but in that each individual tube consists both of hair-fine sections and far
wider ones. Thus in one duct the water will not rise beyond a particularly
wide void, where capillarity is at a discount, while at the same level immediately beside it there may be a narrowing in which capillarity can easily
raise the water up to a widening section far higher up. As a result, if we
have an imaginary surface passing through the tops of all those columns of

water, we shall find that its level is most erratic. All the water retained above the ground-water table in this way is called *capillary water*.

A further distinction can be made between the water below a comparatively level plane through the surfaces of the water in the widest tubes (hence there is no air in the ground beneath this plane) and the water rising above it, i.e. that standing in more or less thin threads above the general capillary plane (Fig. 104).

If, therefore, the ground-water rises in an arid mass of sand and then becomes stationary, a zone of capillary water will be formed above it and the voids higher up will remain empty. Should the ground-water rise to the surface, however, and then fall back to the level just mentioned, the situation will have changed in two respects. Firstly, the water level in many of the tubes will be considerably higher than in the above case, as the water remains standing in thin sections, where the greater capillary force will be able to cope with a longer column of water than that drawn up in the wider opening farther down (Fig. 105). This means that with falling water the capillary zone is thicker than with rising or stationary water. Secondly, water will be retained by capillarity between the grains of the whole mass of sand in small corners and crevices and wherever the grains touch. This water, though not directly connected with the capillary zone, represents isolated outposts. Its official name is *pendulate water*. It is completely independent of the level of the ground-water and it is quite immaterial whether there is a superimposed thick or thin layer of sand and whether the capillary zone is half an inch, or a couple of yards below it; for the quantity of water is determined solely by gravity on the one hand and the capillary forces retaining the fluid on the other.

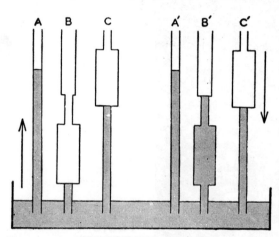

Fig. 105. Capillary force, (left) drawing up water and (right) retaining water, after tubes have been filled. Note difference between B and B'.

As a rule the capillary zone is not formed by suction from the ground-water lower down; nor does the pendulate water reach the site by a temporary ascent of the ground-water. It is precipitation which gives pendulate water to the soil and feeds the capillary zone from above. In the course of a dry period, some of the pendulate water will evaporate into the air between the grains and thus escape above the surface, and some will be imbibed by plants. The first shower breaking such a drought is used primarily to make good this loss; the capillary voids will claim it and let nothing pass until the imprisoned water becomes heavier than the capillary suction power can stand. Then and then only will the surplus trickle down into the depths and restore the original pendular condition at lower levels also. Hence there is a very well-defined amount of moisture in every cubic foot of ground at which it is saturated pendularly; with a little less, it is not filled up; with a little more, it overflows. So, although an imaginary piece of soil in the

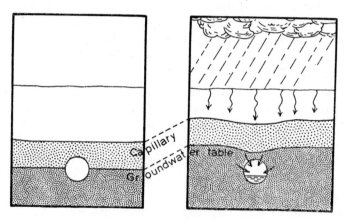

Fig. 106. Action of tubular drain.

ground has neither sides nor base, it is in a sense a vessel of certain dimensions.

It will now be clear that by no means all the rain that falls after a prolonged drought serves to replenish the ground-water. The entire rainfall is often required to restore the saturated pendular condition in the upper layer of the soil. Not until this has been accomplished can the surplus seep down to the capillary zone. The ducts in this zone are filled up from above; hence the surface of the zone is raised to a higher level.

It may be asked how the ground-water table fits into all this. Now, the phreatic surface is not visible but is only a theoretical level, for the layers of water below and above it are in unbroken contact. To make this clearer, let us imagine a drain exactly on the original ground-water table (Fig. 106); this will not drain off any water, because capillarity is holding all the water above the tube in the capillary zone. When the ducts in the ground are filled up with rain-water, capillarity is unable to cope with the lengthened column and some of the water oozes out into the drain until the formerly prevailing condition is restored. Thus, before it has come to this, the ground-water table will have risen to above the drain. It is well to remember that the ground-water table has *risen*, though there has only been a *downward* movement of water. The only thing that has changed at the site of the drain is the pressure. Accordingly, the ground-water table may aptly be defined as the plane in which the pressure of the ground-water is equal to the atmospheric pressure of the air. Hence the ground-water table rises and falls, however infinitesimally, together with the barometric pressure, though the water itself may not move by so much as a millimetre.

Water in the ground is not only replenished, of course, but also suffers loss. We have just seen an example of artificial drainage, and natural drainage will be dealt with presently. But, in addition, there is also some loss towards the free air, primarily through evaporation and also through absorption by the roots of plants.

Where not filled with water, the pores of the ground contain air completely saturated with water vapour. As the ducts freely discharge upwards, they give off moisture to the atmosphere and are therefore always able to absorb water from the pendulate and capillary zones, as a result of which the surface of the capillary zone descends. With it, the level underneath, where the pressure is equal to that of the atmosphere, naturally goes down as well. This is tantamount to saying that the ground-water table drops. The greater the depth to which the capillary zone descends, the more difficult will it be for moisture to escape to the surface, so the slower will be the depression of the ground-water table. A table at very great depth will accordingly suffer scarcely any loss at all through evaporation.

We shall see later on that there are some places in the soil to which water is constantly being supplied, such as the banks of a river, the shores of a lake, places where a spring rises through débris, etc. In such cases the ground-water table will be unable to drop, notwithstanding upward escape, for the capillary forces then draw up water to the same constant level from an inexhaustible supply. Such places are, however, relatively few and far between. The sucking action of capillarity is often compared with that of a suction pump, which compensates for upward loss by drawing on a supply at depth. Actually, the water-air boundary in the ground rises and falls with supply and loss just the same as though there were no capillary forces at work, except that thanks to these forces the boundary lies constantly at a slightly higher lever than otherwise.

Plant roots do not generally reach down to the completely filled level, where they would drown for lack of air, but just above that zone water and air occur together, and hair roots can penetrate everywhere between the granules and suck up the water. After superabundant rain, this layer of the soil retains as much water as can cling to the grains without yielding to gravity; so in this state of fine balance the roots need only the minimum of force to draw up the water they need. But the larger the amount of water withdrawn, the more tenaciously does the residue cling to the grains. The maximum suction power of the roots is 7 to 8 atmospheres and, once the attractive force exerted by the grains has reached this figure, the plants are unable to absorb any more water and they begin to wilt. Evaporation, however, may continue for a long time to withdraw water; indeed, right up to the moment when the force by which the last molecules of water are being held fast to the particles of the soil has attained a magnitude of thousands of atmospheres.

In most regions the roots do not go down farther than six feet. This zone contains at most 10 cubic inches of water per square inch of surface. As the roots extract twice to five times this amount per year over and above the loss by evaporation, the pendulate water needs replenishment once a year at least. In arid districts the activity of vegetation prevents any water from reaching the phreatic level. Exceptionally, lack of water forces the roots to go on growing downwards to the ground-water lying at very great depths and to draw on what they find there.

We must now consider in what way different soils affect ground-water. Grains of sand being relatively large, the ducts are wide and the capillary zone is therefore thin, being at most one or two feet thick, while the points of contact between the grains are few in number. Clay particles, on the other hand, are minute flakes, too small to be visible as loose fragments even under the microscope. Consequently the pores are likewise exceedingly small, whereas there are an enormous number of points of contact. The aggregate surface of the grains in one gram of sand is one square foot, but in one gram of clay it is no less than 1000 square feet. This implies that the capillary zone in clay is far thicker, at least three feet, and, moreover, that more water is retained per unit volume. Another difference between the two soils is that the pores in sand occupy about a fifth of the volume, whereas in clays sometimes half or more is occupied by water. Finally, clay particles, on absorbing water, are liable to swell, stick firmly together and cause the clay to become plastic.

The differences are most evident when the two soils are parched. The structure does not change when moist sand loses enclosed water, because the hard rounded grains were already packed close together and supported each other in rigid stacking. Clay, the particles of which swell on absorbing water, contracts considerably when drying. Moreover, the flakes of which clay consists are pliable and can therefore be more closely compacted when the intervening water is expelled. At first, a shrinking layer of clay merely becomes thinner, but it is not long before cracks develop as the result of growing tensile stresses in the horizontal plane. These cracks run in all directions and cut up the clay into angular pillars separated by straight or curved rents called *shrinkage cracks*, which may be a few inches wide and become more than a yard deep, tapering downwards (Fig. 107 B).

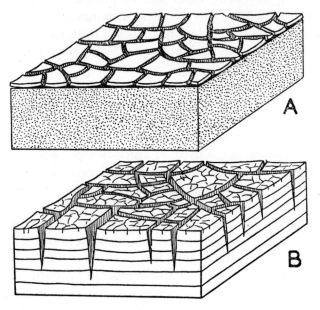

Fig. 107. Shrinkage cracks caused by drying of (A) a thin layer of clay on sand and (B) a thick pack of clay.

Curious patterns occur if a thin layer of clay lies on sand. The contracting skin cracks and detaches itself in scales, because the substratum is not shrinking with it. The polygons of clay curl up at the edges because desiccation proceeds fastest at the top (Fig. 107 A).

If sand or dust blows across the cracked surface, it fills the crevices. Also in any sudden flooding the cracks may be sealed before the clay has had a chance to re-absorb water and to close them. In this way cracks may be preserved. Geologists frequently come across these petrified shrinkage cracks in ancient sediments.

There is a great deal more to be said about the structure of the soil and the colloidal properties of clay, but it would take us too far from our true subject. We shall therefore revert to sandy soil and at once consider a complication.

Ground-water Flow

Generally speaking, ground-water is no more stationary than water at the surface and, like the latter, flows by gravity to the lowest point it can reach. As this movement is not apparent, some aspects of the matter strike us as strange when they are brought to our notice for the first time. The principles are nevertheless perfectly simple: water in the ground moves in the direction which tends to reduce its pressure; whether it moves upwards or downwards, directly or indirectly, the internal pressure to which we are now referring is not only the atmospheric pressure, but the resultant of that and the weight of the water itself. Water in a bucket does not flow upwards, even if the pressure near the bottom is greater than that at the top. But let there be made only a small hole in the bottom of the bucket and this higher pressure will cause the water to run out. The same thing happens underground: the pressure increases with depth and if in one of two connected channels it comes to exceed that in the other, the excess pressure may even force the water in the latter upwards. Where there is unequal pressure at two adjacent points in the same level, the water flows horizontally from the higher to the lower pressure.

There is a second principle which affects the velocity of flow. Given equal excess pressure, water flows more quickly in the wider ducts, because there is less friction against the walls to impede it. Thus water runs through coarse gravel almost as rapidly as through an open canal at the same angle of slope. There is appreciable retardation through sand, while clay, with its system of minute ducts, is, for all practical purposes, impenetrable.

For simplicity, we shall now ignore the capillary zone and assume that the ground-water table marks the boundary between completely saturated soil and dry ground.

Applied to water in the ground, this assumption enables its behaviour, the points of emergence and disappearance, its velocity, to be clarified in broad outline. Anything in the nature of the unpredictable must be denied to water under the surface. Although we cannot follow its course and are therefore inclined to suspect it of illicit divagations, not a single molecule evades the all-seeing eye of nature, which imposes strict obedience to her laws. It is not an inner urge to rise to the surface which causes water to well up in a spring, but the law of communicating vessels; so one can be quite certain that somewhere in the vicinity a mass of water at a higher level is providing the hydrostatic pressure necessary. If water somewhere dips down into the ground, it is not to be thought that it has disappeared for ever in the bowels of the earth; at some distance, whether short or long, it will reappear at a lower level. Water flowing under the surface needs a head just as it does in an open river bed. It need not necessarily flow to a lower level, however, provided there be a pressure head like that existing between the water-tower and the tap in our bathroom on the first or second floor, to which the water "drops" up from the ground floor or basement.

The simplest example that suggests itself is that of a mound of sand surrounded by a ditch at constant level. When a shower of rain has saturated the whole mound with water, the pressure in the plane AA (Fig. 108) will be greater than the atmospheric pressure through the weight of the column AB.

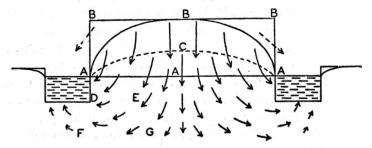

Fig. 108. Flow system of ground-water draining into ditches.

The water will sink downwards and sideways, first to ABA. At that moment a system of flow will be operative as indicated by the arrows—not only above the plane AAA, as might be supposed, for a difference in pressure also prevails lower down. The pressure at E, for instance, will be greater than at D, which implies that there will be a pressure head and, therefore, flow. Even at G the pressure exceeds that at F, but in proportion the disparity is already narrowing and, owing to the longer distance, flow is also progressively impeded by friction. Hence, the movement dies out at greater depths.

The water continues to drop even after reaching ABA, passing ACA with considerable reduction of pressure and speed. It eventually comes to a standstill on reaching the line AAA. If there are repeated falls of rain before the AAA line is reached, a hillock of ground-water will remain standing and a more or less stationary condition will be established, with continual drainage towards the ditches.

The difference between sand and that vastly less permeable material, clay, is that the flow is so much slower and the ground-water hillock higher in the latter. With the same amount of rainfall, in sand far less difference in height will be capable of providing the necessary pressure to drain off the water, because there is so much less friction during flow through the wider ducts.

Let us now see how our theoretical model fits the vagaries of a natural landscape. We find that the ground-water table shows roughly the same topography as the surface, but subdued, lying high under the hills and low under valleys and near the sea. Flow, however, is perpetually at work, undermining ground-water hillocks and filling the depressions up to the surface, with the result that the ground-water mounds are lower than the

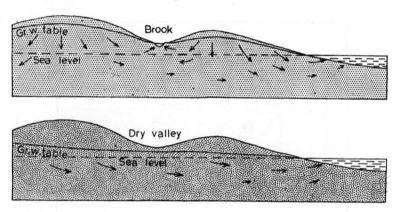

Fig. 109. Drainage system in fine soil (top) compared with that in a coarser, more pervious material.

topographical elevations and that the ground-water table meets the surface in the valleys.

The coarser the material comprising the soil, the sooner will the water cancel out inequalities and the more featureless will the ground-water relief become. This being so, some hills find no counterpart in the ground-water table and, instead of rising, the water drops away from the valleys (Fig. 109).

Let us now see how pumping water out of a bore-hole affects the ground-water. Prolonged pumping at a constant rate causes a depression to be formed in the ground-water table (Fig. 110). Close to the drill-hole the gradient is considerable but, flattening progressively outwards, finally it merges into the initial ground-water table. The head induces flow towards the boring but, as the water coming from all sides has to flow inwards through an ever narrower cylindrical section, the speed towards the hole must steadily increase. This requires the upward bulge of the cone.

If the water is imprisoned below an impervious layer, a vacuum will not, of course, be formed; consequently there will be no conical depression in the water surface under the sealing layer. Instead, pumping causes a *conical depression in the pressure* of the enclosed water. This depression is much larger and develops far sooner than the depression in the phreatic surface of the former case; for, the slightest movement in water brings about a change in pressure, because water is scarcely compressible or extensible at all. The pressure head towards the bore-hole now induces flow and when pumping stops, the original condition is restored long before it would be with a free ground-water table.

The movement of water in the ground is far more complicated than in our

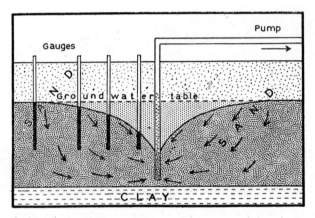

Fig. 110. Formation of conical depression in ground-water table through continual pumping from bore-hole.

theoretical examples, because of the alternation of strata of varying permeability and irregular shape instead of the uniform mass we have postulated.

Rocks and sedimentary deposits of the earth's crust, in their relation to ground-water, can be divided into the following groups. 1. The sand and gravel strata, through the large pores of which water can easily percolate. 2. The clays and marls (i.e. clays containing lime), which are virtually impervious to water. 3. The solid rocks, consisting of watertight strata and irregular masses, but invariably in some degree jointed and with planes of division. Some water can therefore usually find a way along fairly wide channels through crystalline rock, even though they may be few and far between. This group includes rocks consolidated from the molten condition at depth, such as granite, the lavas, also sandstone and conglomerates, gneisses and other crystalline schists. The limestones, which likewise belong to this category, stand apart because they are soluble. In them, the fissures

through which water percolates widen sufficiently to allow almost unimpeded flow, as though in an irregular water-main system. We shall deal
with this matter in full detail when considering the hydrography of the Karst.

Springs and Water Supply

Taking once again the simplest case, to begin with we shall consider how
water moves in a hill of which the upper part consists of permeable rock,
resting on a flat, watertight base (Fig. 111 A). The infiltrating rain is now
brought up short on the impervious layer but, as there is nothing to hold it
back at the sides, it will ooze out plentifully all along the upper margin of
the impermeable layer. If the hill is a small one, the soil here will only be
slightly moist and vegetation only a little more luxuriant. The geologist,
however, will call it a "spring" because, being a specialist, he has to give

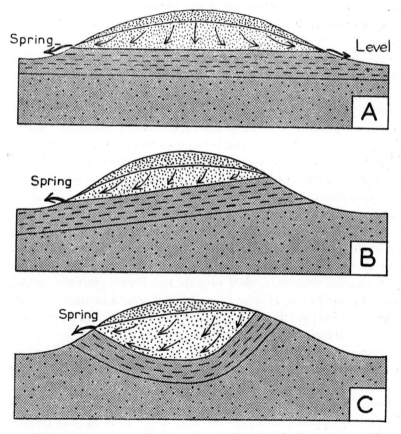

Fig. 111. Ground-water and springs in sand on an impermeable stratum of clay.

careful attention to any spot where water wells up, seeking a cause for its accumulation. On a bigger hill, there will be more water seeking an exit; it will scour out wider channels for itself along certain paths, thus running out in concentrated, manifest springs here and there along the edge of the lower layer. The spectacle of a large spring is fascinating because it gives some idea of the great amount of rain that falls in the catchment area.

If the impervious stratum is inclined, ground-water will emerge in still greater concentration at the lower end (Fig. 111 B). But the strata will not always be flat; on the contrary, the mountain-forming forces often wrinkle the earth's crust. Rocks may have been locally depressed, for instance, with the result that the watertight stratum forms a kind of basin; this will fill with water until it overflows at the lowest point of the periphery, as though it were an open basin (Fig. 111 C).

These, then, are a few forms of springs. It will be evident that the most abundant water in proportion to the size of the hill will be produced by the form represented in Fig. 111 C, because it alone drains off all the water in one place.

There is far greater variety than this, however. A reservoir full of ground-water, which is called an *aquifer*, can be formed where strata are intersected by a fault (Fig. 112 I). If a water-repelling stratum comes to lie next to a permeable material during the shifting of the strata, the ground-water collects in the permeable material until it ultimately overflows somewhere in the form of a spring. Should sand be sandwiched between two sealing layers of clay, it may carry the water under a region situated at a higher level (Fig. 112 II) towards the lowest attainable exit (unless, that is, the strata are situated in a dome). In that event, the water flowing from the spring into the valley derives from precipitation which has fallen on the hill to the right. The same applies to the lowest profile of Fig. 112 III, but here folding has caused more marked distortion of the strata and a subsequent fault has added complications. Faults need not necessarily give rise to seepages; on the contrary, if caulked with clay, they provide excellent watertight partitions in the soil. In our profile III the ground-water would in that event stagnate and the precipitation falling on the catchment area would have to drain off as a brook or remain stationary in the form of a lake.

Where ground-water is held between watertight, firmly-sealing rocks and there are only limited ways of escape (e.g. the cases represented in Fig. 112, II and III), it will stand under hydrostatic pressure and will be expelled with force. Under natural conditions, however, such a situation would not persist for any appreciable length of time, as the running water soon scours out a wider passage for itself and the pressure then automatically declines.

It is a different matter when man intervenes and narrows the opening artificially or cuts a new exit for stagnating water under pressure. The ancient Egyptians drew off water under pressure in wells 2000 years before Christ, but it was not until the twelfth century A.D. that anything similar was done in Europe. The first "artesian well" was obtained in this way in

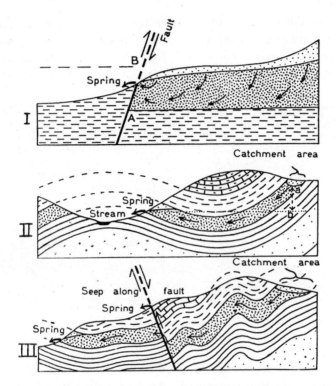

Fig. 112. Springs from three types of aquifer or ground-water reservoir. I held up by a fault (movement B to A). II hydrostatic pressure *a* to *b*. III escaping along fault.

the province of Artois in northern France in the year 1126 and supplies water to this day.

It took seven years of unremitting labour to drill the first deep well with cable tools, a work which was completed near Paris in 1841. A powerful source of artesian water was struck at a depth of 2000 feet, certainly a technical feat of the first order at that date. Later on, the technique of drilling, especially as practised by oil engineers, was raised to such a high pitch of perfection that it now takes as many days as it then did years, and the number of artesian wells being sunk all over the world is rapidly increasing. Vast areas in arid regions, particularly in the United States, depend entirely on artesian water for their supplies. Thousands upon thousands now make a living in agriculture and stock-breeding in regions where nature had only subterranean pressure reservoirs to offer. Hundreds of miles away, in rainy districts, the feed-water sinks away into the ground, flowing through the strata deep under the surface, finally to emerge through borings to irrigate these deserts.

The smaller the pores in the water-bearing stratum and the farther the distance from the catchment area to the boring, the greater the loss of pressure. Once the well "comes in", friction caused by the flowing water will increase the loss of pressure. That is why the pressure seldom reaches

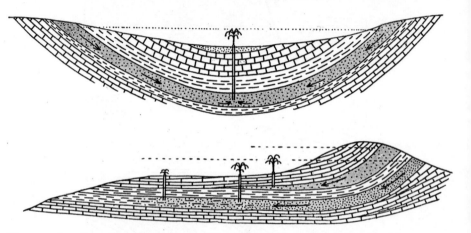

Fig. 113. Artesian wells: (above) in a syncline; (below) in tapering stratum and in a stratum gradually becoming impermeable towards the left.

high figures, even if the mouth of the drill-hole is at a considerably lower level than that of the feeding-ground. Artesian wells jetting water a couple of dozen yards upwards are exceptions, and an initial pressure measured at the surface of more than 20 atmospheres is extremely rare.

The ideal case is the aquifer between two watertight beds, the whole curved in the shape of a basin, for thus artesian wells can be sunk anywhere in the basin (Fig. 113, above). But if the resources are drawn upon to excess, the pressure diminishes as does also the yield of the first wells, to the prejudice of those working them. Sometimes artesian water derives pressure not from the basin-shaped dip of the strata, but from tapering of the porous layer or from lateral cessation of the porosity (Fig. 113, below). Such a case is when sand contains a progressively larger admixture of clay the lower down it gets on a slope.

It has been tacitly assumed so far that our springs come straight out into the daylight and do not, therefore, conceal their whereabouts. But this is by no means a hard and fast rule. Often enough the outlet is buried under a thick layer of débris or topsoil and the rising of the ground-water is therefore betrayed only by a moist patch, possibly with bogs. When all is said, the difference between a spring and an area of oozing ground-water is one of degree only.

The yield of a spring, like that of a river, may vary. Some springs produce large quantities of brown, muddy water shortly after a heavy downpour of rain and then run almost or entirely dry. These, of course, are quite unsuitable for catchment and consumption. The best water-producers filter through thick, cleansing strata. The outflow of clear water, free from bacteria, coming as it does from a very large reservoir, fluctuates very little from year to year, showing a maximum only slightly in excess of the normal yield and coming several months after the wet season. Another advantage is the equable temperature of the water. From the fact that it may be some degrees above the yearly average of the neighbourhood, we may infer that the water has passed hundreds of feet beneath the surface and carries off some calories of the earth's heat.

An interesting calculation can be made if it is exactly known what area is being drained by the spring. Rain-gauges installed in the catchment area record the amount of precipitation accurately and drainage through the spring can likewise be ascertained with precision. These figures show at a glance the percentage of precipitated moisture which has penetrated deep down into the soil and has flowed via the ground-water towards the spring. The balance has run off on the surface, or else has been absorbed by the topsoil and the vegetation and has then evaporated. In European districts where precipitation consists mainly of rain, one-third to half penetrates into the ground and reappears in springs. Where snowfall is the main form of precipitation, as much as two-thirds to nine-tenths may go underground, because slowly delivered melt-water sinks into the ground more easily than rain coming in sudden showers; there is, moreover, little evaporation, owing to the paucity of vegetation in the vicinity of the snow-line.

Thermal and Mineral Springs

These are in a category apart. There is no clearly marked distinction between them and normal springs, but if their temperature is more than 10° Centigrade above the yearly mean of the surrounding air, they are called *hot* or *thermal springs*, and the term *mineral springs* is applied to those containing a noticeable percentage of dissolved substances (more than about 1 in 1000). Not surprisingly, most thermal springs are rich in dissolved substances, while most mineral springs are warm. These properties may be due to two causes, either singly or combined. The ground-water may have been in contact with hot rock material, either recently solidified igneous rock in the outer crust of the earth, or rocks at great depth which are maintained at high temperatures by the earth's heat. It is also possible that hot water containing dissolved material is expelled during solidification of molten magma. Five to ten per cent of water may be dissolved in the original fluid melt; but there is no room for moisture in the crystallising minerals. As solidification proceeds, the water collects in the residue of the melt until it is finally ejected. Several other substances, likewise repelled by the developing crystals, will also concentrate in the aqueous residue. When water of this kind escapes to the surface, it is called *juvenile* because of its recent birth from the bowels of the earth; and, by contrast, ground-water which has seen the light of day before is called meteoric.

Indications may be obtained of the degree of participation of juvenile water in the formation of mineral thermal springs. If the hot spring reacts strongly to the quantity of precipitation, it is a fairly sure sign that it is pre-dominantly meteoric water, which is ultimately arriving at the surface after having travelled deep down in the subsoil. The dissolved materials will be mainly those encountered on the way and carried along—for the most part silica, carbonate of lime and rock salt. The hot springs at Baden in Switzer-land are an example. The water takes two years to complete its underground journey and flows under Zürich at a depth of 5000 feet.

When dissolved carbon dioxide is a conspicuous component of spring waters, and a variety of substances, such as sulphur compounds and boric acid, occur in them, it may safely be assumed that juvenile water plays an important part, though it is unlikely ever to be predominant in a spring. It will be obvious that the majority of the medicinal springs and those from which soda water is made (Apollinaris, Ems, Aix-la-Chapelle, etc.) belong to the juvenile category and therefore owe their utilitarian properties to the slow de-gassing and dehydration of the deeper strata of the earth.

Geysers

Those intermittent eruptions of boiling water which we call *geysers* are undoubtedly the most remarkable natural phenomena in the realm of springs. On the whole of our globe there are only three areas of appreciable extent in which geysers occur, viz., the classical region of Iceland, from which they have taken their name; that of Yellowstone Park in the U.S.A., where more than 3000 hot springs and nearly 200 geysers occur; and New Zealand, where there used also to be a fine display of geysers, until a few decades ago the terrain suffered badly from a volcanic eruption (Plate XIV, 1).

The activity of geysers varies considerably. With the utmost regularity, "Old Faithful" gushes every 65 minutes up to 130 feet, whereas the "Beehive", likewise in Yellowstone Park, erupts only once a day, but when it does, it flings its jet of boiling water no less than 200 feet high. New Zealand holds the world record for height in this respect also. Right at the beginning of this century, a geyser which was in action for several years reached 1300 feet, a height which makes the most powerful fire-hoses at our disposal look like mere toys.

The sequence presented by the eruptions of the "Great Geyser" in Iceland is highly complex. In the centre of a shallow basin 60 feet in diameter there is a narrow eruption channel. The perpetual, gentle overflow of water is punctuated now and then by subterranean explosions which cause the water to boil up and run over. Explosion follows upon explosion, the noise grows to a deafening roar, belching steam whips the water in the basin into stormy waves and the whole culminates in the emission of a jet of water 80 or 100 feet into the air. This is soon followed by a second and third rocket of water and then for a few minutes the geyser disgorges a hissing stream of water and steam soaring sometimes to more than 200 feet. The water dropping back is carried again and again from the basin up into the air and much also overflows. In a comparatively short time the monster's energy is spent and hours, days, or even months pass before the motive forces have re-assembled in sufficient strength for a fresh display. But for many years now this gusher has been inactive.

After some time, possibly after a violent eruption, a geyser may become an ordinary hot spring or the channel may get choked; but as a rule the loss is compensated for by the break-through of new gushers in the vicinity.

One or two geysers show tongues of flame apparently playing far down the column of water in the eruption channel. These, of course, are not actual flames of fire, but jets of burning-hot gases which help to heat the water.

The deposition of lime or siliceous sinter appears to be an invariable concomitant to a geyser. Obviously, the hot water and gases must act as strong solvents upon the rocks through which they pass. When the water cools on arriving at the surface and liberates the dissolved carbon dioxide, it automatically precipitates some of the mineral constituents. The sinter thus deposited consists of silica or calcium carbonate. Not only does this act as a sealing agent in the eruption canal, but at the same time it forms a mouthpiece at the outlet of that tube, or a rim on the wider basin around the channel. On the flanks of hills the sinter sometimes forms a flight of steps or bastions, each encircling a dribbling pool of turquoise-coloured water.

The coloured mud wells, like the Fountain Paintpot of Yellowstone Park, are also an amazing sight. They consist of a group of small cones, each perpetually throwing up lumps of mud. A visitor to Yellowstone Park, a General, said: "It reminded me of a group of politicians, each one trying to outdo the other and, although most of the mud falls back into the same cone from which it is emitted, occasionally it falls into another. But", he added, "this mud is clean."

The mud is conspicuously coloured pink, blue, yellow and white and, if of the right consistency, the rising bubbles unfold into tulip-shaped flowers of soft pastel hues. Expressed in less romantic terms, the fact is that if too little water issues to form a spring and if the rocks have been weathered to clay with compounds of iron, the result will be a "paint-pot".

In and around the true geysers and hot springs, too, the most resplendent and contrasting colours heighten the vivid spectacle presented to the visitor traversing Yellowstone Park. For there are several species of intensely pigmented algae, able to tolerate the hot water, which suffuse the bottom of the water and the sides of the basins with indigo or sapphire blue, red or brown, mother-of-pearl, green, white or yellow. As the differently coloured algae also thrive at different temperatures, some other colour is usually to be seen on the outside of the sinter deposit (also known as travertine). It is, therefore, natural enough that many geysers should have been nicknamed after jewels. Thus, the sinter deposit of one geyser being grey, olive-green and bright yellow, arranged in a very intricate pattern, it looks as though a casket of vari-coloured jewels had spilled over on to the white earth, so that when, moreover, the emitted water rises in a thin iridescent spray sparkling in the sun, the spellbound spectator feels that "Jewel Geyser" is no misnomer.

Many have been tempted to seek a reasonable explanation for the intermittent activity of geysers. One hypothesis formulated a century ago was later translated into the form of a model with which periodic eruptions in fact can be obtained. But neither this hypothesis nor many later suggested explanations would appear to be entirely satisfactory. The over-all picture must be something like this: Largely, the water of a geyser is meteoric, but is warmed by the intrusion of juvenile steam rising from hot masses of igneous rock at shallow depth. Standing in a tall column, the water is first gradually heated up to boiling temperature. Below the surface the latter is higher than 100° C. owing to hydrostatic pressure, and increases in proportion to the depth. If somewhere in this column of water the temperature is raised above the boiling point valid at that spot, the water will be partly converted to vapour and therefore expand enormously. As a result, the superincumbent water is ejected and the pressure reduced in the whole of what remains of the column. The residual superheated water will begin to boil violently and this leads to a powerful eruption. Some of the ejected water falls back into the basin, but it has cooled off so much on the way that there can be no further eruption until the juvenile steam has started all over again to super-heat it.

The active element in geysers and paint-pots is the ground-water itself; but there are other kinds of bubbling springs, in which the water is entirely passive. Its only participation in the formation, for instance, of the peculiar little erupting cones known as *mud-volcanoes* consists in imparting the particular consistency to the mud. The motive power is supplied by gases emanating from oil deposits. Accumulations of the latter tend to lie in

Fig. 114. Poeloe Kambing, a mud volcano rising from the sea near Timor, seen from the North East. Cr = Crater; M = Mangroves.

sandy strata far below the surface and often contain dissolved gases like methane and ethane. If the expansive force of these gases becomes excessive, they will seek some outlet, blow a hole right through the covering strata, and escape. Should they, in the process, first pass through a coarse-grained aquifer containing much ground-water, this will be carried along with them. If a layer of clay is then encountered, which the mixture of gases and water whisks into a soft slurry, mud will emerge and build up a cone on the surface. Within its centre a cauldron of thin mud bubbles and splashes; every so often the bubbles lift the mud to above the edge of the crater and it overflows onto the flanks of the cone. As it dries out, it hardens and in this way the mud-volcano continues to grow. Around Timor, huge examples are found, arising out of the shallow sea (Fig. 114). Escaping volcanic gases may produce mud-volcanoes in a similar manner, but these are very small.

The Karst

Reverting, after this digression, to ordinary cold-water springs, we can now look at some examples with superabundant water supply. In our search for these we always come upon hilly or mountainous country, where the earth's crust consists mainly of limestone ($CaCO_3$), even though other rocks, particularly argillaceous limestones or even pure clays, be prominent components. This location of the great springs of the world in limestone regions is explained by the fact that calcite is virtually the only rock-forming mineral which dissolves readily in water. Its solubility in pure water is not striking, but rain-water and ground-water always contain a considerable percentage of carbon dioxide; if the ground-water has passed through wooded soil, this will be enhanced by addition of traces of humic acid. Both these increase the solvent action on lime very considerably.

Limestone possesses other important properties besides solubility. In structure it is a compact mass of closely contiguous crystals and it occurs in thick, coherent beds, which renders it completely impermeable, except for joints and fissures. Limestone is, moreover, a strong building-stone, a fact to which its technical use in the form of marble, paving slabs and for building purposes testifies. Owing to this solidity, once cavities have been formed in limestone mountains, they will not readily be closed up, and will only cave in when the dimensions become excessive.

As the result of this combination of properties, cracks and fissures in limestone rock are soon widened by the invading ground-water, open communications are formed and drainage from then on takes place for the most part underground. All this is conducive to the development of a strongly individual kind of landscape, called *karst* after the region of that name along the Adriatic Sea, which exhibits the typical features to perfection.

This is a kind of country in a class all its own. The soil, which in any event is not fertile, is very dry because the ground-water seeps quickly through the innumerable cracks in the underlying rocks. No rivers irrigate the valleys to lay down at least a strip of greenery as do some desert rivers. Bare rock shows everywhere through the scanty earth, and its white colour and rounded shapes betray the calcareous nature of the subsoil. It was forest country in ancient times, but the Romans disforested the district, which was hence denuded of good soil; while grazing goats hold back the growth of new plantations. Wherever the vegetable kingdom is allowed free play, timber seems to be able to re-establish itself fairly quickly, thanks to the ample rainfall; but the renewal of soil and humus takes a very long time.

Lack of running water has prevented the development of continuous valleys but the Karst landscape presents a kind of depression peculiar to itself. This consists of a large number of round to oval pits, called sink-holes or, from their Slavonic name, *dolines*, varying in diameter from a few to hundreds of yards. Where such a depression is very deeply excavated, or if drainage is choked, a stagnant tarn may collect at the bottom. Usually, however, the bottom is covered with a layer of clay different from the surrounding bare hills in that it is somewhat moister and more fertile and therefore bears a little more vegetation. It is these oases that the impoverished peasantry has to cultivate as best it can, but treacherous cloud-bursts which

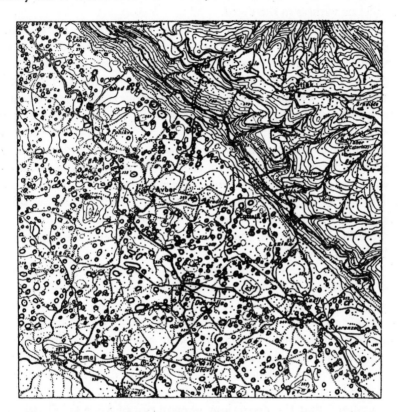

Fig. 115. A Karst area to the North of Trieste (Scale approx.: 1 : 60,000 or 1 in. to mile). The south-west shows typical characteristics of limestone areas with numerous sink-holes and no surface drainage pattern. The north-east corner of the area, not having a limestone sub-soil, shows a normal pattern of surface drainage. (After Escher.)

are liable to flood the dolines are feared more even than aridity, the commoner enemy.

The sink-holes always drain downwards, frequently through hidden crevices, but occasionally a round swallow-hole may be found at the bottom, leading to an irregular tube widening as it descends. The system is comparable with a large kitchen sink. By throwing in a stone and listening as it goes clattering down, the fathomless depth of some of these shafts (called *ponori* (sing. *ponor*) in the Karst, and *avens* by the French) can be realised. We have to assume that the dissolving of limestone is responsible for the formation of the dolines, the clay being the insoluble residue of this gradually denuded material. A possible alternative is that by solution a cavity was first hollowed out at depth and the roof later collapsed, leaving a surface depression as witness to the event.

Solution cannot have created the larger basins in the Karst landscape (*Polja*; sing. *Polje*), for their surface area may amount to many tens of square miles. They must have been formed as depressions in the mountains through movements of the earth's crust (so-called *synclines* and fault troughs). Sometimes there is a spring at the margin, feeding a good-sized stream; this winds through the polje until it vanishes in a *ponor* on the other side, or maybe on the way.

It is peculiar to ponors in a polje that their action may be reversed. Thus, not only may a spring dry up after a prolonged drought, but a swallow-hole, into which a stream tumbles under normal circumstances, may, after a period of heavy rainfall, change its tactics and begin to throw up water instead. If this goes on for a long time, the whole polje is inundated. Eventually, the ground-water in the vicinity seeps away and the hole returns to its ordinary swallowing habits.

All that water which has sunk into the soil in areas of this type must reappear somewhere. If the limestone region borders the sea, as does the Karst itself, full-sized rivers will issue in large springs at a short distance from the coast, carrying the efflux to the sea in flat, short valleys. There must also be any number of submarine springs, but only a few are conspicuous by their large output or abnormal qualities. Moreover, some springs of brackish water discharge above sea-level, no doubt having drawn up an admixture of sea-water by siphon action.

It is assumed that the mysterious phenomena of *sea-mills*, likewise derive from siphon action. On the island of Cephalonia off the west coast of Greece, for instance, are to be found swallow-holes close to the sea, towards which sea-water flows, disappearing into the limestone. Quite a sizeable stream of sea-water can be seen vanishing from sight into such a hole. The inhabitants use this force for the operation of water-mills; hence the name (Fig. 116).

When a district of the Karst type is remote from the sea and surrounded by impervious rock, the drainage system will have to discharge somewhere above the surface. Since the material in these surrounding rocks cannot be dissolved, there will be no subterranean rivers of any significance. The discharge will therefore have to take place in low-lying parts of the area, where several springs of great capacity and constant yield will be found. Here we have a typical example of the classical rising of a river from a spring. With the exception of glaciers, these are the only cases of the emergence of full-scale, ready-made rivers. We shall see later how rivers usually do rise.

The most celebrated spring on the margin of a limestone plateau is La Fontaine de Vaucluse near Avignon. It was described by Pliny, while Petrarch and many others have sung their praises of this mysterious, copious flow of crystal-clear water. The Sorgue, a river of considerable size, here has its source in a small cave slanting downwards, funnel-wise, in the base of a perpendicular wall 600 feet high. The feeder has been plumbed down to 160 feet below the surface of the water. We apparently have here the rising branch of a very deep, natural siphon, but, although a survey has been made of many of the avens on the plateau, it has not, at the time of writing, been possible to detect the earlier course of the underground stream. The Sorgue generally carries roughly 400 cubic feet of water per second, but after much rainfall no less than 550 cubic feet of water per second are produced from

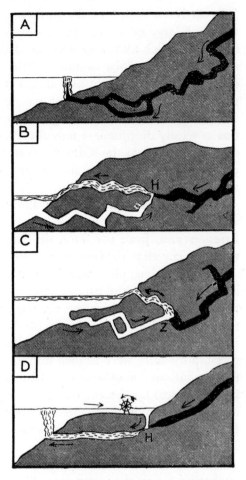

Fig. 116. Underground streams in limestone country discharging into sea. (A) Outflow of fresh water below sea-level. (B) Spring of brackish water due to siphon action at H. (C) Brackish spring due to pressure of sea-water at Z. (D) Siphon action at H causes flow of sea-water which operates sea-mill.

the interior of the limestone world, the largest yield of a spring ever measured.

Casteret's account of the search some years ago for the sources of the Garonne makes exciting reading. This river is formed from two confluents, one of them issuing as a waterfall from a large spring, the Goueil de Jouéou. The problem to be solved was: Where does this abundance of water come from?

In the Esera Valley, on the southern side of the watershed of the Pyrenees, there is a large swallow-hole, known as the Trou du Toro; the thunderous roar with which all the melt-water of the Maladetta glaciers and adjacent snowfields pours down it makes "the bull's hole" a fitting name. The destination of this torrent had always been a profound mystery. Some suggested the existence of a through-passage running under the mountain ridge towards the north, thus feeding the source of the Garonne; but the notion was generally dismissed as unrealistic. In the common opinion, the water disappearing down the Trou du Toro under the Esera Valley emerged as pools, springs, and mountain streams, eventually thus reaching the Ebro and the Mediterranean.

Yet after years of investigation, the conclusion was drawn from the available evidence that the Garonne does in fact rise on the southern slope of the Pyrenees and, from the Trou du Toro, dives under the mountain ridge whence it travels to the Goueil de Jouéou two and a half miles distant.

Just at this time, plans were being made in Spain to catch the water before it disappears into the ground and to use it for working hydro-electric power plant, from which site drainage was to be conducted above ground to the Ebro. Under this threat, the French raised funds to finance an expensive but conclusive test. Sixty kilograms of fluorescine, a very strong, greenish dyestuff, were thrown into the Trou du Toro and the protagonists had the satisfaction of seeing the Goueil de Jouéou temporarily transformed into a magical fluorescent waterfall, bright green in colour. This provided incontestable proof of the direct subterranean communication and enabled France to contest the plans for removing the drainage from the Trou du Toro to the Ebro.

Although in Karst country rivers formed from precipitation arise only on the border, where the water runs off, there are many instances of rivers flowing in from elsewhere. Sometimes the entering stream soon disappears in a hole, thence flowing as an underground Karst-river and, mingled with water of local origin, reappearing at the margin in a spring. Elsewhere the stream succeeds in traversing the dangerous zone without noticeable loss of water, like the Tarn in the *Causses*, the characteristic limestone plateaux of south central France. Where this river reaches the Karst area, the bed is so deep that the water cannot dive underground; on the contrary, it is fed laterally with extra water from the Karst districts. In a deeply incised, steep-sided valley, the Tarn winds on a few dozen miles, finally to emerge unscathed from the limestones on to the safe, impermeable granites and gneisses farther on. The gorges of the Tarn are justly famed for their serpentine picturesqueness, seen to best advantage from a punt. Actually, however, the Tarn is not a representative Karst-river, which should properly be subterranean. We shall now proceed to explore the fairyland that is found to exist underneath the Karst landscape.

It is not a hard and fast rule that any fissure in limestone must be widened by trickling water; on the contrary, if it is so narrow that the water is held by capillarity, lime dissolved elsewhere may be deposited there and seal the crack. Some of the cracks and planes of division in the limestone are wider, however, owing to tensile stress set up here and there by movements of the earth's crust. The water is quick to seize these opportunities of escaping downwards; it dissolves lime on the way and widens the fissure further still. Thus a swallow-hole may be formed, for instance, where two cracks intersect. Eventually the water will arrive at a dead end and be forced to continue more or less horizontally through the bowels of the mountain chain until it emerges in a spring; but on the way, the initial trickles will have united into runnels and finally to real underground streams, or even veritable rivers.

In comparatively dry periods, the water accruing to the subterranean streams will have become saturated with lime on its way down, so that the river will no longer corrode its banks; but after heavy rainfall, even the larger watercourses will drain unsaturated water. Hence they will be widened from time to time by solution, as well as scoured by the running water, though in minor degree for lack of scouring material. These tunnels ultimately grow to such a size that they are not filled up to their full capacity even in the event of an underground spate. The roofs may collapse, or the stream may work its way ever deeper into its bed. Enormous caverns may finally be formed in this way. All the rock once filling these caves has been dissolved, molecule by molecule, in the ground-water and carried away in solution; the Timovo, for instance, a comparatively small river rising in Dalmatia, carries away annually 210 million kilograms of lime from caves through which it passes, equivalent to a cube with sides of 140 feet. Yet where water has been able at a later period to wear a passage lower down, such caves may now be bone dry.

These highly complicated paths through the rocky subsoil of a Karst-type region might have been designed by a puckish spirit giving full rein to its inventive powers. At one point the roof of a large cavern vaults an unruffled, clear lake, so large that it would take the stream many days to fill it. This reservoir is invisibly fed and drained under the surface of the water. Before reaching and leaving the lake, the water flows rapidly through straight, twisting or curved tubes. Then, of a sudden, it will reach a widened fissure, of which only the bottom part is occupied by water. At one place

o

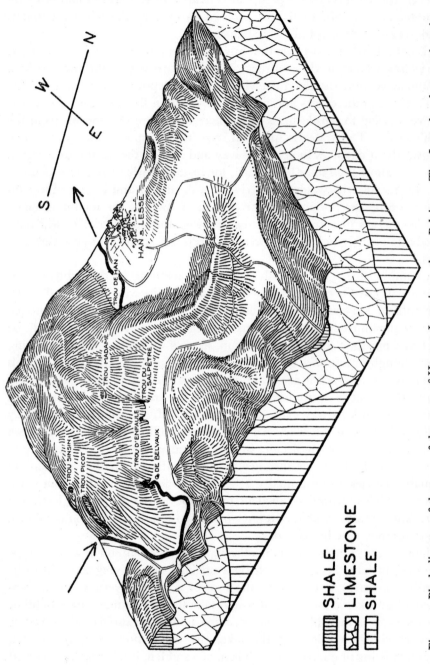

SHALE
LIMESTONE
SHALE

Fig. 117. Block diagram of the area of the caves of Han-sur-Lesse in southern Belgium. The Lesse has burrowed underground through the limestone and abandoned the old meander ("la Chavée"). (After Hol.)

the stream meanders lazily through a spacious, elongated chamber; at another it dips down into a natural tunnel or siphon under a partition, only to re-emerge in the next chamber of the underground palace. Sometimes it laps boulders of lime or insoluble fragments loosened from the limestone; elsewhere it is turbid, especially after heavy rainfall, owing to clay carried along from the surface which will be deposited in thick, slimy mud on the bottom in quiet, uneventful stretches of its course. Along its course, a deathly silence and everlasting peace will be followed by chattering, gurgling or chuckling noises. When, after exceptionally heavy downpours, water is pouring into the ground and the air in every nook and cranny is therefore forced out by its growing volume, a fierce draught often gets up in some narrow passage connecting larger chambers, roaring and howling as enormous quantities of air flee from the subterranean deluge towards the open.

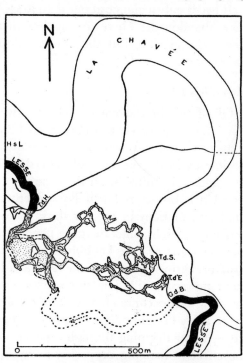

Fig. 118. Map of area illustrated in Fig. 117, indicating the underground passages made by the Lesse.

The Lesse, a rivulet in the Ardennes passing through the celebrated Han caves, may serve as an example of the underground course of a river. The block diagram, Fig. 117, and the map in Fig. 118 show the old, sub-aerial valley of the Lesse (la Chavée), with the stream vanishing at the Gouffre de Belvaux, to reappear about a mile farther on at the Trou de Han. There is too much run-off at high water for all of it to be absorbed and the dry valley is then flooded. Losing some of its water in the Trou d'Enfaule, the Lesse then follows its old course along la Chavée, uniting with the underground branch again at Han. In former times the Trou du Salpêtre and the now collapsed Trou Picot and Trou Sinsin must in a similar manner have provided swallow-holes for the underground course of the Lesse. Apparently successive passages through the limestone hills developed at lower and lower levels as the river flowing on the surface cut out a deeper path for itself and the old entrances to the caverns were abandoned one by one.

Shortly after entering the Gouffre, a big, vaulted cave, the Lesse plunges down obliquely for many feet and then lazily moves onward in a hidden bed, about $1\frac{1}{2}$ miles long, in the limestone. Not until twenty-four hours later does the water reappear in the Han Caves; just below ground-level it throws off a branch, then dips down twice through siphons, picks the branch up again and finally flows towards the exit.

It needs only a glance at our map to see how complex were the old courses, now abandoned. There are no less than three miles of known galleries under the ground, but the inaccessible stretches undoubtedly add up to many more.

Cave Deposits

Of all this lime carried off by the water, a minute proportion, only a fraction of one per cent, is re-deposited and this produces the most arresting features of this cavernous, underground world. There is something very fascinating in the spectacle of, indeed in the mere speculation upon, stalactites and stalagmites in all their variety of colour and shape. Side by side with black, brown, red or milky stalactites or stalagmites may hang or stand similar formations in pale or dark yellow or pure white; next to slender, perfectly straight, smooth tubes pendent for several feet from the roof, we may see short or long knobbly shapes many inches in circumference. The structures growing up from the floor are, by their very size and freakishness, more impressive still. Gigantic masses of stone weighing hundreds of pounds, towering castles complete with battlements and bastions, may be surrounded by an army of rigid pillars of varying length and thickness. In some of these caves, water dripping through a system of chinks in the roof has produced the effect of hanging draperies, many of which are semi-transparent and striped yellowish-white and dark brown, so that if a light is held behind them, they look for all the world like huge slabs of streaky bacon (Fig. 119).

But, apart from the beauty, multiplicity and variety of these naturally sculpted figures, there is something else that lends enchantment to a stalactitic cavern. The immense slowness of the building-up process will be brought home to the visitor who notices how seldom a drop is actually seen to fall. The complete furnishing of a stalactitic cave must take hundreds of centuries. What speaks to the imagination still more, however, is the fact that all this elaboration has taken place in the pitch-dark, with not a single animal, let alone a thinking human being, there to witness its gradual unfolding. At most, swarms of bats may have fluttered cautiously around the stony icicles, or blind newts have slithered along the bases of the mounting columns. By human standards, the pyramids of Egypt are immeasurably old; but for ten, possibly a hundred, times that span of time, the growing stalactites in caverns such as those of Han, or the Carlsbad Cavern of New Mexico, awaited the advent of their first discoverer. There must be numerous entirely inaccessible caves hidden away in many limestone regions which the eye of man will never be granted an opportunity of admiring.

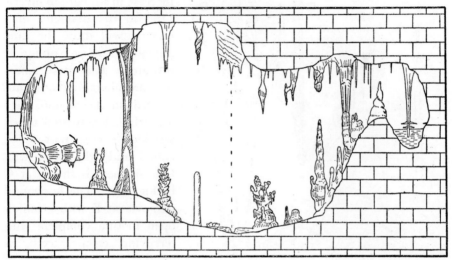

Fig. 119. Typical stalactites and stalagmites. Note the toppled column on the left and the pool on the right which has deposited collars on the stalactite at varying high-water marks.

The process in itself is quite a simple one. If a narrow crack cuts the roof of a cavern, the water saturated with lime will drip through it here and there. Should there be any circulation of air at all, some of the carbon dioxide will escape from the water, or the latter may itself evaporate to some extent. In either case a small proportion of the dissolved lime will be deposited. Since a drop evaporates at its surface, this lime will be cemented to the roof in a ring around the point of exit. The next drop will deposit its contribution at the same place and in this way these very thin rings are successively placed one under the other and cemented together. As the drop always grows to the same size and then falls, all these rings have the same diameter. Ultimately a short tube is formed, suspended from the roof, with walls less than a millimetre thick. These suspended "icicles" are called *stalactites*. From day to day and year to year the little tube of calcite goes on growing. Sometimes it gets choked if, for instance, the dripping is too slow in a year of very dry weather. On renewed supply, the water will then burst open an outlet for itself at the root and proceed to drip down the outside of the stalactite. As it does so, it deposits lime on the original tube like a skin and from that time the lime "icicle" grows not only in length but in girth also.

If the stalactite is closed at the base, a microscopic crack may be formed under the pressure of the water, somewhere along the tube. The capillary forces, which, as we know, increase in strength in inverse ratio to the diameter of a crevice, will draw the fluid out laterally or even obliquely upwards. The most amazing protuberances are thus formed on the wound, such as carbuncles, twisted tubes, wrinkled leaves or root-stocks, cables and what you will. One of these is shown at C in Fig. 120. The horizontal gargoyle at E with grinning open mouth, complete with terrifying calcite teeth, is another curious expression of the whimsical tastes of the djinn responsible for the interior decoration of stalactitic caverns.

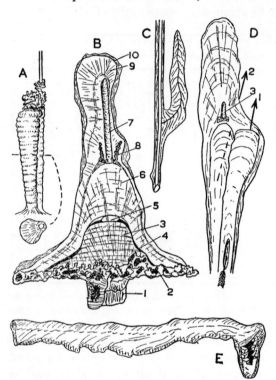

Fig. 120. Various stalactites from the Ardennes, reduced in size. (A) one seventh, (D) one quarter, the remainder half full size. (The foot of B and beak of E have been completed from other specimens.) See page 216.

The colours are due to minute contaminations, usually compounds of iron or constituents of clay, which are left behind with the lime. Nothing so clearly illustrates the variety of routes by which ground-water has reached adjacent points in the same cave, as the juxtaposition of quite differently coloured stalactites.

As only a small amount of the water entering has time to evaporate before the drop has passed its limit of expansion and falls, water charged with lime also reaches the floor of the cave, with the result that this and the walls likewise become covered with lime deposits. A little mound of lime will be formed on the floor at the point on which the growing stalactite above drips all down the centuries. Sometimes the process begins by the hollowing out of a shallow cup in the soft clay floor, but eventually the deposited lime glazes the clay and that is the first step in the upward growth of a *stalagmite*. Naturally, this form is never hollow and, thanks to the spattering of the

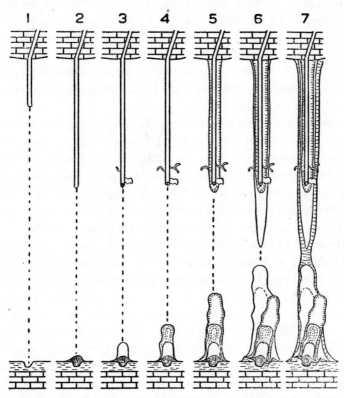

Fig. 121. Successive stages in the formation of a stalactitic pillar. A small depression is made in the clay floor (1) which soon fills up with deposited limestone (2). If the stalactite gets choked, lateral excrescences are formed on it (3 and 4), which themselves become choked. The stalactite then continues to grow in length and girth by deposition on the outside (5). In (6) the stalagmite has tipped sideways, but continues to grow vertically; eventually both coalesce to form a pillar (7).

falling drops, the lime covers a larger surface. Accordingly, the girth of most stalagmites is about that of a human arm or thicker (Plate XIII).

The stalactites and stalagmites thus grow towards each other and when their junction is finally effected, water can no longer pass through the tube of the stalactite. Hence, if the latter has not already become stopped up, the growth in circumference as the effect of water running down the outside will now begin. In the end, a huge pillar is formed which does in fact support the roof (Fig. 121). Now and again the two members are unable to coalesce, due apparently to the development of capillary side tubes. A case of the kind is illustrated at A in Fig. 120, where rosettes on both stalactite and stalagmite show how the water was forced sideways and deposited lime there instead of effecting a sound joint. There is, however, an illuminating piece of history to be recorded where this particular specimen is concerned. Obviously, at an early stage in its growth, the stalagmite began to slant and then, after a time, continued to grow vertically. Such oblique parts of stalagmites are often found; nor is it difficult to realise that the tumbled down blocks or the clay floor on which they stand will sometimes tilt or subside and then set again.

The history of the stalagmite represented at D in Fig. 120 shows traces of having been more complicated still. The hollow tube at the right slanting upwards must undoubtedly have been part of a stalactite which coalesced with the floor. During an earthquake, or some other movement of the earth's crust, the tube broke off and sagged obliquely. At some later period, further violence was done to the structure (direction of arrow 2), after which it settled down to its present position, and grew to its final shape.

A whole series of events can be reconstructed from a cross-section of the stalagmite shown at B in the same figure. After the depression had been formed and filled up (1), a short, stumpy stalagmite began to grow (3). At some time or other there was such heavy rainfall that the muddy water of the inundated cavern rose to above the tip of the stalagmite. After having deposited a thin layer of clay upon it (4), the water dropped away and the bedaubed incipient pillar stood out again. The drip from above rinsed and cleaned the crown and growth was resumed; but it was only upon this cleaned crown that the lime would adhere in crystallographic contact. It was not until a lump (5) of considerable size had been joined on that the new layer spread over the clay and sealed it off. After centuries of undisturbed growth (6), the stalactite (7) descending from the roof almost touched the stalagmite, but, as contact could not at first be made, wrinkled, leafy figures developed at the site of the join (8). After some kind of rough coalescence had been achieved at last, the thin tube broke across, but the lower section remained, standing upright in the stalagmite. The continuous deposition of carbonate of lime (9 and 10) ultimately produced a smooth, handsomely finished figure, the exterior of which betrays nothing of all these vicissitudes.

And with this we must take leave of these fascinating caverns and return to more normal regions.

Ground-water as a Reservoir

The percolation of rain-water through the soil and its evaporation from it are processes with their specific problems to which soil specialists have devoted extensive study. As a matter of fact, the practical gardener knows as well as anyone that "hard rain makes hard ground" and does not do the plants anything like as much good as "a nice, soft, growing rain". In sand, well-worked vegetable mould and loose woodland soil, rain-water can be sucked up by capillarity immediately, the surplus being passed on to lower strata. The air expelled by the invading water has no difficulty in escaping. If, however, the topsoil consists of heavy clay, or has not been adequately worked, a thin skin absorbs the water to repletion and seals off the sub-stratum hermetically. The air, unable to push aside water so strongly bound by capillarity in that skin, cannot escape into the open. As the ground has now become impermeable, the rain collects into puddles and runs down any available slope, in which case precious mould is carried along with it and the scene is set for that notorious soil erosion which has reduced so many disforested and cultivated districts to stony deserts.

If the topsoil is loosened, it has little contact with the subsoil; the lumps of earth cannot extract moisture from below and will soon dry up. After-wards, however, the loose fragments protect the lower strata from evapora-tion and tilled soil therefore does not dry out so quickly. Paradoxically enough, a light shower or spraying may now cause the loose fragments to spread out plastically, with the result that contact with the subsoil is restored. The topsoil will soon be dry again, but this time evaporation can continue and the water will be constantly drawn up to the surface. Under certain conditions the ultimate effect of spraying, therefore, is that the plants will have to do with even less water!

It is evident that precipitation provides the foremost constituent of ground-water, even though, as we have seen, some are of opinion that con-densation of moisture constitutes a by no means negligible factor. Locally or temporarily, however, ground-water may be supplemented in an entirely different manner, viz., from rivers or lakes. For, when a river flows in a wide bed of loose material, the ground-water table will, as a rule, stand in the banks at a higher level than the surface of the stream (Fig. 122, left). Surplus precipitation runs off towards the river and, in between showers, this inflow will be the stream's chief source of working capital and therefore regulates its yield.

When, however, the river begins to rise after heavy rainfall, the head of ground-water towards the river disappears and is even reversed if the rise continues. Then water starts to percolate from the river into the spongy material of the banks and it is the ground-water table that rises now. Thus the stream lays up a store of water in the adjacent soil, upon which it can draw as soon as the level starts to subside. If we consider that the loose soil bordering the Rhine between Bâle and Mainz contains per running kilometre an amount of water equivalent to one day's drainage of the river, we shall realise the immensity of such a reservoir. Partly lying, as it does, below the bed of the river, however, it cannot take part in the drainage to its full extent.

Again, there may be a constant flow from the river to the ground-water.

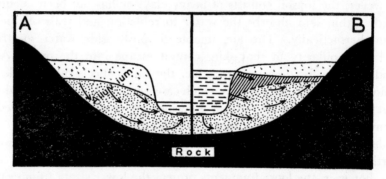

Fig. 122. Section through river flowing in its own alluvial deposits (A) at low water and (B) when water is rising, showing flow of ground-water. Hatched portion in (B) indicates rise in level of water table which builds up a reservoir of ground-water.

This may happen where a river flows into a desert or steppe, where the ground-water, being at a far lower level than the bed, is always the recipient. Something similar occurs when a mountain stream enters a plain or wide main valley from a steep tributary gorge. In this case the freight of débris carried along is deposited in a kind of delta, an alluvial fan of rock-waste. These matters will be dealt with in greater detail in the chapter on surface water; it will suffice to say here that generally these cones steal some of the water from the stream and lose it again in small springs and damp zones near the base. Were it not for algae and depositions of clay, which seal off the bed, many a stream would remain entirely hidden for a large part of the year in its own alluvial fan. It need hardly be said that such cones are likely sources for public water supplies.

Nowadays, river water is sometimes conducted to the ground-water by artificially induced inundations of certain infiltration areas. This is a safer and cheaper reservoir for use in dry months than can be produced by building a dam. The latter type of reservoir is costly and, in countries subject to earthquakes, like California, is not as innocent a scenic adjunct as it may seem. Furthermore, the evaporation of the open water spells a loss which should not be underestimated.

Drinking Water Supply

The demand by civilised societies for water and yet more water poses a first-class problem. More exacting demands in the matter of purity are naturally made upon water to be used not only for irrigation but also for human consumption. This usually necessitates drawing upon sources at deeper levels. In mountainous districts, where precipitation is plentiful, there are generally many springs of clear, pure water for the asking, though it may often be chalky, which is admittedly troublesome. In arid lands, however, laborious search has to be made for scanty sources of supply. Nowadays, the geologist is able in the majority of cases, provided he has enough time and funds at his disposal, to discover exactly where a boring should be made. He can even predict the approximate depth at which water will be found.

Freezing of Ground-water

In any climate subject to frost, the ground-water is liable to freeze and we shall see presently the part this plays in the weathering of rock. But in polar regions certain unusual conditions prevail as the result of the perpetual frozen state of the ground. If the mean temperature is below zero, frost in winter penetrates to a depth beyond the reach of the subsequent thaw in summer. If this goes on year after year, the ground-water freezes to progressively greater depths and only the top layer of a few inches or yards thaws during the warmer season. On the other hand, the flow of heat from the earth's interior will tend to arrest the progress downwards of the perpetual frost, limiting it to a few hundred yards.

The specific effects typical of the frozen ground, however, do not actually derive from that layer itself; for this, being in the iron grip of winter, is rigid and inert in every respect. It is, rather, the impermeability of the layer, with its component parts immutably welded together, which is responsible for the special conditions prevailing above and below it. One has only to imagine undulating country covered with a watertight sheet of ice to realise that the ground-water deep down below is imprisoned. As a result, artesian pressure may prevail in the valleys and if for some reason a crack is formed anywhere, this ground-water wells up. No sooner does frost clamp down on the surface than the outflowing water freezes and a hummock of ice is formed with a core of water. Given sufficient pressure, this crust will again burst open and the process may be repeated many times until considerable mounds of ice are formed (Fig. 123). Finally, these crusts close the wound in the icy ground and the frost begins again to creep down into the crack until it has completely healed. Siberia is the best-known scene of these strange icy blisters.

A thin layer at the top of the eternally frozen ground thaws almost everywhere in summer. To this the winter's snow, likewise melted, adds its ample quota of water, while the frozen substratum hermetically seals off every downward line of escape. Since, moreover, in the preceding period of freezing, innumerable small horizontal cracks filled with ice will have been

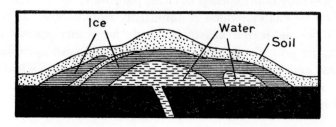

Fig. 123. Hydrolaccolith or hummock caused when ground-water under artesian pressure is checked by formation of layers of ice.

formed, the thawed surface must inevitably be swamped with water and will become an impassable slush. This pulp tends to creep slowly down even gentle slopes—a phenomenon known as "solifluxion" and typical of arctic climates.

Large wedges of ice may develop near the surface as the result of cracking. After the first autumnal freezing, the temperature may fall so low that the ground contracts and cracks open. Sometimes the pattern is reminiscent of shrinkage cracks in desiccated mud. In other cases huge fissures, several yards deep, can be traced for considerable distances and these may fill up with snow, which eventually turns to ice. The sequence of thawing and freezing year after year widens the crack more and more, up to several yards. Sand will also enter the fissure. In the end, if the ground thaws permanently after an improvement in the climatic conditions of the region, the fissures become filled with washed-in material differing from that of the walls. We can thus detect in our own soil such petrified wedges dating from the Ice Age.

If strata of varying composition and, above all, containing different percentages of water, alternate in a thawing zone (even if they lie horizontally), deformations are bound to occur. Heavily-soaked strata are liable to become so "hydroplastic" that they yield to every change of pressure. Such movements may be initiated by differences in the weight of snow carried, by heavy beasts walking over the surface, by local inequalities in the degree of thaw, or by the superincumbence of a layer of greater density. When the water in the pores freezes again in the autumn, the strata containing most moisture will be subject to greater expansion than the drier ones.

This explains how the soil, after thousands of seasons, gives the impression of having been thoroughly kneaded. The thawing of buried ice-wedges,

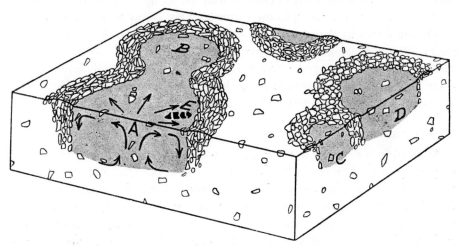

Fig. 124. Polygonal soil with stone rings. A and B have coalesced, the partition has disappeared. The stones are turned on their sides: C and D have formed a common wall with the stones on the surface lying flat. E is a cracked rock torn apart. The stippled areas indicate loamy soil.

when the covering layers sag down into the evacuated spaces, also has much to do with these transformations. Owing to their very high water content, thin strata of peat lying between strata of sand are very active and the striking effect is enhanced by the strong colour contrast between pale yellow and dark brown.

There were similar occurrences all round the land-ice during the glacial period. Thus much disturbed soils in vast areas of Europe and America witness to the former prevalence there of a grim polar climate.

Another phenomenon of the upper layers of perpetually frozen ground is that of *polygonal soils*. If the soil is stony, the larger fragments are found to be piled up in rings, usually several feet or yards in circumference, with predominantly fine-grained material in the centre, which is slightly lower than the ring. The ground may be so thickly studded with these rings that, the points of contact interfering with their circularity, they tend to become angular.

The true cause of the formation of polygonal soils is not known. It has been suggested that the ground undergoes something like convective flow after the spring thaw (Fig. 124). Water is heavier at 4° C. than at freezing point. If the ground thaws and slushy mud is formed at the surface, this, warming up on top, will increase in specific gravity, while the further melting of ice will maintain the subsoil at 0°. Under such conditions it is conceivable that a convection current may be set up in the slurry, with the cold, light suspension rising in the centre and the heavy material warmed to 4° sinking down at the margins. Owing to the high specific gravity of the slurry, stones floating on it would perform a centrifugal movement at the surface, would be dragged towards the periphery, and finally come to rest there as a girdle of fragmented rock. It yet remains to be seen whether this ingenious hypothesis is a true representation of the facts.

Ground-water and Weathering

As a fitting conclusion to this chapter, we may now turn briefly to the part played by ground-water in the weathering of rocks. Under dry conditions their constituent minerals persist unchanged; chemical weathering in the desert is almost non-existent. The grains are, admittedly, loosened and parted by the rapid and extreme variations in temperature in arid regions, and then become the playthings of the wind. Moreover, the absence of a vegetable covering connotes lack of humic acid, which is a highly active chemical agent. Carbon dioxide only corrodes minerals when it is in the dissolved state. It is therefore true to say that water is the most potent agent in the chemical weathering of fresh rock in the earth's crust, whether by its direct or indirect influence.

Once water permeates the rocks, and particularly if it contains CO_2 and humic acid, the majority of the ingredients of the crust fall a victim to it sooner or later. Oxygen, both that dissolved in the water and the atmospheric oxygen held between the particles of the soil, is also actively involved in the process. We have already seen what solution does to limestone; but rocks such as granite and lava also consist largely of vulnerable minerals. Felspar, comprising more than half the volume of the earth's crust, is altered by chemical weathering into clay, which is insoluble, while the calcium and sodium compounds in particular go into solution. Indeed, almost all the clay known to us is formed in this way from felspar, hence likewise all slate, which was developed from it deep down in the crust by tectonic stress. Quartz and mica are the only resistant minerals among the common kinds, and it is accordingly of these that sand is mainly composed.

The dissolved material drains downwards with the water and proceeds as a component of the ground-water to its final destination, the oceans, either by a direct route or after mingling with a river. In certain chemical conditions, and especially where the drainage is poor, some of the dissolved materials, especially iron salts, may be precipitated around ground-water level; it is thus that have been formed those hard layers of "pan" so obstructive to agriculture. The sodium salts, however, evade capture and reach the oceans, where they remain during evaporation and therefore take no further part in the cycle. In the life of the earth's crust, therefore, sea-water has gradually been becoming a salt solution of ever-increasing concentration.

Ground-water can be very active mechanically as well as chemically in the disintegration of solid rock, but in this work needs frost as an accessory. In high mountainous country and in polar regions the temperature may fluctuate around freezing point *every twenty-four hours* for months on end. The snow melts in daytime and all the cracks are filled with water, but with strong radiation towards evening the temperature drops to far below freezing point. At first a layer of ice hermetically seals the fissures, but as the frost penetrates to increasing depth, the enclosed water expands with irresistible force, the walls of the joints are pressed apart and the crack extends inwards. This goes on day after day, the fissures becoming ever deeper and wider, until the moment comes when a fragment of rock is precariously held in place only by the ice itself. Then, when the morning thaw sets in, the block is released and rolls down the incline. All Alpine climbers regard a steep wall of rock above frost level basking in the early morning sunshine with suspicion, and know that at any moment chunks of it, large and small, may give way and come crashing down.

And so the water in the underground section of the cycle is perpetually at work disintegrating and pulverising the solid structure of the earth's crust in various ways. These loose fragments fall on glaciers, slip down along gentle slopes into the beds of streams and, with the dissolved components, follow their downward course.

Without the preparatory work and unremitting help of weathering, streams and rivers would be incapable of wearing down the earth's crust and transporting the mountains, as débris, to the sea; nor would the action of the glaciers be anything like as intense. In the next chapter we shall see what the effects are of flowing water upon the crust.

VI

Water on the Surface

After water has evaporated from the oceans, passed through the atmosphere and returned to the earth's surface in the form of precipitation, a clear division takes place. Most falls straight into the sea again; hence this itinerary is a short one. The fortunes, however, which await rain or snow falling on terra-firma are many and various.

Solid precipitation which comes to rest on the continents may sooner or later evaporate again, possibly after having formed a component part of glaciers; or else the snow may melt quickly, or only after persisting for a considerable time, first as snow and subsequently as ice. The term "eternal snows" should not be taken too literally, for, although such country is perpetually buried under snow and ice, the older crystals are constantly being replaced by new ones, the annual surplus moving down with glaciers and avalanches to lower regions.

Melt-water is subject to the same vicissitudes as ordinary rain: it may evaporate while still on the leaves of plants or on the surface of the earth; it may, however, penetrate into the soil and mingle with the ground-water. In the preceding chapter we saw how some of the ground-water is lost, partly via vegetation or by direct evaporation, and some pursues its subterranean course until it returns to the surface in well-defined springs or as amorphous and diffuse oozings. This issuing ground-water unites with the precipitation which neither percolated nor evaporated, but drained along the surface or stagnated there. It is with these combined waters, derived from precipitation, melting and emerging ground-water, that we shall now be concerned and we shall have to follow this water on its travels back to the sea to complete the cycle.

River Feeding

We have seen that, wherever the ground-water table intersects the earth's surface, there is a boundary above which water can penetrate into the soil and below which the ground is entirely saturated; it is from the latter that

PLATE XV

(*a*) Water seeks the route of least resistance, not the shortest: meanders of the
Geul river in South Limburg, flowing to the right.

(*b*) Damming of the Red River in the U.S.A. by a compacted mass of tree trunks.
(*Photo U.S. Geological Survey.*)

PLATE XVI

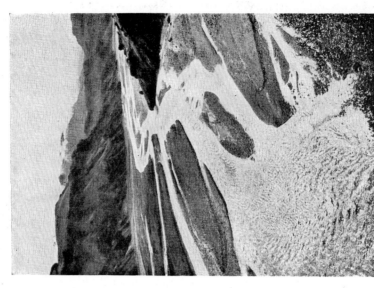

(a) The wall of water of the Skógafoss, Iceland. May it never be tamed by turbines! (*Photo Ehrhardt.*)

(b) Interlacing channels with gravel-banks, Thorsmörkdal, Iceland. (*Photo Ehrhardt.*)

water issues into the open. If, as sometimes happens, this line of intersection is situated in the middle of an incline—e.g., just above an impervious stratum—there will be found concentrated springs or else damp areas with more diffuse emergence of water. More commonly, however, this line runs along the water-line of a lake, a river or the sea, in which case the ground-water stream remains invisible, notwithstanding the fact that the open water is undoubtedly fed by water welling up from the ground, especially near the banks. It depends predominantly upon the nature of the bed of the river or lake whether this feed is allowed access at depth in the floor, or whether the impermeability of the basin and its banks forces the water prematurely

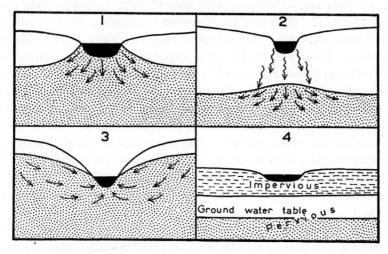

Fig. 125. Relation between ground-water and rivers. A ground-water reservoir is being fed by a river directly in (1) and by seepage in (2). In (3) the river is being fed with ground-water, whilst in (4) an impermeable layer prevents contact.

to the surface, where it is dissipated in brooklets or manifests itself as a general sogginess of the land. In the latter case, the line of intersection of the ground-water with the surface is, therefore, slightly above the bank (Fig. 125).

We have also seen that the exact reverse may take place when ground-water, instead of emerging, is, on the contrary, the recipient of water percolating through the bed of a river or lake. It is clearly evident from the interplay between ground-water and the free water surface that the latter is to be regarded as a place where the phreatic surface is situated above ground.

Water drainage can only be properly understood by thus considering a river system in intimate association with the ground-water in and around its basin. For, when all is said, conspicuous springs from which water can be

P

seen welling up in a concentrated stream are comparatively few in number, and the amount of melt-water liberated by the glacier fronts is only a small percentage even of rivers rising in mountains. Hence only a fraction of all the water in rivers derives from these never-failing sources.

As a rule, all rain on the surface disappears a few hours after a heavy shower, and surface feeding of the streams thus comes to an end. Two or three days later, all the water collected in the brooklets and rills will have united in rivers and have been carried off to the sea. Hence a river like the Meuse, which receives no melt-water in summer, would be reduced to a mere trickle if, apart from this, it depended entirely on the few springs in its basin. We now know, however, that ground-water comes pouring in along all the banks of the river and its numerous tributaries. Every shower feeds this invisible store, from which an uninterrupted supply is distributed to the river system. Thanks to the immense capacity of the ducts and cavities in which the ground-water accumulates, there is a large stock of water in the ground, especially in loose gravel and sandy soils. The fissures in hard rocks also provide considerable storage space, though much less, of course, than that available in gravel, sand or clay. The stocks which are situated above the level of the river can be drawn upon in periods of drought. In low-lying undulating country, such stocks are naturally small compared with those in an Alpine mountain range. Nevertheless, the strata of loose soils which are good ground-water containers usually being thicker, the water held in reserve is ample.

The intercalation of ground-water in river economy, therefore, means that precipitation is in large part absorbed and that a limit is thus set to direct drainage. These hoarded savings are put by for a rainy day, as it were, and are doled out in a dry period, which in this case constitutes a "rainy day". Owing to the great friction in the narrow channels in the soil, ground-water movement is far slower than the surface drainage and in this way ground-water regulates the volume of rivers. The longer the drought lasts, the smaller becomes the available reserve of water and the flatter becomes the ground-water table. The pressure head which forces the water towards the bed of the river is constantly diminishing, with the result that the velocity of the ground-water also decreases gradually. It is as if soil keeps a wary eye on its dwindling stocks and imposes rationing upon rivers. A further glance at Fig. 122 reminds one that ground-water beside a river may alternately give and receive, a far more effective regulative process than the mere withholding of supply.

Clarity is another important effect of the circuitous underground passage of most of the feed-water. Anyone walking in hilly country in pouring rain may see for himself how little rills and runnels of dirty, muddy water collect and scurry down paths and roads and across the fields. Dark-brown, turbid water will also be found in the permanent brooks, or even in larger streams. This may be due in part to churned-up sediment, but it is caused mainly by grit and dirt washed in by surface water. As soon as surface drainage ceases and ground-water is the only source of supply, all turbidity vanishes; at most, the water may still be strongly tinted by humic substances.

Having disposed of the common misconception that rivers are fed by springs or glaciers only, it will be obvious that it is by no means always easy to discover the source of a river. The first step is to discover which is to be deemed the main river and which the tributaries, since it is not a foregone conclusion that the former is the longest branch; there is the familiar case of the Missouri, tributary to the Mississippi. Again, tributaries may bear a larger volume of water than the recognised main stem. As a rule, the branch following most nearly a straight course is regarded as the main river. Secondly, the quest for the source usually leads the seeker to watercourses ever diminishing in size, until the birthplace is ultimately found to be a marshy plateau, an insignificant pool, a soggy field or a dry bed along the surface of which water seems only occasionally to flow.

The annual variation in the drainage of a river depends upon so many factors that no two systems are entirely alike in this respect. These factors fall into two classes, viz., those which are conducive to a fairly uniform distribution and those which produce marked differences in volume. It goes without saying that a climate in which wet and dry seasons alternate must necessarily give rise to pronounced disparities in water-level, the supreme example of which is the desert, where rivers sometimes dry up altogether, as in vast tracts of Australia every year. Unrelenting drought may even persist for several years in succession, until suddenly torrential rains fill the dry river beds with turbulent, rushing streams in a matter of hours. A few days later, all that water will have percolated into the soil or have evaporated and it may well be that decades pass before there is any further appreciable precipitation.

The thinner the loose soil in the catchment area and the more compact the rocks underneath, the less effective is the regulating action of the ground-water. Pulsating drainage also results from a dry land climate with plentiful snowfall, with all the melt-water having to be drained in the brief spring season. Rivers exposed to the steady alternation of a dry and a wet monsoon are transformed each year from beds almost dried up to wide, turbulent streams and vice versa.

In the wet season, the rivers in the island of Timor, to the north-west of

Australia, are raging, almost impassable cataracts, but at the end of the dry monsoon a man may wander along a river bed, walking over sand and picking his way among boulders without coming across a single drop of water. Here and there the natives may know of a place where a small well can be exposed by turning over a boulder. A pitiful amount of water can be collected here, a remnant of the ground-water stream threading its way in the coarse-grained deposits of the river bed.

A sea climate in temperate zones has the reverse character. Scarcely a month passes in Scotland without rain or thaw after snow, and the streams drain off without intermission. Thick beds of gravel and wide deposits along the courses of the rivers likewise sustain even distribution.

The drainage of a river like the Rhine is exceptionally constant (Fig. 126). Down to near Basle, the Rhine is pre-eminently a glacier river with a maximum volume in summer, through the melting of glaciers and mountain snow, and a minimum in winter. Its tributary, the Main, shows the highest water-levels in spring, when the snow melts in the secondary mountain chains along its course, and the lowest in summer; while the Moselle has a minimum drainage in summer and a maximum in winter, when precipitation is plentiful and evaporation limited. The volume of the Rhine when it enters the plains is remarkably constant, thanks to the superposition of the various maxima and minima, with only very modest peaks in spring and summer.

Lakes intercalated in a river course help to iron out inequalities. It is interesting to note that the North American lakes would practically abolish fluctuations in the water feeding the Niagara Falls, were it not for the changing force of the wind driving the water towards the outlet or away again.

We may take as our second example the water-levels of the Niger at various points (Fig. 127). It rises in the coastal mountains of West Africa near Sierra Leone, where heavy tropical rain falls, with a maximum in autumn. Accordingly, the highest recorded water-levels at Kulikoro are in September. The river receives no further feed worth mentioning in the next 2000 miles of its course. Half-way down, at Timbuctoo, the maximum drainage becomes less pronounced because the river slows down here and is therefore somewhat better regulated. Near its mouth, the Niger traverses the littoral of Nigeria, where it again receives plentiful supplies of tropical rain (indicated in black at Badjibo in Fig. 127). Hence the river, which might otherwise cease to flow in some months of the summer as the result of the heavy losses incurred in its long passage through the desert, is well fed during the critical months.

The precipitation falling on the Continent of Europe is of the order of

25,000 cubic miles a year and the estimated drainage from it comes to 9000 cubic miles, hence a third. About 25 per cent is calculated for the drainage of Central Europe, 44 per cent for the Rhine, 27 per cent for the Dnieper. The percentage of the drainage is much higher in the upper regions of mountains. Thus the Rhine empties quite 80 per cent of the precipitation

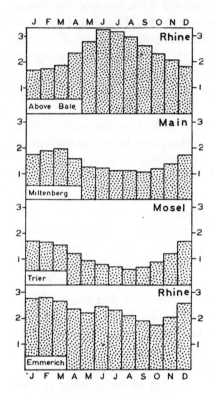

Fig. 126. Monthly mean water-levels at four places on the Rhine (upper and lower) and its tributaries the Main and the Mosel (metres above low-water mark).

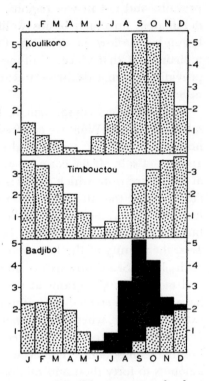

Fig. 127. Monthly mean water-levels at three places on the Niger (metres above low-water mark). Black = rise due to precipitation in lower course.

of its upper region into Lake Constance, while the Iller drains off 72 per cent as it flows down from the Allgäu Alps to the Danube at Ulm. How much of this runs off immediately along the surface and how much has flowed via the ground-water, it would be hard to say. In mountainous country on almost impervious rock the percentage of direct surface drainage will naturally be larger than in low-lying country with thick, permeable deposits. Probably the temporarily percolating water always predominates and in plains the surface drainage is of little account.

Clearly, in regions where precipitation predominates over evaporation, water must normally drain off towards adjacent areas and eventually to the sea, while conversely, in areas where evaporation exceeds precipitation, there can be no drainage to other parts. In the latter case there will either be no rivers at all, or the water will flow towards a salt lake at the lowest point.

The reader may wonder why such basins should occur where a dry climate prevails, and not in wet regions. The answer is that, if precipitation predominated, any such basins would be filled up and, once the water had begun to overflow the lowest part of the rim, the river would soon scour out a channel at that place, draining the lake initially formed, and eventually providing normal drainage towards the sea. In a dry climate this would never happen.

Now, all rivers contain small, but not negligible percentages of various salts in solution. What we call fresh water is, therefore, by no means entirely innocent of salinity; we have already seen that even rain contains a small amount of salt. If we consider an undrained basin with a river and a lake at the centre from which water is again continually evaporating, we cannot fail to realise that the river is constantly feeding salt to the lake and leaving it there. The water evaporates because the precipitation is less than the loss, but the deposited salt remains behind. Hence gradually, as the centuries pass, the salinity of the lake must increase. The salt content at the surface of the Dead Sea is upwards of 200 grams per litre (six times that of the sea) and more than 300 grams at the bottom, which is 1300 feet down. Plants have now been erected for pumping the water from a depth of 200 feet into extensive ponds, where it is evaporated by the heat of the sun. Common salt very soon separates out, followed later by potassium and, more especially, bromine compounds. The accumulation of dissolved salts in the Dead Sea amounts to forty thousand million tons. Nature has probably been at work for several hundred thousand years collecting this store and a huge mass of common salt has already been deposited in the surrounding area as the result of evaporation from what was originally a far larger lake. This would account for the comparatively high percentage of the precious bromine and potassium salts.

Change of climate or other conditions may cause such a salt lake to evaporate until the water disappears altogether, leaving salt steppes or even thick deposits of salt. In some districts this drying out may recur every year, after which the wet season supervenes and re-creates a salt lake.

Lakes. *The Origin of their Basins*

Whereas a salt lake may be regarded as the deepest part of a basin-shaped

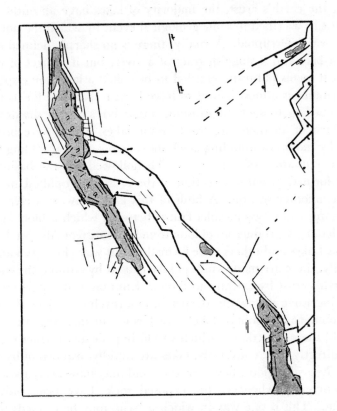

Fig. 128. The African fault or rift valley system within which are situated lakes Tanganyika and Nyasa. (After Krenkel.)

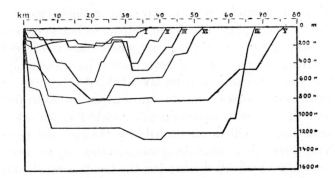

Fig. 129. Various cross-sections through lake Tanganyika (vertical scale × 25). The faulted nature can be clearly seen. (After Krenkel.)

hollow in the earth's crust, the majority of lakes have an outlet and their origin must be ascribed to some geological event by which the normal grade of a river was interrupted. Actually, there is no sharply defined distinction between a lake and a sluggish tract of a river, but if a sheet of water is so large that it seems naturally entitled to be called a lake, some special event or circumstance is almost bound to have been responsible for its formation.

It is according to such circumstances that lakes can be divided into five classes. First of all there are the tectonic lakes, which were brought into existence by mountain-building earth movements. Either folding took place and it was curvature of the crust which hollowed out the basin; or else a fault was formed, when one section of the crust was uplifted or depressed relative to another section. A fault of this kind athwart a river may well act as a dam, while two parallel faults, between which a block of the crust has subsided, may produce an oblong trench. The great African Tanganyika and Nyasa Lakes and others were formed in this way (Figs. 128 and 129).

Secondly, there are many kinds of lake caused by erosion, the eating-away of the earth's crust by extraneous forces. Running water may erode, but it has little incentive to saw out deeper in one reach of a river than another; for, the moment an embryo lake were formed in this way, the velocity of flow would there slow down, which would impede any further erosion. We shall see directly that, conversely, lakes are rapidly disposed of by the action of rivers. In arid regions, however, the wind may blow away loose sand and do so recurrently whenever the exposed rocks have been pulverised by weathering. This is one way in which a basin may be formed; then, if the climate changes at a later period, bringing more moisture to the district, the basin fills up and becomes a lake.

Lakes formed by the erosion of glaciers are far more numerous and well-defined. The grinding action of ice-streams was touched on in a previous chapter and it was pointed out that, thanks to its thickness and rigidity, a glacier is capable of creeping some distance up an incline in its bed. A valley may be scoured to greater depths at places where there is soft rock or at the confluence of two glacier tongues. Former glaciers have also scraped shallow hollows in very many corries, leaving lakes behind (Figs. 130 and 131).

Barrier lakes, with various kinds of dam thrown up, form the third distinctive class. If part of a mountain side tumbles down into the valley during a landslide, it will in all probability obstruct the passage of the stream flowing there. As a rule, lakes formed in this way are very transitory for, once the water overflows the barrier, the fast-flowing stream will soon carry away the pile of rock débris and soil thrown down during the landslide. In this way the dam is sawn through and the barrier lake is drained.

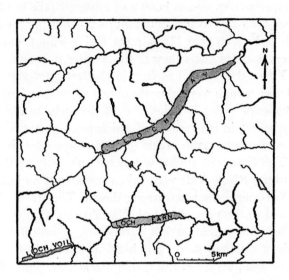

Fig. 130. Loch Tay, a typical glacier lake in the Scottish Highlands.

Fig. 131. Three tarns situated in shallow rock-basins hollowed out by glacial action in Alaska, with a corrie visible in the background. The erosive action of the connecting waterfalls (W) and the silting up of the basins with detritus will soon result in the disappearance of the tarns. (From an aerial photograph.)

The most impressive specimen known of a barrier lake formed by a land-slide succumbed long ago to this suicidal process, but the imposing remains are still plainly to be seen near Flims in the Rhine Valley above Chur. The Ice Age glaciers had cut the valley of the Vorderrhein into a deep, steep-sided gorge. When the ice had melted in the last inter-glacial period, the walls of the glacier trough were so undermined at one particular spot, that a gigantic block beside what is today the Flimserstein broke loose and fell into the valley below, in the process of which more than two cubic miles of limestone must have been crushed and ground to fine waste in the space of a few minutes. This limestone rubble was swept some way up the bank on the opposite side of the Rhine Valley and then spread out on both sides. One-third pressed upstream, the rest turning down. The tip of this monstrous landslide reached to the present site of Reichenau, six miles from the start-ing-point. When movement at last came to a standstill and the heavy, eddying clouds of grit had shed their burden of lime-dust and were dissipated, a massive dam, 2000 feet thick, had blocked the valley in the vicinity of Flims.

The Vorderrhein must have been pent up for many years, gradually forming a barrier lake. This became deeper and deeper and extended farther and farther upstream, before the waters had risen sufficiently to find an outlet over the lowest point of the dam and to unite downstream with the Hinterrhein as of old.

For thousands of years the summits of the Alps were reflected in the quiet waters of this vast mountain lake, brought into being with such shattering birth-pangs. Although the stresses and pressures involved in this event had consolidated the pulverised limestone into a hard mass, the water foaming over it in a long rapid was able to erode it in a comparatively short time. It had sawn a fairly deep cleft through the dam, which had largely drained off the lake, when the glacier of the last Ice Age came creeping along, pass-ing through the cleft and over the dam on its downward path. When this latest mass of ice had, in turn, disintegrated in the warmer climate following the glacial period, the river returned to the attack, finished its cleft and there was soon nothing left of the lake. The pulverised landslide rubble can still be seen in the steep, bare walls of the gorge at Flims. The many huge boulders strewn over the face of the original body of shattered rock bear witness to this prehistoric catastrophe.

As most of the major landslides were, like the greatest of them all at Flims, initiated by the tremendous excavating action of the glaciers in the Ice Age, the climatic changes of the past are, by and large, responsible for the formation of barrier lakes. Many, probably most, of the great Alpine lakes were formed behind barriers also to be attributed to the Glacial Period, namely, large terminal moraines. In that age the massive tongues of ice crept down to the foot of the mountain chains and even into the surrounding plains, huge amphitheatres of moraine material being piled up in the process and acting as natural barrages as soon as the ice melted away. Thus the North Italian lakes roughly mark the outer limits reached by such glaciers.

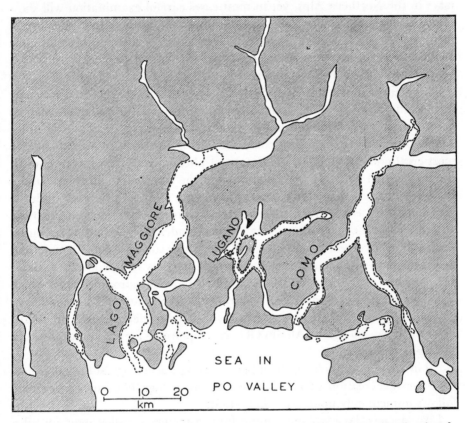

Fig. 132. Southern margin of the Alps at the end of the penultimate Ice Age showing the sea covering the Po valley and transforming the glacial valleys into fjords. When the sea-level fell, terminal moraines deposited during the last Ice Age created lakes, which were reduced by alluvial deposits to the present size (shown by dotted lines).

In the interglacial periods the sea-level was higher even than it is now and Fig. 132 shows how an arm of the Adriatic ran along the foot of the Alps in the plain of the Po. The deeply eroded, glacial valleys formed deep fjords penetrating far inland. The last glacial age left crescentic terminal moraines behind at the foot of the mountains and the lower extremities of the valleys therefore collected large lakes. In post-glacial times these were drained to a lower level by some hundred feet through breaches made in the terminal moraines, while heavily laden streams and rivers tipped their burden predominantly at the upper end of the lakes, thus starting to fill them up.

Although terminal moraines are not always as obvious a feature of the lakes in the Northern Alps, yet in most cases careful examination will show that the formation of the basin was due to glacial erosion and glacial sedimentary deposits farther downstream. It is, however, just possible that some of these trenches were produced by down warping of the valleys due to a general subsidence of the Alpine massif during the Glacial Period.

There are circumstances in which a glacier may take a more direct part in blocking a stream. If a tongue emerging from a side-valley encroaches upon a main valley which is not itself occupied by a glacier, a barrier of ice will be formed. Lakes which come into being in this way are among the most erratic and dangerous of all natural phenomena. At a given moment the tongue will suddenly be floated up and the lake water can escape under the lifted barrier; then again the ice may begin to break up, when both the lake and the ice-floes rush down the valley in an overwhelming torrent. In other cases the lake water melts a tunnel under the ice, finding an outlet that way. In certain places where glaciers now advance and then retreat again in perpetual alternation, treacherous barriers of this kind are liable to be formed over and over again, entailing those catastrophic floods which are their natural consequence. Notorious examples are the Vernagtferner in the Austrian Alps, to which we have already referred, and the Mattmarksee at the foot of the Allalin Glacier, responsible for fifteen outbreaks in the eighteenth century.

All in all, glaciers hold pride of place among the geological forces responsible for the creation of lakes, especially in an age like our own, which follows immediately upon a glacial period.

Like glaciers, lava streams issuing from a tributary valley may cut off a main valley or, conversely, following the course of a main valley, may block a side valley. Obstacles like these are far more enduring than landslides and a lake hemmed in by a lava dam may enjoy a long life.

Crater lakes, which are formed if the strata constituting the volcanic cone are impermeable to the rain-water falling into the crater on the peak of the mountain, are also in the barrier category. The volcanic gases which sometimes bubble up through these lakes are apt to impart unusual colours to the water. The most striking case is that of the Gilimutu in Flores, Indonesia. This high volcano has three small crater lakes at its summit, one bluish-green opal in colour, another a cloudy yellow and the third dark wine-red. The many *Maare* in the Eifel are more accessible. These are likewise small crater lakes in a way, though it can scarcely be said that they occur in the cones of volcanoes, as the subterranean forces only blew out deep funnels when they erupted, emitting insufficient lava and ash to build up mountains.

The lakes along the Red River in Louisiana came into existence by a remarkable series of circumstances (Fig. 133). At some prehistoric time a

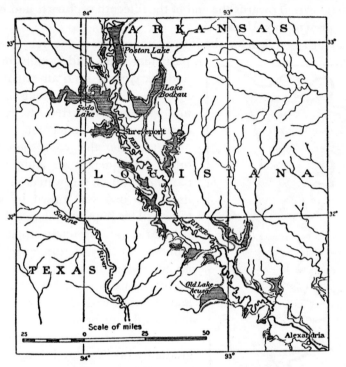

Fig. 133. Barrier lakes along the Red River formed between about 1500 and 1873 as the result of blockage by tree trunks. (After Veatch: cf. Pl. XV, 2.)

vast number of trees must have been uprooted during heavy floods and carried down the river. At some point below what is now Alexandria, the branches and roots must have become so inextricably intertwined that the trunks were brought to a halt, piling up one upon another. A barrier was thus formed by thousands of closely compacted forest giants. Sediment was soon deposited in this barraging tangle, for the river carries much silt, to which it owes its peculiar colour. Owing to this silting-up, the water upstream was halted at the barrier until it had found the lowest point from which it was able to overflow at the side and circumvented the barrier by a circuitous path in the surrounding alluvial plain.

It was not long, however, before driftwood, which the river always sweeps along with it when it is in spate, began to accumulate at the mouth of this new outlet. Thus a second barrier was formed above the first and the process was repeated again and again, each time at a point higher upstream. The distance between the successive barriers varied considerably according to the circumstances, but on an average the front shifted about a mile upstream each year. Towards the end of the fifteenth century it had reached a point near present-day Alexandria.

After having stood firm for about two hundred years, the trees forming any

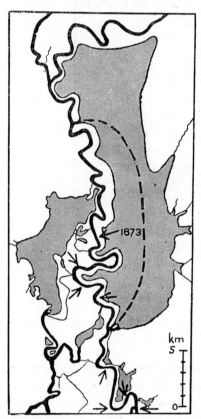

Fig. 134. The last lakes to be formed alongside the Red River. Arrows indicate where piled-up tree trunks barred the passage of the river, and the broken line the route of the steamship service. (After Veatch.)

particular dam had usually mouldered and decayed to such an extent that the obstacle collapsed, liberating the old bed and enabling the river to resume its former course at that point.

Meanwhile, this congestion had another consequence; in addition to the damming up of the waters of the river itself, the bed was raised by sedimentation. This impeded the free flow of the tributaries into the main stream at their mouths and they in turn were dammed up into oblong lakes. It was not until the timber dams downstream of these lakes had disintegrated after 200 years' existence and had been washed away, that the waters in these tributaries were gradually liberated and drained off. All the sediment accumulated during the period of stagnation, however, had to be cleared away before the tributaries could return to the original level.

This is how, in the course of years, the obstruction travelled upstream in the Red River by jumps of varying length. In 1873 the barrier farthest upstream was formed near the north border of Louisiana. The latest lake to be formed, called Poston Lake (Fig. 134), was even used for a steamer service from 1868 to 1872. Then man intervened at last and, by blasting the strangulating growth, cured the river of its crippling disease.

As soon as the Red River was free to pursue its true course, the water began to cut rapidly into the accumulated deposits. At some points the river has already incised its bed more than 17 feet in these deposits and this has enabled most of the lakes to drain away, leaving vast tracts of fertile arable land behind them.

For all that, the original system will never be restored entirely. Some tributaries have entered on a new course and even the main river has shifted permanently below Alexandria. Formerly the Red River flowed towards the S.S.E. and discharged into the Gulf of Mexico far to the west of the Mississippi. Owing to the barrier, a lake was formed to the south of Alexandria, which found an outlet to the north-west, as the result of which the Red River became a tributary of the Black River, which, in turn, drains into the Mississippi. This breach was sawn out to such depth before the old lower course was liberated, that it has remained the outlet of the river to this very day (Fig. 135).

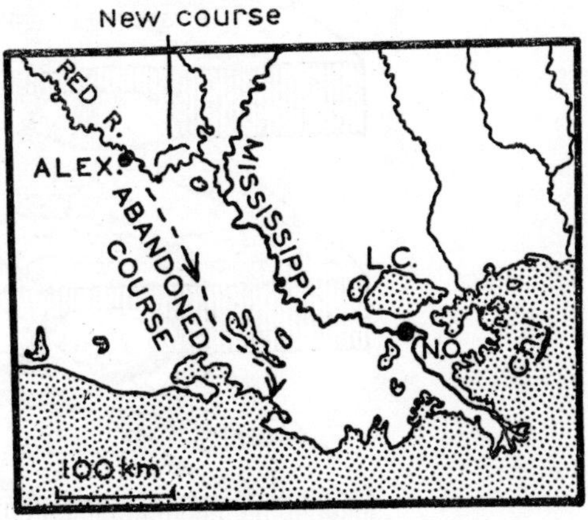

The fourth class of lakes consists of those formed by solution in limestone regions, giving rise to hollows extending to below the ground-water table, or by obstruction to downward drainage above the ground-water table. Many

Fig. 135. Diversion of the lower course of the Red River owing to obstruction by trees. N.O. = New Orleans, L.C. = Lake Chartrain, Ch.I. = Chandeleur Islands.

dolines, or sink-holes, contain a lake and poljes may also be filled temporarily or permanently with a sheet of water.

Artificial lakes may be taken as representing the fifth and last type.

The shape initially assumed by a newly formed lake does not persist indefinitely. Cases have been mentioned in the preceding pages in which water was drained off. Conversely, the basin may be filled with detritus carried downstream by rivers which are gradually extending their deltas. This process can be seen at work in the Swiss lakes, either by a river building through a lake from one end to the other, or by a side valley constructing a delta in the centre and thus ultimately cutting the lake in two. Examples of the former are the Rhine in Lake Constance and the Rhône in the Lake of Geneva. The second case is illustrated by the Maggia delta at Locarno in Lake Maggiore and the delta of the Adda in Lake Como. Since the last Glacial Period the surface area of lakes in Switzerland has decreased by about half, for many flat, fertile valley floors are nothing more nor less than silted-up lakes (Fig. 136). Only the larger and deeper lakes and those situated farther downstream have continued to exist, but even these are doomed and there is every reason to believe that the Alpine landscape will be deprived of all its lovely lakes in the course of the next 40,000 years.

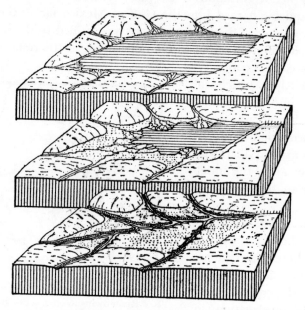

Fig. 136. Stages in the development of a lake. First an upthrust at right top has thrown a barrier across the stream system, making a barrier-lake. Deltas are then formed, which gradually coalesce. Finally, the outlet cuts in so deeply that the lake is drained off and the deposits become the victims of river erosion. (After Longwell, Knopf and Flint.)

Lake Water

Lakes receive some water by direct precipitation, but as a rule drainage from adjacent areas is the main source of supply. Only the steep surrounding slopes enlarge the catchment area of crater-lakes and small tarns high up in the mountains, but one or several rivers debouch into most lakes and thus add to the drainage basin. The number of streams discharging into an Alpine lake may be anything up to a few dozen.

Somehow or other this increment has to be disposed of. As we have seen, in arid climates, evaporation does most of this work of clearance. If it is the only means by which water is withdrawn, it is ultimately responsible for the formation of salt lakes. Other things being equal, the vaster the sheet of water, the less will be the evaporation from it, because the atmosphere becomes saturated with water vapour and new, dry air cannot be supplied to the whole surface of a large lake as quickly as to a small one.

The vast majority of lakes, however, lose some of their water by drainage. In some, e.g. many crater-lakes, the rock of which the basin consists is so permeable that the water simply trickles away without cutting an outlet for itself at ground level. Ordinarily, however, an outlet exists at ground level through which the whole surplus of precipitation plus feed left after loss by evaporation flows off.

The Norwegian lake of Lesjö, which is drained by two canals, forms one of the very few exceptions to the general rule that a lake has only one outlet, irrespective of the number of streams feeding it. It is not difficult to see why this should be so. If at any time more than one overflow should be in operation, one of them will erode its bed quicker than the others, either because the subsoil at the site offers the least resistance, or because the largest amount of water is drained there. The deeper the trench is scoured out, the greater will be the proportion of water escaping here and the more rapid will be the erosion, until finally all the other outlets will run dry. This is tantamount to saying that multiple overflows from a water basin are subject to a kind of labile equilibrium.

The properties of water running into a lake always differ from those of the discharge. The silt brought in is deposited; consequently the effluent water is much clearer. This is very marked in glacier lakes, because opaque, silt-laden glacier milk enters and a perfectly limpid stream, from which the sediment has settled on the floor of the basin, passes out. That there is ample time for the sedimentation of even the smallest particles is evident from the fact that the water of the Rhône, for example, needs on an average more than eleven years to pass through the Lake of Geneva.

Dissolved substances do not settle out, of course, but the daily, seasonal and, in large lakes, even the yearly changes in composition of the feeding arteries are well mingled and thus reduced to a general mean. Further, if there is more than one feeding canal, the waters will be thoroughly mixed, and moreover diluted by direct precipitation. Biological processes in the lake also tend to change the character of the water. Nutrient salts may be withdrawn and waste products added, changes which are, of course, governed in large measure by seasonal variations.

Q

The temperature of the water in the lake follows the fluctuations of that of the atmosphere, though very gradually and in a minor degree, and is therefore subservient to the climate of the immediate surroundings. In this respect, too, the drained water is far more uniform than the water entering the lake.

Another very important factor is the regulative effect of a lake upon the run-off of the river running through it. The utility of a lake in this respect may be inferred from the more obvious efficacy of a man-made barrage. What may not be common knowledge is the fact that the services of several Swiss lakes have been enlisted by artificial means for the better regulation of a water-course. Time and again the Linth, in central Switzerland, used to burst its banks, bringing great inconvenience and incalculable damage to the wide, thickly populated valley, until someone hit upon the ingenious idea of intercalating the Wallensee in its course. This large lake was situated at quite a short distance from the course of the Linth and, by digging a canal towards it and a drainage canal back from it to the river a little farther downstream, the surface of the river was extended enormously. The Wallensee now acts as a kind of buffer, able to cope with a huge amount of water in any sudden emergency and then to pass the surplus on by degrees to the next section of the Linth. So effectually did this put an end, for good and all, to inundation of the land below the Wallensee that this highly successful expedient was adopted elsewhere in similar circumstances.

It should not be thought, however, that the incoming water travels steadily from the entrance to the exit of the lake, passing uniformly through the whole cross-section of the basin. Like the waters of the ocean, those of a lake are stratified, with the heaviest water underneath and the lightest on top. If incoming water is as light as or lighter than the superficial water, it will spread over the surface and the lower part of the basin will receive practically no fresh water at all, since drainage is likewise from the surface, leaving the water at depth untouched. But if the incoming water is heavier than that at the surface, it will plunge down, seeking a level at which it is in equilibrium with the deep water. It is reminiscent of the heavy current which dips down to 3000 feet when it issues from the Strait of Gibraltar and only begins to spread out in the Atlantic Ocean when it reaches that depth (see page 67).

The temperature and mud content of fresh water are the two factors which govern its density. The water in a lake basin will always be clear, and if the inflowing water is likewise free from silt, the sole determinant is the temperature. The river water will, then, sink until it reaches water of the same temperature as its own. If it carries much suspended sediment and is therefore relatively heavy, it may sink to a level where the lake water is much colder before equilibrium is established. Once the river water has come to rest in the depths of the basin and has shed its burden, it would be reasonable to expect that it must rise again until it finds its proper level according to temperature. Chiefly through mixing, however, it has meanwhile transmitted its surplus heat to the adjacent waters and it is in this way that turbid river water may warm the deep waters of a lake.

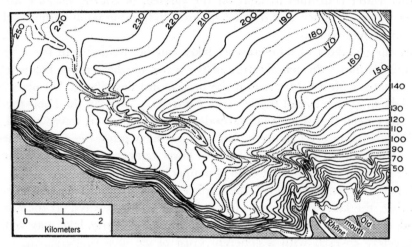

Fig. 137. Winding channel in the floor of the Lake of Geneva, opposite the mouth of the Rhône. There is also a nearly blotted out channel in front of the old mouth. Note the raised margin of the gully and the greater depth at the outer bends of the meanders.

In many instances the incoming water will only be heavy enough to dip down at certain times of the year, more especially in summer, when the water of the lake is warm. A stream then coming from a glacier will be relatively cold and, moreover, laden with silt derived from the melting glacier tongue and the ground moraine. In an Alpine lake the cloudy water can sometimes be seen plunging below the surface at a short distance from the inlet. By taking soundings to considerable depths it is even possible in some lakes to discover a channel on the bed running downwards from the entrance of the stream along the front of the delta. This channel is kept open by the continued flow of the river under the surface during those months in which its heavy waters travel to the lowest levels of the basin (Fig. 137).

The Freezing of Lakes

Many lakes are frozen over regularly every year, or at any rate in hard winters. As has been stated before, the greatest density of pure water is at four degrees above freezing point. Since it is always the surface which is affected, the chilled—and therefore heavy—water sinks and is replaced by warmer water rising from the depths. When the whole mass of water has been cooled down to 4° C., the basin is filled with water of maximum density. Heavier water than this cannot be formed; on the contrary, continuous loss of heat causes the surface water to expand and it becomes lighter. This lighter water continues to float on the surface, of course, because all the other water is heavier, and it can cool down to freezing point without suffering further convection.

By the standard of temperature, lakes can be divided into three types. In mild climates the temperature of the water nowhere drops below 4° C. In climates with a colder season the process just described takes place and the lake may or may not freeze over. Conversely, lakes in the Polar regions and very deep basins at lower latitudes, like Baikal Lake, never rise above 4° C. in temperature. Hence in this last case the depth water at 4° C. carries a superincumbent layer which cools to lower temperatures in winter but is never warmed to above that critical temperature in summer.

When the temperature of the surface water drops to 0° C. in frosty weather, the lake will begin to freeze in either of two ways. If there is no wind, a layer of ice will be formed at once. Even a large lake may well be completely covered with a coherent crust of ice in a single starlit, frosty night; and if the period of frost is prolonged, the crust will gradually thicken. Wind and waves, however, alter the picture entirely. The process begins with the formation of small blobs of ice, but wave action prevents them from joining. Repeated collision and mutual rubbing rounds off their corners, while a raised edge of spongy ice is built up at the periphery by detached fragments and frozen spray. The floe grows steadily in girth and depth, but the weight of the upright rim holds down the surface and spray covers it with a thin film of water gently swinging to and fro to the rhythm of the wavelets. This is perpetually pushing the upright rim to the outer edge of the floe and the so-called "pancakes" thus increase in size until they attain to a diameter of more than a yard, invariably flat on top with a raised margin and rounded below. As soon as the wind abates, the pancakes coalesce to a coherent layer, but it is spongy, friable ice, light in colour owing to the large amount of enclosed air.

If a crust of ice on a lake is exposed to abrupt changes of temperature due to nocturnal radiation alternating with warm sunshine during the day, it begins to work. On cooling, it contracts and, with a sound like muffled thunder, breaks up into separate floes. Naturally, the water in these cracks freezes immediately and if, in daytime, the floes begin to expand again under the heat of the sun, space becomes cramped. With irresistible force the ice then encroaches farther and farther up the shores. In other cases the ice piles up in the centre, often forming large barricades of upright floes. A fall of snow will bring this upheaval to rest, as it shields the crust from the effects of sharp variations in temperature.

On smaller sheets of water the wind produces something quite different, i.e. air-holes. It may at first not be clear how the wind can keep these patches open, though it will be evident that ice cannot be formed on the lee-side, which is lapped by rippling wavelets. But the first few feet of water on the windward side are perfectly smooth. Why does not this open water

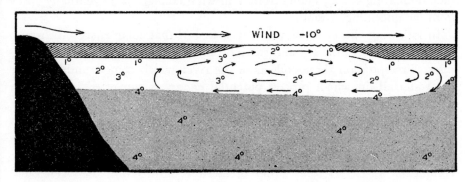

Fig. 138. How the wind keeps an air-hole open in a small sheet of frozen water.

close up if it continues to freeze day after day for weeks on end? The answer is: the circulation induced in the water by the wind, which is constantly pushing the water over the air-hole and under the ice crust again, on the lee-shore (Fig. 138). To compensate for this loss, new water from underneath the ice is drawn up on the wind-side. This water is just above freezing point and before it has had time to cool and attach itself to the ice sheet it has been carried past the hole and pushed under at the other side. It may even be that, in spite of severe frost, an air-hole grows larger towards the wind-ward side as the edge of ice melts where warmer water is being sucked up. Sometimes the action of the wind is assisted by a large flock of water-birds milling around the air-hole and churning up water of a higher temperature.

Once a thaw has broken up the ice sheet into floes, a strong wind will effect a thorough mixing of the waters and hasten the melting process. A thick crust of ice can be disposed of in an incredibly short time in this way.

Waterfalls

Lakes are not the only phenomena a river may meet on its journey from source to mouth. It also has to pass waterfalls, which we may now consider (Plate XVI, 1).

What could be a more imposing and fascinating spectacle than a large waterfall? The thunderous booming, the iridescence produced by the play of the sun's rays in the finely atomised water, the moist breeze rising from the base, the slight fluctuations in supply causing spurts like rockets, shooting down in front of the fall; all these irresistibly hold the spectator and start him wondering how such a phenomenon ever came into existence, where such unabating energy comes from, and what changes will eventually ensue from the unceasing erosion.

In following the cycle of water it was seen that solar energy draws up water vapour from the sea and carries it off at a high altitude to the mountains. Precipitation there collects in the river which comes tumbling over the waterfall, in which process potential energy is converted into motion and subsequently, partly through friction, into heat.

What standard are we to take if we want to know which is the greatest waterfall on earth? Some might take width and height, hence the surface of the curtain of water, as their criterion, whereas others might choose the volume of water. If some order of merit is insisted on, then generated energy (height times quantity of water) would surely be the most objective basis; only, it is then a moot point whether the maximum at high-water mark should be taken, or the mean for the whole year. The pragmatic modern, with a calculating eye on the possible conversion of this energy to electric power, would no doubt choose the latter.

In the following table the standard is the maximum display of energy. It may surprise many readers to see that by that standard the Niagara Falls take ninth place among the great cascades of the world. While this waterfall owes its world-wide fame in great part to its easy accessibility, there is undoubtedly one other important point. If waterfalls are arranged according to their *mean* volume, the Niagara Falls cut a far better figure and are surpassed only by the Guayra Fall. The Aughrabies is then outclassed, and even has to give place to two waterfalls not mentioned in the table. They now come in the following descending order: 1. Guayra, 2. Niagara, 3. Paulo Affonso, 4. Khon, 5. Kaieteur ($2 \cdot 3 \times 10^6$ h.p.), 6. Iguazu, 7. Victoria, 8. Grand Falls ($1 \cdot 3 \times 10^6$ h.p.), 9. Cauvery, 10. Gersoppa, 11. Aughrabies. Hence the maximum generation of energy of the Aughrabies is six times that of Niagara, but the mean is only $1/7$, while Guayra's volume exceeds Niagara's $4\frac{1}{2}$ times at high-water and $1\frac{1}{2}$ at mean level. The lowest level of this waterfall is also twice the minimum of Niagara.

Some of the giants among the waterfalls will now be briefly described. South America, it appears, is the continent of cascades *par excellence*. The basin of the Alto Paraña—called Rio de la Plata farther down—is particularly rich in waterfalls, to which none of the European falls can hold a candle. Among them are Guayra and Iguazu, while Paulo Affonso is situated in North Brazil and Kaieteur in British Guiana.

GIANT WATERFALLS OF THE EARTH

Name	Height in feet	Mean Volume		Maximum Volume		Width in yards
		Cusecs.	Million H.P.	Cusecs.	Million H.P.	
1. Aughrabies	465	11,000	$\frac{1}{2}$	500,000	30	20
2. Guayra	110	470,000	8	1,800,000	27	5200
3. Cauvery	241	33,000	1	670,000	24	920
4. Paulo Affonso	275	100,000	4	500,000	17	19
5. Gersoppa	829	5,000	1	120,000	15	800
6. Khon	60	410,000	3	1,800,000	13	14000
7. Iguazu	237	62,000	2	450,000	13	4300
8. Victoria	295	38,000	$1\frac{1}{2}$	250,000	10	1500
9. Niagara	67	212,000	5	300,000	6	1300
cf. Rhinefalls, Schaffhausen	67	13,000	0·1	38,000	0·3	125

The Guayra Falls, on the borders of Brazil and Paraguay, are commonly held to be the most powerful in the world. The Paraña River widens above the falls into a lake, which drains through a deep and narrow gorge. This gorge cuts some distance into the bed of the lake and is fed by eighteen gigantic waterfalls all round it. Hence, like most big waterfalls, this is divided up by islands. The Iguazu and Victoria Falls are somewhat similar in type. The individual falls of the Guayra are situated at the head of short side clefts cut out by the falling water at right angles to the main channel. A few similar lateral branches are found downstream of the falls, but they have now run dry (Fig. 139). As the main gorge continues to extend upstream, the most southerly falls of the present day will also presumably dry up. The cleft obviously follows a weak strip in the earth's crust which is being washed out by degrees.

Like the Iguazu and other waterfalls of the Paraña basin, the Guayra Falls owe their origin to huge fields of lava poured out in earlier geological periods and laid down in a number of superimposed horizontal layers. Owing to a dense network of vertical cracks, the lava fields perpetually tend to break off in perpendicular ridges. It is thus that the abrupt leap over a sharp edge of rock is maintained, notwithstanding abrasion and the gradual backward shifting of the cascades.

Even more imposing than the Guayra Falls themselves, which, as a matter of fact, cannot all be seen together from a single vantage point, is the spectacle of the water gushing at furious speed through the gorge. This is 300

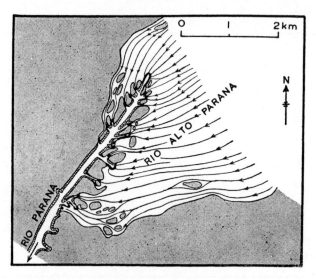

Fig. 139. The Guayra Falls. Each individual fall, lined in black, is cutting back in a separate small gorge.

feet wide, but the whole mass of the Paraña shoots through it, at the rate of 20 to 30 miles an hour, a quantity of water which is about equivalent to the normal volume of the Niagara, Paulo Affonso, Iguazu, Victoria, Cauvery and Kaieteur added together! The following description comes from Hills and Dubar:

"Below were the great rapids. The river poured in thunder through the opening, lumps of shattered water, foam and spray, amber and ivory. You cannot compare it to water at all. It was a substance compacted of air and liquid and froth, and yet there was nothing light or foamy or airy about it. The rush and the stress and the drive of it hammered it into a solidity; and yet it had that sameness of outline, that moving quality, which is given you by the unchanging movement of a great waterfall; for it was always changing, never the same, tossed and twisted and tortured now into this shape and now into that."

The Iguazu, a tributary of the Paraña, is enlivened by several falls and rapids. The largest occurs twelve miles above the mouth and, as the table shows, this fall is twice as high as the Guayra fall, but its volume is considerably smaller. This is another instance of a broad, shallow river drained by a fissure only about 170 feet wide into a ring of many independent falls. It is on record that, during the exceptional flows of the Paraña in 1905 and 1929, the level of this river rose so high that the waters of the Iguazu piled up in its gorge and the waterfall was effaced, as it were. This tributary then burst its banks and inundated the surrounding jungle on its way to rejoin the Paraña.

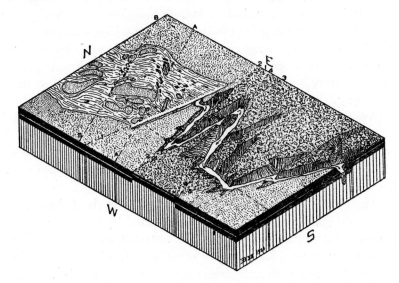

Fig. 140. Block diagram of the Victoria Falls on the Zambesi River. (After Escher.)

The most remarkable among the giant waterfalls are undoubtedly the Victoria Falls of the Zambesi. Geologically, they most resemble the Guayra. Here again a shallow, very broad river, spanning a mile from bank to bank, flows across a plateau of lava sheets and then drops down a deep, narrow cleft which had been excavated along a fault plane (Fig. 140). But the fissure of the Victoria Falls stands almost exactly perpendicular to the direction of the river and, instead of linking with an outstretched canyon, is followed by a chain of short cross-channels which carry the river in a zig-zag line through many miles of the arid plateau. All these are scoured sections of faults almost at right angles to the direction of the river. The lava lining these vertical fault-planes was pulverised and thus became an easy prey to the erosive action of the falling water. In the geological near future a new bend will be added to the zigzag gorge along a fault which begins on the right bank of the Zambesi where it falls into the first branch of the gorge and crosses over obliquely parallel to the penultimate section of the canyon. The former bed of the Zambesi can easily be reconstructed on the obvious assumption that its banks followed the tangents at the extremities of the zigzag gorge.

This geological history in itself would earmark the Victoria Falls as one of the great wonders of nature. What particularly strikes the spectator is the comparative placidity of the broad river before it is so abruptly cut off by one of the widest and highest falls in the world, converting the previously calm waters into a deep, turbulent torrent swirling through the canyon. The first section of the gorge is so narrow that the falling water beats against the opposite side. The in-sucked air shoots up as a stiff breeze, sweeping with it a dense mist of spray. As the falls are always enveloped in this mist, particularly during heavy flows, they and the yawning canyon at·their feet are never completely visible together.

The Orange River, South Africa, which is the next to be considered, is far more variable in point of volume than the Zambesi. Nevertheless, the drainage, which under normal circumstances is much inferior to that of several other falls, is of the same order as of the Niagara Falls at the highest water-levels.

The Aughrabies Waterfall in the Orange River is different: a concentrated type with one very high drop preceded by sizeable rapids. The whole body of water does not go down the waterfall, as some of it is diverted by a complex system of large, interspersed islands which here divides the river. The Orange River, true desert stream as it is, is subject to marked variations in volume. At high water its volume is immense and the energy generated by the lofty fall is unequalled anywhere. The mean horse-power, however, is quite low, owing to the fact that the annual drainage of the river is no more than moderate. A more striking contrast could scarcely be found than between the Aughrabies Waterfall, with its brown, turbid waters, sharp variations in volume, insignificant width and enormous height, and the Niagara Falls, the North American giant. Their only resemblance is in the length of the gorge below the fall, which is half a dozen miles in both cases.

The striking variations in volume also occur in the Cauvery. Whereas in the dry monsoon the river is little more than a trickle of water, in the wet season it produces a waterfall only third from the head of the list in point of volume. The fall is divided into two branches, each of which is again subdivided, so that it is impossible to get a full view of the whole from the ground. Generally speaking, these branches constitute very steep rapids rather than sheer falls, with a drop of a hundred yards, over which the water rushes at immense speed. The variegation of colour produced by purple rocks, tropical vegetation and glittering white churned water makes these falls at high water an amazing and fascinating sight.

Paulo Affonso, as the great fall in the Rio Saõ Francisco, Brazil, is called, is the most varied of all the great cascades. Just above it, the river divides into two. The smaller branch forms a waterfall; the larger plunges through a gorge and in turn divides into two rapids. After uniting in an enormous pot-hole and flowing towards another, the mass of water divides again, this time into four tremendous rapids, and races obliquely down the 60-foot drop at terrific speed. All the waters of this great river then collect in a huge pot-hole and drop in a single fall of about 200 feet, after which they are drained in a canyon, in places less than 300 feet wide and 42 miles in length, through the arid plateau towards the coastal plain. The rapids above the fall are unparalleled and are certainly the most magnificent of their kind on the face of the earth.

There could be no more striking contrast than that presented by the Kaieteur Fall of the Potaro River in British Guiana. The volume of this river is moderate, but the fall measures 822 feet, with the upper 741 feet a sheer drop. The river flows placidly upon hard conglomerate until it reaches a very sharp, horizontal edge, where it plunges vertically straight into a wide pool. The sandstone under the conglomerate having been hollowed out at the back, it provides a tall, dark arch as a background to the silvery jet of water. High water transforms the Kaieteur into a veil more than a hundred yards wide, hidden largely by clouds of mist of its own making. Similar in appearance is the Gersoppa Fall in the Sharavati River in southern India, but it is slightly superior in height, namely, nearly 829 feet in one sheer drop, while the maximum drainage is as much as 120,000 cusecs (= cubic feet per second), in spite of the short length of the upper reaches (70 miles) of the river. Unfortunately, the waterfall is completely hidden from view by the veils of spray which are swept upwards from its foot, filling the whole precipice below the cascade with thick mist.

The Niagara and Kaieteur Waterfalls are due to the same geological cause, for in both cases hard rock is undermined by easily eroded formations beneath. Now and again some of the overhanging ledge breaks off and drops into the chasm, so that every time this happens the waterfall moves a step farther upstream. The falling waters then begin to disperse the débris beneath and when that task is completed the undermining starts all over again.

Niagara, however, is outwardly altogether different, not only in its far greater width and incomparably larger volume of water, but also in point of height, which is only a fifth that of Kaieteur. The fact that the Niagara drains a lake, viz., Lake Erie, affects the falls in several ways. First of all, the colour of the cataract is an intense greenish-blue owing to the limpidity of the water. Secondly, the volume of the waterfall varies little because inequalities in precipitation are smoothed out by the large surface of the lake. Variations in discharge are caused principally by the wind on the lake, which either raises or depresses the water level at the outlet. Once only, on 31st March 1848, an ice-dam was formed athwart the outlet of Lake Erie, when, as a result, the waterfall ran practically dry. There was nothing to prevent anyone who wished from taking a stroll along the bed of the river and the edge of the precipice.

At the foot of the waterfall there is a gorge seven miles long, through which the water courses at great speed in angry waves and eddies towards Lake Ontario (Fig. 141). The origin of this fissure is an interesting fragment of geological history. When the last Ice Age had passed its zenith and the ice-sheet had retreated, the Niagara River drained only the water of Lake Erie and therefore contained only 15 per cent of its present volume of water. In a low, broad, waterfall 35 feet high the primeval Niagara fell into Lake Ontario. The work of cutting back began at once and the waterfall remained as it had been because the hard stratum was being perpetually undermined, breaking off every so often. Only its height varied, reaching at one time more than 320 feet (see Fig. 145). More than 25,000 years must have been required to saw through the first three miles of the gorge. Subsequently, when the river began to drain the other large lakes as well, its volume increased enormously. This also accelerated the backward movement of the waterfall. It could not have taken more than 3500 years to cut out the remaining four miles of the gorge. Hence, in a comparatively short space of time the waterfall will have cut back to Lake Erie, thereby pronouncing its own death sentence.

The Grand Falls of the Hamilton River in Labrador rank second among the North American waterfalls, followed by the Shoshone Falls of the Snake River in Idaho. The latter have virtually disappeared, having been tapped for electric power and irrigation.

The Khon Falls of the Mekong in Indo-China are situated well over 400 miles from the mouth of the river. They are not high and might as aptly be called rapids. It is, however, the enormous volume of water of the Mekong, surpassed in this respect by one fall only, the Guayra on the Paraña, which exalts the Khon Falls to the ranks of the giant cataracts. At this part the river is divided by a large number of islands into a network of water-chutes. These fall over a steep ledge of about 70 feet, some gullies being worn down to a species of rapids, while others are true falls. The total width amounts to no less than eight miles, which places the Khon Falls in a class by themselves.

Among the very high, but not voluminous waterfalls, are to be reckoned some, not yet thoroughly explored, in the Roraima massif in British Guiana;

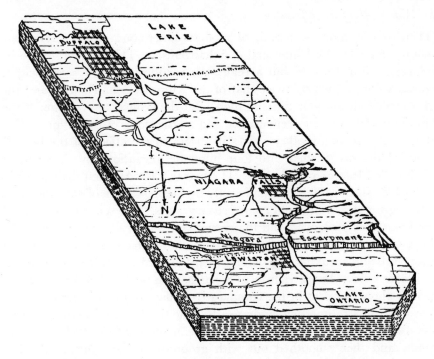

Fig. 141. Block diagram of Niagara Falls region. (After Longwell, Knopf and Flint.)

also the Yosemite Falls in Yosemite National Park, consisting of two sheer drops of 1430 feet and 320 feet and several shorter ones, together amounting to 2425 feet, and the "Ribbon" of more than 1612 feet. There are also the Chirombo Fall of the Ieisa River in Tanganyika, Africa, nearly 880 feet high; the fall of the Wollomombie in Australia, nearly 1100 feet high; the Sutherland Falls in New Zealand with three jumps of 815, 751 and 338 feet, together 1904 feet, with greater volume, hence more compact water jets than the slightly higher Yosemite Falls; the Cascade de Gavarnie in the Pyrenees, with a sheer drop of 1384 feet; and, finally, the Staubbach, which drops 900 feet from the valley of the Pletschenbach into the Lauterbrunnen

Valley. Owing to its small volume, however, the water is scattered in spray before it reaches the bottom.

There are no giant waterfalls in Europe. Powerful though the great falls of Iceland (Dettifoss and Gullfoss) be, as well as the Scandinavian cascades (Sarpsfoss, Rjukanfoss, Skjaeggedalsfoss and Vöringfoss in Norway, the Stora Sjöfallet and Harsprånget in Sweden and the Imatra rapids in Finland), they are not comparable with the greatest of those we have mentioned.

The Waterfall of Schaffhausen

There is one more waterfall, of modest dimensions, which claims our attention, namely, the Rhine Fall of Schaffhausen. This is often said to be the largest fall in Europe, but actually the Sarpsfoss is of the same height, its mean volume is nearly twice that of the Rhine at Schaffhausen and the high-water levels are four times as high. But the geological evolution of the Rhine Waterfall was very remarkable and merits closer examination. This waterfall, like so many others, owes its origin to the effects of the Glacial Period. This was divided into four immense glaciations by three warm periods called Interglacial Periods. The first two Ice Ages left their mark in the North Swiss Lowlands predominantly by the deposition of vast and thick tracts of ground-moraine and coarse river gravels. The second Interglacial Period was very prolonged and the rivers had time to saw steep, gorge-like valleys out of the foothills of the Alps, draining the water in a winding course. Broadly speaking, the Rhine then followed much the same course that it does today. In the vicinity of Schaffhausen the bed had been cut to a depth of about 700 feet in the comparatively flat land consisting of glacial deposits with hard limestone underneath. The third Glacial Period covered these districts with glaciers and the Rhine canyon was first filled with river deposits and then smoothed out with ground-moraine. During the last Interglacial Period the Rhine tried to clear its old bed, but long before it had been able to do so another ice age supervened and the glacier buried the foothills of the Alps for the fourth and last time. When this latest ice-sheet had likewise retreated, there remained a gently undulating countryside with faintly marked valley remains here and there, large crescentic terminal moraines and shallow, tortuous river beds.

Upon retreat of the ice, the Rhine was at first divided into four sections which issued from various points in the front of the Rhine glacier. But when the tongue of the glacier had shrunk sufficiently to liberate Lake Constance, all the melt-water collected in this basin and overflowed at the lowest point in the surrounding ridge. The river was thus concentrated into a single copious stream enabled by a steep grade to scour out its bed. As a result, its winding course was perpetuated, as it were, in the more or less haphazard twists and turns it had taken in the fairly flat terrain left behind by the glacier; and that course had little if any relation to the form of the deep-seated canyon formed in earlier interglacial periods. After the post-glacial Rhine had entrenched itself 150 feet down into the landscape, the stream for the first time struck the hard limestone under the glacial deposits. This must have been some 10,000 to 15,000 years ago. It was far more difficult to scour the bed of hard rock than the loose ground-moraine and river gravels with which the river had previously been dealing; and so from

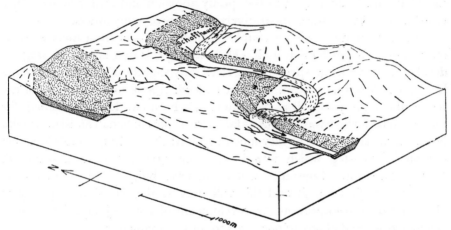

Fig. 142. The Rhine Waterfall at Neuhausen near Schaffhausen formed where the river flows over a stretch of hard limestone before returning to the old glacial valley which had been filled with easily erodible moraine materials.

that time on the cutting of the Rhine bed progressed at a far slower pace. The first point of contact with the hard substratum was where the waterfall now seethes to the south of Neuhausen (Fig. 142).

Upstream, scouring proceeded at first without hindrance and the outlet of Lake Constance was therefore constantly dropping to a lower level. This, however, gave the river less and less grade until it finally became so sluggish that it was unable to cut any farther. But below this stretch of hard rock the Rhine followed its ancient bed and had no difficulty in disposing of the loose material; so in that section the river continued to dig itself in. At the edge of the hard limestone a step was thus formed which became progress-ively higher until, about 6000 years ago, it reached its present height. The Rhine Fall at Neuhausen had come into being.

While at work in this way, the river had succeeded in cutting an eighty-foot trench into the limestone, but as the upstream slope was being levelled and is now so insignificant that practically no rock-waste or boulders are carried along, cutting has as good as ceased. The Rhine, moreover, drops all its sediment into Lake Constance, which is another reason why it is quite transparent when it reaches the waterfall. Hence the river lacks the tools for corrosion and foams over the limestone bed, powerless to modify its shape. In addition, thanks to the clarity of the water, large colonies of algae, which would be destroyed in other streams by sand and gravel, have been able to settle on the rocks. These colonies help to shield the limestone from denudation. The waterfall at Neuhausen has come to stay, in a manner of speaking, and is not subject to the speedy abrasion and transformation into tame rapids which is the comparatively early fate of many others.

A similar situation exists a couple of miles upstream from the waterfall, quite close to Schaffhausen itself. This, however, is in a far earlier stage of development, with the speed of the river only slightly accelerated over the limestone. A second cascade will not be formed here until the bend of the Rhine above the waterfall at Neuhausen has been cut down far enough for the bed to be further washed out as far as the rapids of Schaffhausen. It will, however, never be a fall of very much account; there will be ample time for erosion of the step which would otherwise have served as a waterfall. Furthermore, Lake Constance will in all probability be silted up by the rivers discharging into it and this will provide the Rhine with plenty of abrasive material to prevent the development of a steep jump. The lake is calculated to need about 17,000 years to silt up completely.

Downstream from Neuhausen the Rhine frequently deviates from the course of the buried, interglacial canyon and is continually being impeded from denuding the ancient valley. For this reason the river has not as yet been able to cut its way down to the interglacial depth. The bed of the ancient Rhine lies another 80 feet farther down and the valley was formerly considerably wider. Indeed, the Second Interglacial Period lasted many times as long as the postglacial age up to the present time and it will be tens of thousands of years before the present Rhine has cut down as deep as its forerunner.

It is a familiar fact, and from the aesthetic point of view a most regrettable one, that more and more waterfalls are being exploited to procure water-power. The total kinetic energy produced by all terrestrial running water is the equivalent of roughly 8000 million horse-power. In a year this is equal to the combustion value of 2 per cent of all coal supply on this earth. Only a small fraction of all this energy can be put to practical use. The potential water-power available on the various continents can be estimated as follows:

Continent	Potential water-power in millions H.P.	Now being employed in millions H.P.
Africa	200	Less than 1
North America	70	16
South America	60	1
Asia	70	2
Europe	50	13
Oceania	20	Less than 1
Total on earth	470	33

Hence of all the available energy 1/17 is utilisable and of that fraction only 1/14 is so far being employed. Yet many beautiful waterfalls have already been largely, if not wholly, deprived of their splendour; e.g. the double fall of the Snake River in Idaho, the Niagara Falls up to a certain point, the Imatra Falls in Finland, the Rjukanfoss in Norway, and the Foyer Falls in Scotland, to mention only a few of the far-famed examples.

General Origins of Waterfalls

In the preceding description of the most celebrated waterfalls, there was here and there occasion to refer to their origins. It will be useful to summarise the circumstances known to the geologist as liable to lead to their formation.

When a fault occurs in the earth's crust, resulting in a disparity between the levels of the two masses of fractured rock, all rivers flowing from the higher to the lower level will plunge down over this step as a waterfall. The head here invests the water locally with great energy and, laden with pebbles and sand carried along, it grinds down the rock with considerable force. As

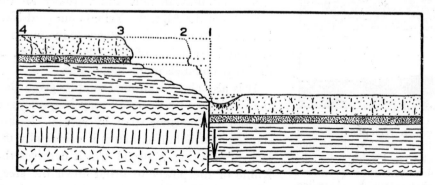

Fig. 143. Abrasion of a waterfall formed by a fault. The steepness diminishes and the fall gradually shifts upstream.

R

a result the step over which the water drops is worn away and shifts upstream. But as the step retreats, the slope becomes less and this leads to the gradual transformation of the waterfall into rapids. In a short space of time— geologically speaking—the waterfall is worn away altogether, leaving as the only trace a slightly steeper grade over a stretch of the bed upstream from the fault (Fig. 143).

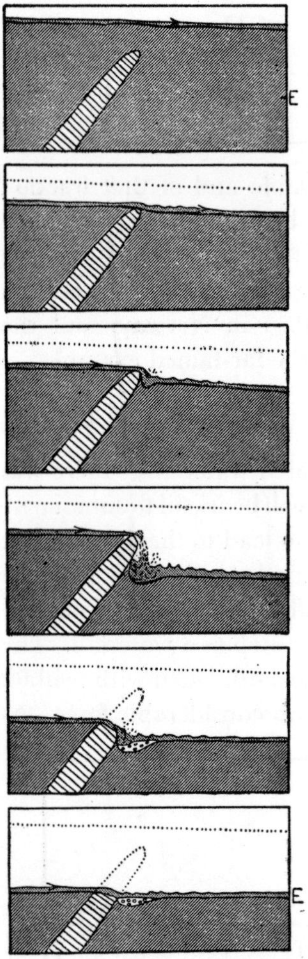

Another occasion for a waterfall may be a thick stream of lava from the surface of which a river comes tumbling down. Sometimes it has entered an existing valley and the fall has arisen suddenly over this new obstacle. In other cases, as the river cuts deeper and deeper into the mountains, it encounters somewhere a stratum much more resistant than the adjacent material. This may either be a deeply buried ancient lava-flow, or a consolidated intrusion of volcanic material; but there are many other very hard rocks besides. A barricade may temporarily develop by erosion downstream of the resistant stratum. This will vanish only when the hard rock ultimately, after a tenacious existence, has likewise succumbed to the ravages of time (Fig. 144).

By far the majority of waterfalls, however, result from the action of glaciers during the Ice Age. The geological origin of the Niagara and Schaffhausen Falls has been discussed in detail. The Scandinavian falls and virtually all the cascades of the Alps, the Yellowstone and New Zealand falls owe their existence to inequalities, created by glaciers of the Glacial Period, in drainage channels in the mountains.

It is also clear from the examples given that the existence of a waterfall may be prolonged beyond the normal span by special circumstances. At Schaffhausen it is principally the lack of scouring material which deprives the Rhine of the power to grind down the steep cliff over which it cascades and it is the horizontal position of the hard limestone stratum

Fig. 144. Waterfall formed by a hard intrusion of volcanic rock. The height of the falls will vary, but the site will remain constant. E = base-line of erosion (see footnote page 267).

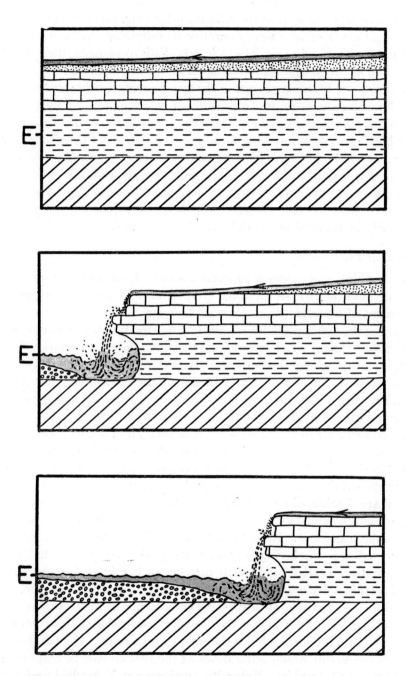

Fig. 145. The retreat of a waterfall formed over a stratum of hard limestone resting on soft clay. The height depends on the thickness of the strata and the base-line of erosion (E).

which maintains the level of the Niagara ledge (Fig. 145). Vertical fractures in the vast cover of lava were operative in sustaining the South American falls in the Paraña basin. The Victoria Falls prolonged their existence again and again on new shattered zones in a lava plateau.

Whether this blunting process of the step be temporarily suspended, as in the above instances, or proceeds without interruption, all waterfalls are doomed to ultimate extinction. Once the after-effects of the Glacial Period have been effaced, in anything from tens to hundreds of thousands of years hence, waterfalls will have become rare relics of the past. At such a time, tectonic forces only will create falls, and then only as an exception; and if those forces should lie dormant for prolonged eons, as they have in the geological past, the last waterfall will shrink to rapids and all rivers will ultimately be reduced to sluggish, steady waterways.

Turbulent Flow

As anything more than a superficial study of water-flow involves complicated mathematics, we shall not trespass beyond some generalities. The movement of a torrent may alternate between a sheer drop and shooting forward of the water particles. A placidly flowing river exhibits two distinct types of movement, viz., laminary and turbulent flow. In laminary flow the particles travel along courses lying parallel to the sides of the channel; hence the lines of flow are parallel to one another. Turbulent flow involves irregular, eddying and rolling movements, hence the lines of flow change shape and direction erratically.

Experiments in tubes have shown that laminary flow occurs at low velocities and that this changes into turbulent flow when a certain speed is reached. It has also been established that, the wider and more irregular the duct is, the sooner does turbulence set in. It may be assumed that all natural watercourses are dominated entirely by the eddying type of movement, with the proviso on theoretical grounds that a narrow zone with laminary flow constitutes the transition towards the solid walls. Large, slow eddies appearing as rounded, low camberings of the surface, are a common sight on great rivers, and are carried along with the current like huge, laggard jellyfish. The dimensions depend upon the size of the river, the rate of flow, etc.

Turbulence is a factor of the utmost importance in the transport of sedimentary particles; for eddying flow involves vertical as well as advancing movement and the former holds the sand in suspension. In plain laminary flow, all the grains would settle down at the bottom, where only a rolling movement can take place. Naturally, particles may be washed up from the bottom by turbulence, but it is not clear at a glance how sediment, once

raised, can be kept in suspension, for, counterbalancing every upward movement in an eddy, there must be a downward one of like momentum. The
suspended material, however, is distributed in decreasing density from the
bottom upwards. Hence in a vertical eddy the rising current carries, against
the pull of gravity, more particles to the top than are borne down with the
descending section. The smaller the particles are, the less readily they settle.
That is why clay is raised in dense clouds right up to the surface and is thus
fairly evenly distributed throughout the cross-section of a stream, whereas
sand accumulates for the most part close to the bottom.

It should not be thought, however, that a bed of sand is safe from attack
by a flowing river and that banks of clay are being persistently undermined;
for it is just the contrary. The vulnerability of the sand is due to the ease
with which turbulent water is able to penetrate between the grains and lift
them. The bed of a swift-flowing river should be considered as a gradual
transition from water with much sand to sand with little water, eddying
round the grains and preventing them from coming to rest completely, one
upon the other. Where clay is concerned, the surface is so smooth and the
interstices are so minute that laminary flow develops along the bed and the
particles are therefore left undisturbed. Thus the result of the fine-grained
structure of clay is, on the one hand, that a river-bed of this material offers
considerable resistance to erosion, while, on the other, particles of clay,
once detached, are easily carried along in suspension. If the water contains
a great deal of sand, however, the clay is blasted off and swept away. Compared with solid rock, clay is very vulnerable. The geological activity of
rivers was not properly understood until the part played by turbulence in
the transport of sedimentary particles was assessed at its true value.

Meanders

The term *meanders*, used to describe the curves from the shape of an indis-
tinct S to an exaggerated horseshoe, which many rivers exhibit especially in
their lower courses, is derived from the Menderes or Meander, a river in
Asia Minor which has developed this type of serpentine bends in a remarkable degree. All rivers bend and wind along their course, but the term
"meander" applies specifically to the comparatively regular, conspicuous
windings through 180° and more which occur almost exclusively in tracts
of insignificant gradient. Hence the amplitude of the curves is so great that
the river is ever and again flowing perpendicular to its general direction,
even turned away from its mouth. A river is barely entitled to be called
meandering if the increase in length through windings is less than half,
while it is very exceptional for the lengthening to be more than three times.

If, in its more hilly reaches, a river were to try to transform a sharp bend into a wide curve, it would also have to remove all the material lying above the level of the stream; and there is so much of this that progress would be infinitely slow. In those places where the stream undermines its banks, the boulders tumbling down are large enough to protect the bank and the river is forced to swerve to the opposite side.

In lowlands, however, the surface of the land is only slightly above the level of the river and the quantity of material that has to be cut away to shift a river bend is trifling. There is always sufficient alluvium, moreover, for deposition in the sluggish water on the opposite bank, so that the river bed is shifted more than widened by this erosion. Then again, the bed is generally composed of sand, clay and silt, i.e., formations showing very little cohesion and hence easily picked up and carried away by running water. In addition, vast stretches of the strata are laid down almost horizontally, with no folds or faults to mar the equality of their internal structure and so to force the river into any one particular course.

Thus a river is free in its lower reaches to cut out its bed in obedience to the laws of hydrodynamics. At every bend, however slight, the water will be impelled by its momentum to impinge upon the outer bank. The details are more complicated than might be supposed at first sight. As the water runs faster on the surface than at the bottom, the centrifugal force will act more potently above than below, causing the faster surface water to travel towards the outer bank, while the slower flow beneath is given a component towards the inner one. Hence the water follows a spiral path in its passage through the bend. The effect is to concentrate erosion upon the outer or concave side which begins to bulge (Fig. 146). Moreover, the obstruction of the bend itself causes strong eddies, which naturally intensify the process.

As a result of the widening of the river and the setting of the current towards the outer bank, the water lapping the inner bank slows down and deposits material. The spiral current drags the detritus scoured out of the outer bank to the placid water of the inner bank, where it settles at the bottom. Hence the centrifugal force within the bend causes the river to meander outwards in an ever-wider curve, without becoming markedly broader.

At the place where the river resumes its normal flow down the gradient, however, a converse bend will have been formed automatically, which in its turn will be subjected to the outward growth of the curvature. A third bend must then develop downstream and thus the meandering proceeds further and further, theoretically until the whole river below the initial kink has become tortuous. In fact, at a given moment, the increasing curve cuts through the narrow neck of the meander (at C in Fig. 146) so that the stream is able to flow straight from the first into the third bend, as shown by the thick arrow. The whole gradient in bend II now becomes available at point C and locally the current is far stronger. This process is called a *meander cut-off*, producing an *ox-bow lake*. The river now has at once to deal with the irregular, pronounced kink at C and the development of a meander will start all over again (Figs. 147 and 148).

The growth of meander curves is subservient to another limiting circumstance. The tortuous windings have increased the length of the river between A and D considerably, say to three times the original distance. But the available drop has remained the same, so that the gradient of the river, i.e. the drop per running mile, has decreased to one-third, with consequent reduction in the speed of flow. But at the same time the river has become wider and deeper to admit the passage of the same quantity of water per unit of time. This increased cross-section, again, favours velocity of flow, so that in the upshot the speed has decreased less than the gradient, i.e. has remained more than one-third of the initial value. There is in sum a certain amount of retardation, which reduces the erosive action upon the outer bank. The radius of curvature in the bend has moreover increased, reducing the centrifugal force and setting the current less at the outer bank, while turbulence abates. Consequently, by degrees the meander loses vitality as it develops. In the end, the stream is incapable of absorbing new material along its concave bank and the growth of the bend comes to a standstill. The limit reached differs in each indi-

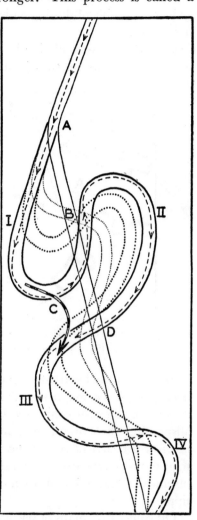

Fig. 146. Gradual formation of a series of meanders following a slight bend in the river at A towards B. Eventually a cut-off will be effected at C leaving the second meander as an ox-bow lake. The river has widened slightly owing to reduced gradient.

vidual case, depending on the size of the river and the slope of the land. This will be further considered presently.

It has long been known that the meanders of a river shift downstream by degrees, as the riverains of some streams know to their cost. In a few decades a river is capable of shifting a distance equal to its own width, for the following reason.

Since the cross-circulation in the river, described above, is to some extent sluggish, this movement will not come immediately into full play at the

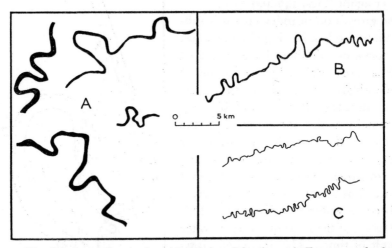

Fig. 147. The size of meanders varies with the size of the river. A. Four examples from the Orinoco delta. B. Clinch River, Virginia. C. Two streams in North Dakota.

beginning of the bend and it will persist after the curvature of the river has been passed. Consequently, the stretches of erosion on the outer bank and deposition along the convexity shift downstream relative to the existing bend. Visualising the erosion of a number of successive bends shifted slightly downstream, it will readily be realised that the meanders in a body must tend to move towards the mouth of the river. Fig. 149 represents a current instance in nature based upon exact measurements made along the Mississippi.

On comparing maps of several meandering rivers, it will be seen that the bends of each stream are of approximately the same size and that they are large or small depending on the size of the river. It is not difficult to see why this is. On geometrical grounds, the radius of a curve must in any event be greater than half the width of the stream (Fig. 150). In a large river, moreover, the huge mass of water has so great a momentum that it cannot be compelled to follow sharp bends. A small stream, on the other hand, flowing

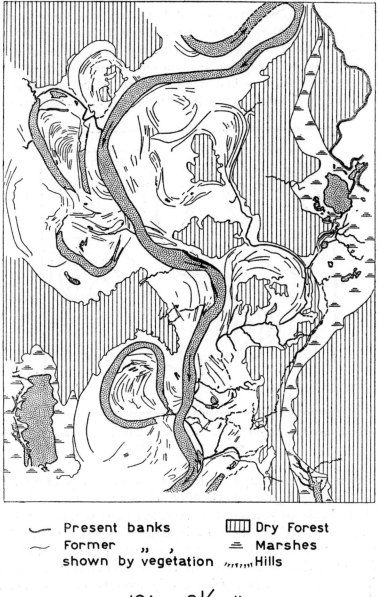

Present banks |||| Dry Forest
Former   ,, ,   ═ Marshes
shown by vegetation ,,,,,,,,,Hills

|← 10 km = 6 ¼ miles →|

Fig. 148. The Barito River, Borneo, showing free meanders and cut-off channels. The growth of meanders can be traced by the contours of the old banks, discernible by differing vegetation and by patches of dry forest surrounded by marshland, formed by levees (see page 276). Top right, plateau escarpment. (After Boissevain.)

in a very large bend will exert so little centrifugal force that any slight disturbance is liable to affect its course. A large river flows faster than a small one with the same gradient. Hence the radius of its curves may also be larger—which would in itself reduce the centrifugal force—and still it will set sufficiently against the concavity of the outer bank to cause erosion.

Geologists have tried to find some standard relationship between the dimensions of the bends and the size of the river, but it appears that it is

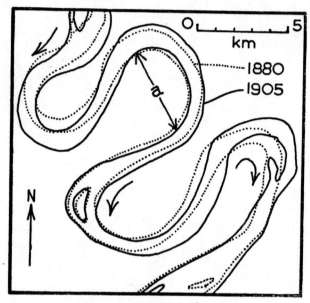

Fig. 149. Meanders of the Mississippi near Memphis observed to grow and shift downstream between 1880 and 1905.

difficult to relate this to any fixed rule. The general slope of the area, the differences between high and low water levels and the nature of the material of which the banks are composed are all determining factors. It is therefore idle to expect that a dependable relationship will be found to exist between the size of the meander and some key measure of the river, such as drainage per unit of time, velocity, depth or cross-section. For all that, the dimensions of the bends appear to depend fairly closely upon the width of the river in the majority of cases; for, if the width of the tract covered by the windings—called the *meander-belt*—is measured and the result divided by the width of the river, the average found is between 15 and 20, with variations seldom below 10 or above 30.

Seeing that meanders gradually shift downstream, it will be evident that a river will have worked over the whole meander-belt in a comparatively short time. When the river has migrated the distance (a) in Fig. 149, it will have passed successively over all the points of the belt. The whole area within this belt must be carpeted with material deposited on the inside of the bends. As the river cannot lay down material above the level of high water, the entire plain within the meander-belt must be on a level with, or lower than, this maximum watermark. A stream in process of depositing material, and thus of building up its bed, will always abandon its old course and even the meander-belt if it should happen to be raised above the general level of the adjacent area. But if the river carries away from the region as much material as, or more than, it lays down in it, the meander-belt will become a broad, somewhat sunken valley. Precipitous banks build up along meanders where they are trying to break out of the belt already worked over and these higher cliffs impede the development of the bends at those sites. Hence the river, hampered in its efforts to widen the existing belt, continues to wind its way through the valley, like a snake wriggling along a gutter.

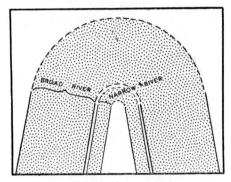

Fig. 150. The sharpest possible bend has a larger radius for a wide river than for a narrow stream.

In both cases considered, there is nothing to prevent the meanders from travelling downstream, in spite of the fact that in the second instance lateral freedom of movement is restricted. Unhindered meanders are therefore called *free meanders* in contrast to *valley meanders* or *incised meanders*. On a map the latter have the normal aspect of such curves, but they are sunk in a surrounding plateau or in a wide, well-defined, steep-sided valley. In some cases all the vertical sections perpendicular to the river are approximately symmetrical and the sides of the valley are uniformly steep (Fig. 151). In that event it must be assumed that the river at first wound on the flat surface of the plateau and then cut its way down, every point in it having sunk vertically. As it has taken time for the river to develop those meanders on the original plateau, by lateral movements without at that time cutting down vertically into the rock, it must be supposed that the plateau was then a plain, roughly at the level of the base-line of erosion.[1] Through sudden

---

[1] Base-line or base-level of erosion is the term used to describe the lowest level which a river can attain. This is usually sea-level or temporarily the surface of a lake.

lowering of that base-line or an abrupt elevation of the plateau, the river must have acquired a steeper grade in a short time and begun to dig itself in. In the process, the meanders were submerged in the mountain massif and the river concentrated all its energy upon cutting downwards. It had no reserves of strength to enable it to make lateral diversions, which would have

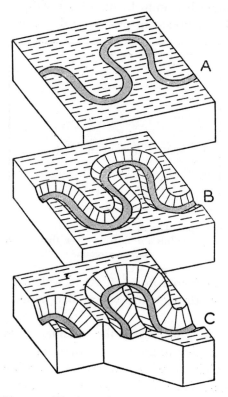

entailed the transportation of far more material. The effect of centrifugal force is balanced by the tendency of the river to restrict the length of its bed to the utmost by always seeking the steepest gradients.

Once the incision of a river has reached a depth which leaves insufficient grade for continued vertical erosion, energy becomes available for the slow work of pushing the curves out sideways. The centrifugal force is now able to dominate the greatly weakened tendency of the river to shorten its course and to direct erosion upon the concave banks. Almost imperceptibly a wider valley with a flat floor evolves and the meander-belt is very slowly levelled down in the same way as with free meanders (Figs. 152 and 153). The Liese at Manderscheid in the Eifel is an example of a little river working over the meander-belt in the initial stages of this process.

Fig. 151. The formation of incised meanders by vertical erosion due to lowering of base-level of erosion. The profile is symmetrical since all the erosive power of the river is spent in lowering its bed.

In other instances the raising of the plateau proceeded at a slower pace and the gradient of the river never increased rapidly. The centrifugal force continued to be operative while the valley meanders were being entrenched and so a certain amount of energy was available for lateral erosion. This attack, of course, occurs predominantly where the curvature of the meanders is most pronounced, which is generally at their outer extremities. The result is that, although the meanders approximately maintain their position, i.e. do not shift downstream, they are constantly increasing in amplitude; the outside valley wall is being continually undermined and retreats; consequently the meander-belt widens. The slope on the inside of the bend is much gentler, because this is the grade down which the meander slides off (Fig. 155). They are, in fact, called *sliding meanders*.

Really vertically cut meanders, like those in Fig. 156, are rare, but sliding meanders are quite common. Variants are known from vertically entrenched meanders, via slightly asymmetrical valleys (Fig. 154), to meander valleys which must have been formed from almost straight river courses.

In course of time the vertical component of sliding meanders will likewise be spent and from that moment the horizontal movement alone will remain, as with incised meanders. The shifting bends then erode wider and wider loops until they finally develop a wide, virtually straight valley.

Complicated forms are produced if the area undergoes a fresh uplift or the sea-level is depressed, hence if the base-level of erosion is lowered during the development of a wide flat-floored valley, or afterwards. In that event, the river is obliged to cut down all over again, leaving terraces along the second generation of incised meanders. There are extant examples of the development of several terrace levels one below the other. Very powerful agents in this respect were the variations in sea-level initiated in the Glacial Period.

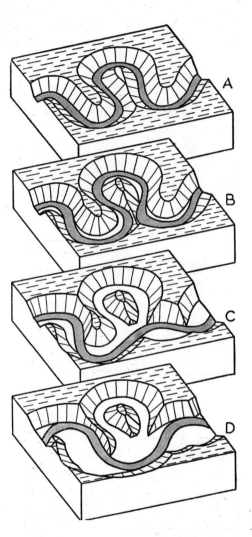

Fig. 152. After the river has attained a profile of equilibrium, energy is once more available for lateral erosion resulting in the formation of cut-offs and a gradual widening in the canyon valley.

Transport and Deposition

There are two main sources from which a river obtains the material which it transports, viz., its bed, from which it detaches material, and the banks and valley walls, from which material tumbles in. A river flowing through a wide, flat valley, with banks consisting of sand, gravel and clay deposits, requires little energy to detach particles and sweep them along.

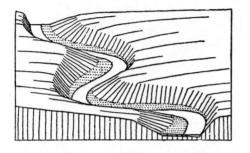

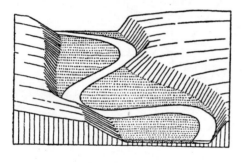

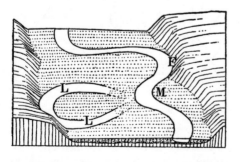

As a rule the load is derived from the older deposits laid down at an earlier stage by the stream itself. But when a river flows over a rocky bed, the slow, laborious work of erosion is carried out by the sediment as it scours and batters the bed.

A stream, however, can only erode the rock with which it is in direct contact. Once the cleft has been sawn to some depth, the upstanding sides projecting above the surface of the water are henceforth immune from any direct abrasion by the river. In fact, all river valleys would remain narrow gorges if denudation and gravity did not lend a helping hand. In the result, fragments of rock are weathered, detached and roll down. Moss and other vegetation begin to cover up the gaping wounds; roots worm their way into cracks and prise the rock open. In a word, the sides of the chasm are attacked and are eaten away. As the walls of the cleft slope backwards, a narrow, V-shaped valley is formed which widens more and more (Figs. 157 and 158).

Fig. 153. A continuation of the process shown in Fig. 152 results in the incised river forming a wide, straight valley. (After Davis.)

At first, all the loosened boulders, fragments and smaller particles, the

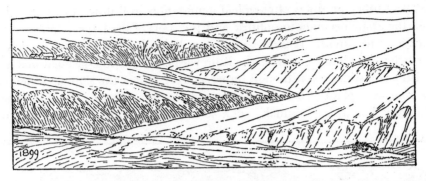

Fig. 154. Incised meanders of the Tardes River (Corrèze, Central France), with almost symmetrical contours. (After Davis.)

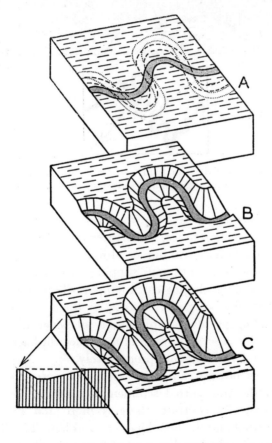

Fig. 155. Sliding meanders formed when vertical and lateral erosion takes place simultaneously. Note the asymmetrical profile.

clay and other products of chemical denudation, roll down the slopes; but soon the angle becomes too obtuse and the roots of the larger plants hold it back to some extent. This does not mean, however, that the destruction of the valley sides has been arrested. Rain washes off the fine-grained material and the soil slides, even though imperceptibly, down the slopes. Wherever the root of a plant penetrates downwards, only to die and moulder later; wherever burrowing animals, such as insects, worms, rabbits, etc., dig

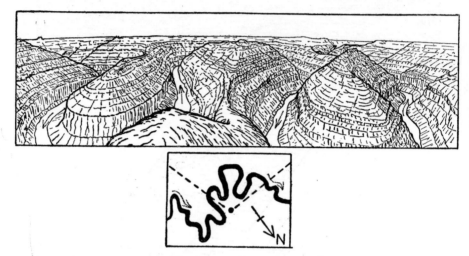

Fig. 156. Valley meanders of the San Juan Canyon, Utah, incised to a depth of about 1300 ft. in horizontal strata with symmetrical valley profile. (From a photograph.)

tunnels, which subsequently cave in; whenever frost causes water to expand in the ground by freezing it to ice, which afterwards melts again; in all these places and instances gravity will induce ultimately a downward movement, an exceedingly slow but continuous slipping, which is called the *creep* of the soil. The layer of weathering earth temporarily protects the underlying rock, but is perpetually being carried away by the action of creep and thus affords the denuding agents an opportunity of penetrating to ever lower levels. Owing to this process the sides of the valley tilt back more and more and the valley therefore widens out progressively.

As a river flows downstream, the volume of water increases and the granular size of the transported sediment diminishes. Both facts should facilitate transport. By contrast, there is more and more sedimentary material to be carried and the bed slopes less and less. This flattening of the bed has the effect of reducing the speed of flow and, therefore, of depriving the river of much of its carrying capacity.

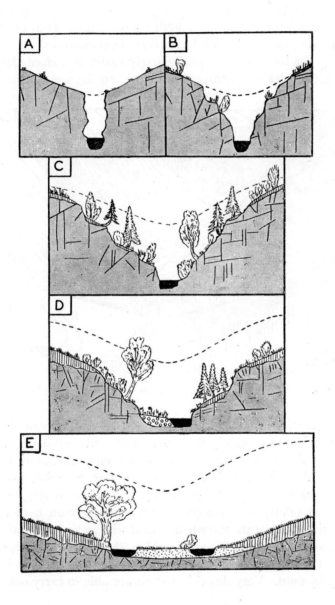

Fig. 157. The gradual widening of a cleft into a gently sloping valley by denudation (weathering, creep and rain wash and lateral erosion).

The reduction in the size of the grains is due to three causes. First of all, the sedimentary fragments are worn down in transit. The larger fragments roll along the bed and the smaller ones jump from point to point or are even lifted entirely off the bed by the eddying movements. Thus the farther the material travels, the smaller will be its component elements.

Secondly, the land becomes progressively flatter as a river approaches its mouth and the work of whittling down elevations is carried on more slowly.

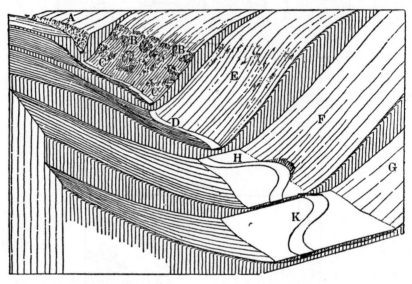

Fig. 158. Successive stages in the evolution of a river valley. (After Davis.)

The coarse kind of denudation which attacks mountainous districts, the weapons of which are mainly frost, waterfalls and seething mountain torrents that break off large boulders, gives way more and more to chemical corrosion of the rocks. This produces very fine material, loose mineral granules or submicroscopic flakes of clay. From the outset, therefore, the new sediment offered for transport farther downstream is of far smaller grain than the material the river had to deal with in the mountains.

Thirdly, as the velocity of flow diminishes, the burden is dropped and left behind; first the larger boulders, then cobbles as well, followed by gravel and finally by sand. Very sluggish streams are able to carry only the finest clay.

A river deposits sedimentary material *within* its bed, *at the sides* of its bed, and at the *end* of its bed.

Deposition of sediment *in a river-bed* is sometimes the result of diminishing volume of water towards the mouth if evaporation and drainage to the ground-water in an area through which the river flows predominate over direct and indirect supply from precipitation. In these arid regions the river possesses less and less carrying capacity as it proceeds downstream and drops its burden piece by piece.

Deposition in the bed is only temporary and local as a rule, due to the waters usually sinking again after a flood and becoming sluggish or even stagnating, e.g. at bends or behind landslides from the banks. Part of the burden is then left behind until some later circumstances provide an opportunity for its removal. Either the banks are raised in this way, or bars are formed in the river, which become gravel banks or sand banks, depending on the size of the grains.

Deposition in the bed can, therefore, also take place in a narrow valley; indeed, it is characteristically developed in the upper and middle courses.

In general, bars move from place to place in the bed of a stream, sometimes travelling downstream, sometimes up. The former occurs when there is comparatively little available sediment, as the water then picks up material at the upper end, drags it over the bar and deposits it again in the still water on the lee-side. If there is plenty of sediment, with a large component of coarse-grained material, the bars shift upstream. Pebbles come rolling down and are plastered against the upstream end of a bar, while here and there at the free lower end the stream may be able to dislodge particles and roll them away to the next bar.

If bar-building takes place on an ample scale and the available valley

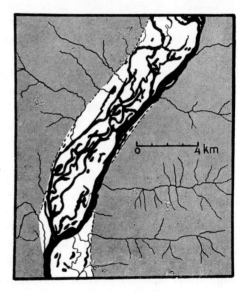

Fig. 159. The Mississippi at Prairie du Chien, showing braiding. River in black and higher ground in grey.

floor is wide, the river piles the bars up to a considerable height, divides and passes around them on either side. The river is said to braid (Fig. 159). It is only at high water that the bars are covered, when the swollen stream swirls down the valley in one coherent mass. As soon as the level drops, the picture reverts to its former character of interlacing branches, though the distribution of the bars may have altered quite considerably (Plate XVI, 2).

Some rivers are permanently overburdened, e.g. where they flow through unconsolidated deposits. It is volcanic débris which overloads the Icelandic rivers, for instance, causing them to braid.

In a narrow valley or under a stream carrying a smaller load, the bars are mostly, if not always, submerged, in which case the undivided river presents a solid mass of water.

Sediment can of course only be deposited *beside the bed* if the floor of the valley is wide enough, and only during floods. When a river bursts its banks, the rapid, turbulent flow in the normal bed has churned up a large amount of

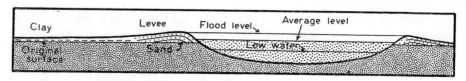

Fig. 160. Cross-section of a river flowing across a low-lying plain, with levees.

sand and clay and the water is laden with a great deal of sediment. As soon as it overflows, the increased friction underneath the shallow flood slows down the speed; eddying ceases and the coarsest components, i.e. sand and, maybe, some fine gravel, are immediately deposited along the edge of the normal bed. All that the sluggish current outside the deep bed can transport is the cloud of fine, clayey substance.

The coarse material forms natural dykes, called *levees*, along the normal bed of the river (Fig. 160), sometimes rising to quite considerable heights. Under ordinary conditions, the level of the Mississippi in its lower course is approximately the same as that of the terrain beyond the levees. It is only at rather high water levels that the river tops these natural dykes; hence the height of the latter approximately marks the difference between high water and the normal level, namely, 15 feet. This is not very much compared with the depth in the central part of this powerful stream, which is 180 to 200 feet, or with its width, which is a mile.

Just because the levees ordinarily provide adequate protection, the exceptional flood is the more disastrous when it occurs. Numerous natural spill-ways are then formed and vast expanses of the surrounding plain inundated. Worse still, the flooding waters have no means of returning whence they came, even if the level of the river drops considerably. There they remain, stagnant, until ultimately part has percolated through the soil and part has evaporated. Thus the whole of the fine silt is deposited outside the levees.

The levees of the Red River stand out clearly in Fig. 134. It will be recalled that the lakes resulted from the natural damming of the river and the strip of higher-lying country can be seen alongside the stream, dividing the Red River from the inundated valley-floor beside it.

The silt thus deposited by many rivers is very fertile, a familiar example being the Nile, the banks of which sustain a dense agricultural population. The great Assuan Barrage has effectively averted the ravages of floods and holds the surplus of water in reserve for irrigation during droughts. The benefits of this curbing of nature are considerable, but the penalty incurred is that fertile mud is no longer spread over the land, the adverse effect of which cannot fail to make itself felt increasingly as the years go by.

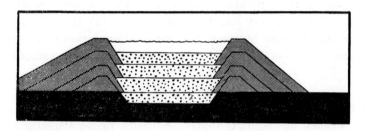

Fig. 161. Gradual elevation of an embanked river through deposition of sediment. Unless such a river is dredged, it is necessary to regularly increase the height of the embankments.

Another human intervention is the building of dykes to prevent damaging spates. These contain the fine mud within the swift-flowing section and it is transported right down to the mouth. Some of the coarser material, how-ever, remains behind and raises the level of the river-bed. Dredging then becomes necessary, as in the Netherlands, where every year 40 million cubic feet of sand and gravel are brought across the frontier by the Rhine and the same quantity is scooped up out of the river and used for building purposes. In many rivers the sediment is allowed to accumulate between the dykes, which necessitates periodically increasing their height. Eventually the river flows in an aqueduct, the floor of which lies some distance above the level of the surrounding area (Fig. 161). It is hardly necessary to say that this creates a dangerous situation which has in the long run to be brought to a halt by either deepening or shifting the bed.

It will be clear from the foregoing that a river is perpetually *exchanging* its load. It deposits material, only to take up new sediment in its place; bars are formed and deposition proceeds in quiet bends; elsewhere obstructions are cleared away and the banks are undermined. This alternating process infinitely prolongs the journey of any particles of sediment from the place where they are first picked up to their ultimate destination, the sea. After being transported some distance, a boulder may remain in a bar for years or centuries before it is cleared away. Now a grain of sand will roll along the rippled bed, bouncing from crest to crest; then it will lie undisturbed for a long time between some stones, in a sandbank in the middle of the stream, or the river bank. Clay particles are the only kind of sediment likely to be carried without interruption from high upstream to the lower reaches; but once arrived there, their further progress will tend to be similarly intermittent with long pauses punctuated by advances.

This interchanging of the river's load has yet another consequence, namely thorough intermingling of all the material carried by the stream. When a tributary passing through abnormal types of rock, empties sediment of a completely different nature into the main stream, this starts by settling out and is then mixed piece by piece into the existing deposits. Hence in this respect transport is effected by a river in the same way as by a glacier.

Deltas

There remains to be considered the deposition of material at the terminal of a river, i.e. the formation of deltas. Actually, deltas are largely formed, especially with very big rivers, not by deposition in front of the river's mouth, but by sedimentation on the banks of its lower reaches, as was shown in the preceding paragraphs. Clarity, however, will be better served by dealing with delta formation as a single process.

Friction and flocculation are the two causes of speedy deposition of sediment outside the mouth of a river. First of all, flow is arrested and all the pebbles which had been carried along are left lying at the mouth. Naturally, the sand in suspension also settles out immediately. A talus is formed, the gradient of which corresponds approximately to the steepest angle at which the material can be stacked under water. Thus the next load brought along rolls down a slope at the edge of the delta. This angle for gravel and sand amounts to roughly 30°, but if finer-grained material is mixed with them, the angle is much smaller and such deposits will not settle at an angle of more than a few degrees.

As large fragments are laid down in most small deltas situated in mountain lakes, the fronts of such dumps are steep. Furthermore, clay cannot settle out so quickly in a lake and is also far less in evidence in the river sediments of steep regions with rapid erosion. For this reason, too, a mountain lake contains very few soft, slope-reducing components.

At the lower end of a great river, clay is the principal constituent of the sedimentary load; moreover, sea-water induces clay to ball together into minute lumps and these settle much faster. This is called the "flocculation" of clay. For the reasons given, the delta of a river advancing into the sea will be rich in plastic clay and will slope gently down. In addition, the fresh water of the river floats on the sea-water, which is heavier, spreading like a huge pancake on the coastal waters before mixing, with the accompanying flocculation of the clay, takes place. This also helps to reduce the frontal slope of great marine deltas.

Wave action is another factor, perpetually rounding off the periphery of the structure and pushing the sediments from the mouth of the river towards

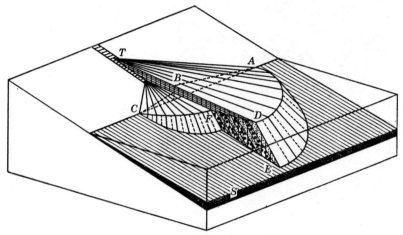

Fig. 162. Formation of an ideal delta on a steep bank. The strata deposited at the maximum angle of rest (foresets) are shown in FDE whilst S is the bottom sediment. Although TBA rests on dry land it must be considered as part of the topset of the delta TDF. The part C represents an earlier stage of growth.

both sides along the beach of the delta, thus assisting the delta front to grow uniformly in all directions.

We have already seen (page 242) what happens when cold, silt-laden water runs into a lake and how this diving current may cut gullies into the front of the delta.

Three types of deposit can be distinguished in the growth of a delta (Fig. 162). The front strata, or *foreset* beds, have just been described and constitute the typical delta-makers with the steepest dip. But in front of these foresets fine silt comes to be deposited, serving as a foundation for the foresets that are extending farther forward. These are the *bottomsets*. Then there are the *topset* beds, which are the normal river-bank deposits laid down upon the delta. Just as the bottomsets farther out gradually merge into the ordinary deposits of the lake or sea-floor, so also do the topsets of the delta merge upstream by degrees into the river deposits. Dropping down a large river, one may well have arrived at the topsets long before one is aware of having reached the delta.

Owing to the steady advance of the delta front, the gradient of the river in its lower course must become progressively less. Finally a lateral slope from the delta apex will become a shorter and, therefore, steeper path to sea-level. At some favourable spot the river will then burst its banks and seek another route to the sea. If this in turn becomes too long and flat, some new

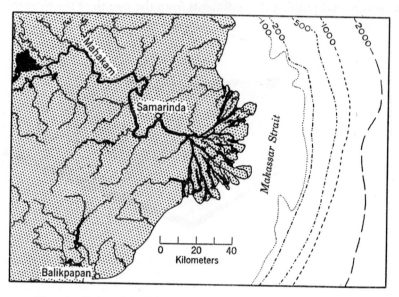

Fig. 163. Delta of the River Mahakam on the east coast of Borneo.

way out will be tried. That is how the river runs now this way then that over the delta, thus building on to it in all directions in an ever-widening arc towards the sea. It is quite a normal occurrence, moreover, for many branches to be simultaneously active, so that the river divides into a number of distributaries in the delta area (Fig. 163).

The fact that the growth of the delta does not eliminate the gradient implies that the total thickness of the successive topset beds must increase in step with the spread of the delta seawards; the topsets must go on growing upstream and extend far beyond the region of the actual delta. It eventually becomes impossible to tell where the delta begins and where the normal river banks end.

A glance at maps of large deltas will show a variety of shape. At one end of the scale there are deltas like those of the Nile, Mahakam and Niger,

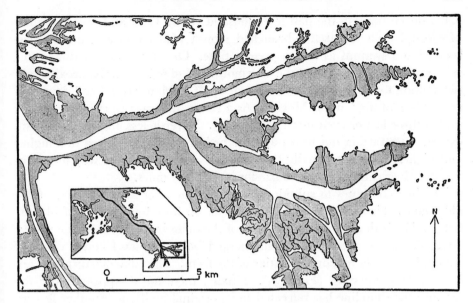

Fig. 164. Part of the Mississippi Delta. The levees project above the water.

which answer fairly well to the above description and can be compared with the small models to be seen and admired in mountain lakes. At the other extreme there is the delta of the Mississippi. This river breaks up into many distributaries, each of which travels far out to sea between two arms of land which are the levees of the river here deposited on the sea-floor (Figs. 164 and 165).

Recent study of the Mississippi delta has resulted in some very remarkable discoveries. The river has completely changed its course in the lower reaches

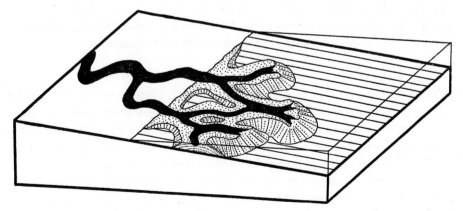

Fig. 165. Diagrammatic representation of a delta of the Mississippi type, in shallow water.

half a dozen times in the past few thousand years. Over and over again the Mississippi built for itself a branched mouth with levees and interspersed lagoons and swamps as at the present time. On each occasion the earth's crust sagged, unable to bear the enormous load of sediment. Approximately two million tons are daily carried down by "Ol' Man River" and deposited at the edge of the Gulf of Mexico. As a result, the crust warps down at the rate of three feet or even more per century. Nevertheless, the ramified delta extends ever farther out to sea and the bed of the river is raised to a higher and higher level, until finally there is a break-through some way upstream and the river chooses a new course for its last fifty miles.

The bed continues to subside for a long time after abandonment of the old course. First, the natural dykes break up into double rows of islands, while a bar is thrown up on the front of the delta by the wash of the waves. Next, the levees are gradually submerged below sea-level and a chain of islands is the only remaining vestige of the front. The Chandeleur island arc has reached this stage (Fig. 135). Finally, these too disappear under the sea and the shoreline has retreated to its original position. Another feature characteristic of the subsidence is the forming of lakes alongside the lower reaches, as, for example, Grand Lake and Ponchartrain near New Orleans, the beds of which still lay high and dry after the beginning of our era.

The silting-up of the Gulf of Mexico by the Mississippi has been going on for millions of years and the Gulf would be very much smaller if the earth's crust were less flexible, and the marine bed here were not for ever subsiding under the load. The delta is estimated to be 30,000 feet thick at the very least, hence extending beneath the floor of the Mexican Gulf to a distance about twice the depth of the Gulf water.

This subsiding movement is not peculiar to the Mississippi delta, for submerged land is found on both sides of many others. Lakes are then formed, as e.g., along the lower reaches of the Mississippi and the Danube, or lagoons, as on the Po, Nile and Rhône, to mention only a few examples.

Fans of Débris

These are closely akin to deltas. They form at places where a fast-flowing stream laden with much detritus suddenly discharges from a narrow, steep valley onto a plain or a wide valley with a broad, flat floor. At such junctures the velocity of flow is abruptly reduced to a fraction, with the result that the load becomes far too heavy for further transportation. A steep cone of sediment is then built up at the exit of the valley; it is called a fan to distinguish it from the screes of weathered débris which are piled up, without the intervention of running water, at the foot of rocky slopes. In the case of deltas, the dividing water level separates the foresets from the topsets, but the fan is constructed in a body by the stream out in the air and there are therefore no contrasting slightly inclined and strongly inclined deposits.

Apart from this, the two forms are closely allied, since the fan also grows with continual shifting of the bed of the stream. The angle of inclination depends upon the circumstances. A small stream carrying coarse-grained waste develops a far steeper cone than a large stream containing finer sediment. As the largest components of the load will always remain behind at the mouth of the valley, the internal structure of the fan will not be uniform. It consists of outward-sloping coarse beds fanning out between deposits of finer material which become thicker towards the foot of the slope.

Fig. 166. Cross-section of an alluvial fan with permeable strata providing artesian wells.

For this reason cones of débris are able to absorb a large amount of ground-water, which gushes liberally when borings are made at the thin end of the coarse-grained beds (Fig. 166).

These fans of débris are conspicuous features in many of the Alpine valleys. So large and thick are they in some cases as they emerge from the tributary glens into the main valley, that they push the river in the latter over to the opposite side. Then again, the meanders of the main river may cut into their periphery leaving steep notches (Fig. 167).

The Profile of Equilibrium

It follows from the process of transport as described that a stream does not necessarily at once carry down to lower sections the whole of the load it receives from above. It takes as much as it can carry and leaves the rest behind. If its carrying capacity temporarily increases during floods, more material will be set in motion, for there is plenty of sediment everywhere waiting to be picked up. During the preliminary work for the building of Boulder Dam in the Colorado River, fresh tree trunks were found to be embedded some tens of yards down in the sedimentary deposits of the river, eloquent evidence, indeed, of the fact that in a recent spate the whole mass of sediment lodged at the bottom of the gorge-like valley must have been set in motion and well mixed.

A river only has surplus energy available in places where its carrying capacity exceeds the load it has to deal with, and that surplus energy is generally used up in the erosion of its rocky bed, which has then been swept

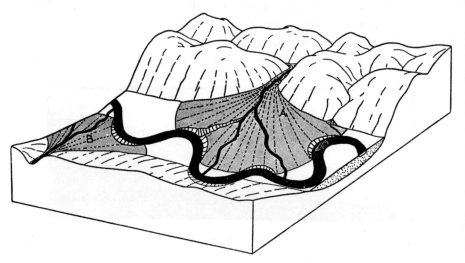

Fig. 167. Alluvial fans formed by tributaries entering a broad trough valley. The large fan A has pushed the main stream to a point where it is eroding the opposite side of the valley.

more or less clean and is exposed to abrasion and deepened. As a result, the gradient and carrying capacity of the river decrease at this spot, but upstream they must increase, so that there is an increment in supply coupled with diminishing capacity until equilibrium is restored.

If, conversely, more sediment is constantly being brought down than the river can cope with at that site, the surplus remains behind, piling up as the years pass. Now the reverse takes place to what occurs with erosion, for with a steepening gradient the river will have greater carrying capacity, this going hand in hand with a slowing-down of the current farther upstream, and, therefore, of supply.

It will be seen, then, that the processes taking place in a river tend to establish a state of equipoise, in the sense that through every cross-section the load brought downstream is not larger than the quantity transportable at the next point. Circumstances, however, do not permit this ultimate result to be attained simultaneously along the whole course of the river.

In the upper course the load delivered is as a rule too small in proportion to the fast current and the immense carrying capacity this imparts to the river. In those reaches, therefore, erosion will be the main work done by the running water. In the middle course the two factors balance each other and the object is therefore achieved. Through every cross-section the average amount of sediment carried away every year is the same as that brought

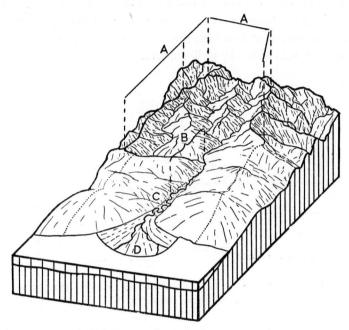

Fig. 168. Mountain stream discharging into lake. A upper reaches, the catchment area; B middle reaches; C winding lower course; D delta.

down from higher up. Moreover, owing to the increasing size of the area draining through the river and the growing capacity this confers, the load in the middle course also gradually increases downstream. The current loses so much speed in the lower course that even the load consisting of fine material can no longer be transported in its entirety and deposition is therefore constantly taking place.

When drainage is developing on a continent after a new and well-marked relief has been created by mountain-building forces, the system will at first be more or less chaotic, comprising a succession of rapids, waterfalls, flat stretches with little grade, or even a slope in the reverse direction giving rise to the formation of a lake. Where the current runs swiftly, gorges and narrow valleys will be cut, while the sediment will be transported to the lakes and flatter reaches. In a comparatively short time, geologically speaking, most inequalities however accentuated, are ironed out, and the rivers run down a more or less regular slope to the sea. Actually, the formation of the relief and the development of the river system go hand in hand, for a mountain chain is not uplifted to thousands of feet in one day. The running water has time enough to adapt its bed in broad outline to changing circumstances during the hundred thousand to million years needed for the uplift, often interrupted by even longer periods of quiescence. When the internal terrestrial forces are temporarily at rest, the river has leisure to attend to minutiæ until finally a system of a very uniform character is brought into being.

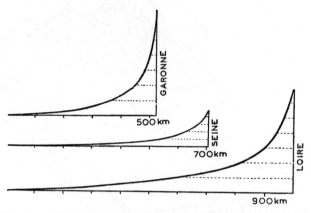

Fig. 169. Profiles of equilibrium of three French rivers rising in non-glacial areas. Horizontal lines 100 m apart.

If the height, as from the mouth, is plotted against the distance in a graph, a smooth curve will be the result. The gradient being too slight to be clearly perceptible, it is common practice to exaggerate the height greatly (e.g. × 500). The result is a curve with the steepest part at the source and the flattest part at the mouth. Once a river has smoothed out all the kinks in this line, a kind of equilibrium supervenes and the ideal of adequate carrying power to cope with the load of débris at every point is then as nearly attained as it is ever likely to be. The term for this state of affairs is *curve of equilibrium* or *profile of equilibrium* (Fig. 169).

The slope will flatten more and more during subsequent development, because little by little the combined action of river erosion and denudation of the slopes tends to lower the surface of the land. The exact shape of the line and whether it will be more concave or more nearly approach a straight line during the development depend upon so many factors that there can be no certainty as to the ultimate picture. A river, moreover, has a very long history, so that a variety of happenings may intervene, again and again post-poning the consummation of the ideal profile of equilibrium. Chief among these obstructionist agencies are glaciation, uplift and tilting of part of, or the whole system, rising and falling of sea-level, volcanic activity, faulting and folding of the crust. There will be one more to consider presently, known as "piracy". Indeed, it is safe to assume that no river course of appreciable extent has ever been able to develop in a body without some let or hindrance somewhere; hence that the curve of equilibrium represents the reciprocal adaptation of numerous segments, each with its own history of evolution. The surprising fact is that one finds so many profile lines vary-ing very little from a smooth curve.

Gradients and Speeds

Actually the gradient of a river is usually very small, and extremely so in its lower course. That of the lower Mississippi is so small that it does not compensate for the flattened shape of the globe, so that the water actually travels farther from the centre of the earth as it flows south. The mean slope of the Rhine from its source to Bale is $1\frac{1}{2}$ in 100, but the gradient from Ruhrort to Rotterdam is no more than 1 in 10,000, i.e. half a foot per mile. In the Hungarian plain the rivers fall only 3 inches per mile. For all that, these mild slopes are capable of imparting considerable velocity to the waters of a great river. The velocity in mountain torrents seldom exceeds 15–18 feet per second, yet the Seine flows at 2 feet per second near Paris and the Rhine at 6–10 feet per second during spate in the vicinity of Strassburg, to mention only two examples.

Pot-holes

One detail of the development of the profile of equilibrium remains to be discussed. Water in mountainous country usually flows swiftly and tur-bulently, its movements being exceedingly erratic. In whirlpools the swirl-ing water laden with sand will drill a round hole in solid rock. These *pot-holes* vary in size from an inch or two to several feet in diameter and are sometimes quite deep compared with their width. Rapids are liable to be so riddled with them that the intermediate partitions eventually break down and the pot-holes are thus strung together. The ultimate picture is that of a narrow gorge, the walls of which everywhere bear the marks of their pot-hole origin. It looks for all the world as though a great many chunks of rock have been scooped out with a half-turn of a huge ladle, for the sides are grooved horizontally with shallow notches several feet high. The major-ity of the Swiss gorges ("Klammen" and "Schluchten") owe their origin to the formation of these pot-holes. They often carve their way across rock sills left lying in the valleys by glaciers of the Ice Age.

The formation of pot-holes takes a comparatively short time. Sometimes this is known for a particular instance, e.g. when it can be watched in progress after diverting a stream into a new course. Thus holes 10 feet deep were cut out of limestone in eighteen months, while it took 75 years to excavate holes 5 feet deep in granite.

Watersheds and Headward Erosion

In the accepted term, a river basin comprises the whole area feeding the stream, irrespective of whether drainage occurs at ground level or below ground. We already know that much of the water in a river does not derive

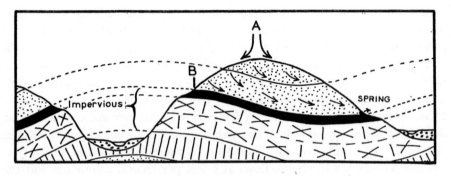

Fig. 170. Undefined watershed: A, watershed for surface water, B that for ground-water.

from the surface of the ground, but has been supplied via the ground-water in the adjacent soil. The confines of a basin can be traced by drawing a line beside a river along all the extremities from which ground-water or surface water is still absorbed. That line is often at the same time the extreme boundary for drainage towards the opposite side by another river system and in that case it is correct to use the term *watershed*. Needless to say, this follows the highest ridges and peaks of the mountains and hills.

It may be, however, that the basins of two rivers separate locally, leaving behind an area which does not drain at all because all the precipitation is consumed by evaporation. Delineation of the watershed is further complicated if surface drainage discharges into a different river system from that into which the ground-water runs (Fig. 170). In extensive limestone regions the erratic drainage by cave rivers bears little relation to surface topography.

All river basins have a tendency to expand, because draining water causes wear and tear, so that the sides of the valley begin to tilt backwards. When *erosion* is said to be *working headward*, it is denudation and not water erosion which is usually mainly responsible. Consider a flat plateau draining largely by means of percolating ground-water. Somewhere a stream may first begin to cut into the slope and subsequently, by headward erosion, be able to excavate deeper and deeper into the pleatau, attracting an increasing proportion of the precipitation (Fig. 171).

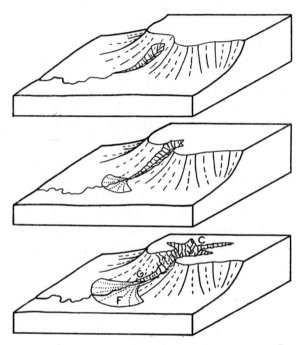

Fig. 171. A mountain stream cutting back by headward erosion into a plateau. C catchment area; G drainage channel; F alluvial fan.

Normally, however, on both sides of the divide, a river system is working at pushing back the surrounding walls. Neither basin will have an opportunity to enlarge itself, but the watershed will be lowered and the mountain chain therefore eaten away by degrees. One of the two may work at an advantage if, say, its base-line of erosion is at a lower level—which implies a steeper gradient—or if precipitation falls predominantly on that side. The favoured system will then be able to enlarge its territory at the expense of its rival, small though the resulting difference may be.

Piracy or Beheading

Under auspicious conditions, however, a river may abruptly capture a

T

considerable portion of its neighbour's territory. This happens when head-ward erosion, as it cuts back, succeeds in completely consuming the water-shed in the middle of the other's basin, thereby tapping the whole of the drainage upstream of that point. This process is sometimes called *beheading*, though the subject is often the head of a tributary to the neighbour's system. An attacker seldom succeeds in capturing a main stream.

Once the decapitation is an established fact, the gain in volume of water to the robber is so outstanding that the victim stands no chance of ever recovering its lost domain, and is likely to be deprived of more of its basin later on, handicapped as it will be for ensuing battles by the aggravation of already adverse circumstances.

At a casual glance, no traces will be discoverable of a beheading con-summated long ago. At the site of the conquest, the robber-river soon adapted itself to the new situation. The passage from one system into the other is unobtrusive and the valleys have also been smoothed by denuda-tion. Closer observation will, however, reveal certain abnormalities pro-viding evidence. For instance, at the site of the event, the river may take a sharp bend and proceed in a different general direction. This *elbow* is clearly the junction at which the two coalesced sections of different river systems join. Or else a fairly uniform valley drains partly in one direction and partly in the opposite one and the volume of water is insignificant in proportion to the size of the valley. This would be the first section below the decapitation of the original course.

Finally, the sedimentary deposits of a river may be found to contain alien fragments of rock, obviously derived from a neighbouring stream, because that particular kind of rock is non-existent in its own basin. The inference must be that the source of the pebbles formerly did belong to the basin of the river's own system, but was lost through piracy.

All these facts are represented by the classical example of the basin of the Meuse. Formerly the upper course of the Moselle above the elbow at Toul belonged to it (Fig. 172). At present the two rivers are connected by a wide, flat valley. Close to the Meuse there is a swamp, on either side of which insignificant brooks flow into the two rivers. A railroad and a canal utilise this natural gap through the watershed between the Rhine and the Meuse. The gravel deposits of the Meuse and the subsoil of this transverse valley contain fragments of a material found only in the present-day Moselle valley in the Vosges mountains. It is even possible to tell by the asym-metry of the incised meanders of the connecting valley that they were eroded by a great river which flowed from Toul to Pagny, and not in the reverse direction (Fig. 173).

The Meuse has, moreover, unquestionably been deprived of a considerable volume of water below the point where beheading took place. The
valley presents the shape of bold, incised meanders, but the present river
does not fit them. It zigzags along, swerving now towards the concave and
then towards the convex meander walls.

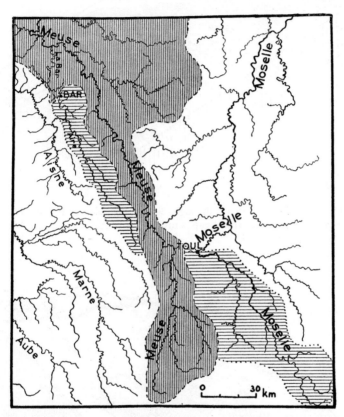

Fig. 172. The "beheading" of the former Meuse by the Moselle at Toul, and of a former
tributary by the Aisne at Bar. The present basin of the Meuse is indicated by vertical,
the lost basins by horizontal, shading.

A second instance is at Bar (Argonne, south of Sédan). The Aire used to be
the upper course of the present stream La Bar, a tributary on the left of the
Meuse. At one time the Aisne, a tributary of the Seine, succeeded in capturing the Aire via a small side-arm (Fig. 172). The marked declivity and
deep incision of the stream between Bar and the Aire and of the latter itself
furnish evidence of beheading, in the sense that the Aisne owed its success
in robbing the Meuse to the fact that the former, flowing at a level 170 feet

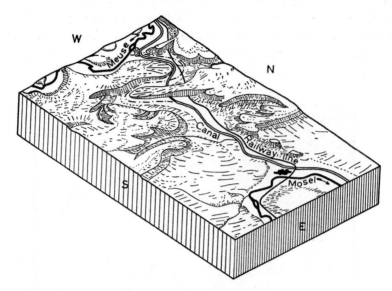

Fig. 173. The abandoned valley, through which the Meuse flowed before its upper reaches were captured. The natural gap is utilised for communications. (After Escher.)

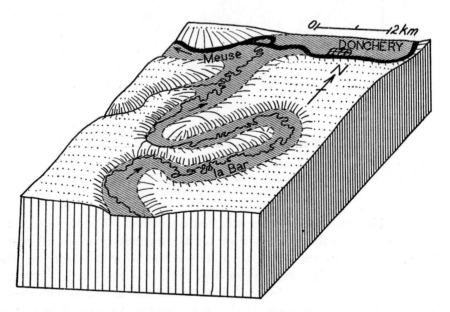

Fig. 174. The Bar, weakened by decapitation, forms small, more numerous meanders within the confines of the original incised valley.

lower, provided a steep declivity for its tributary streams, which were thus able to cut back vigorously. Once the capture had been made, this lower base-line of erosion effected a deep incision of the new members of the system.

Between Bar and the Aire Valley a brook now flows in the opposite direction. The declivity at that village is so imperceptible that in the eighteenth century engineers were able to drain the upper course of La Bar into the Aire to supply water for a factory, with the result that Bar, the village,

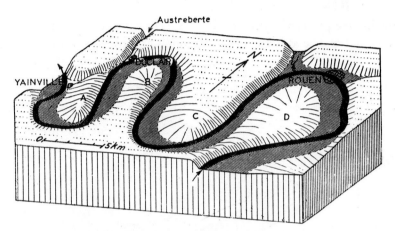

Fig. 175. Active meanders of the Seine below Rouen. The Austreberte, which formerly entered the Seine at the present site of Yainville, has been "captured" by the swerve of the meander at Duclair. Note that the upstream facing sides of the ridges A, B, C are the steeper. The levelling of the meander belt has just begun.

is no longer situated on the rivulet La Bar. Thus man was an accessory to the robbery perpetrated by the Aire. Eventually the whole course of La Bar will be reversed and then the radical decapitation of the Meuse will be imminent.

Again, pebbles in the valley of La Bar bear witness to the fact that formerly the Aire drained in this direction. Like the truncated Meuse, the pitifully attenuated Bar looks puny in the old valley. The river threads its way in innumerable wrinkles along the generous loops of the formerly incised meanders. The striking difference between it and a river like the Seine, which is actively and steadily cutting out its bends, is at once evident on comparing Figs. 174 and 175.

It is in this way that the basin of the Meuse has become narrower and narrower until a mere strip has been left over between the systems of the Rhine and the Seine. And even this, as we know, will eventually be squeezed out of existence.

The Danube is another river which has been forced to surrender vast tracts to the tributaries of the Rhine. The Wutach and Neckar have already captured several of the Danube's former tributaries and, in a geological sense, it will not be long before one of the two will snatch the head of the river itself. Figs. 176 and 177 represent the position as it is today and as it is likely to become in the future.

Drainage Patterns

A distinctive pattern is discernible in the river systems of a landscape and even a casual glance at a few maps is enough to show how different they are

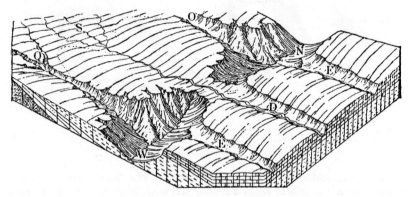

Fig. 176. Tributaries (OE and QE) of the upper course of the Danube SD in Baden, have been captured by the Neckar (N), and the Wutach (W), both tributaries of the Rhine. (After Davis.)

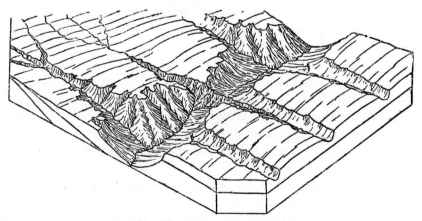

Fig. 177. Eventually the Danube itself will be beheaded by one of the marauding rivers as shown.

in design. The more outstanding patterns are: 1. dendritic (= branching tree-like), 2. pinnate (= feathered), 3. parallel, 4. radial, 5. trellised, 6. rectangular, 7. anastomosing (= intercommunicating).

1. *The dendritic pattern* (Fig. 178) branches at random, apparently, with no definite preference for any one direction, and minor branches flowing into another at every conceivable angle. The branching is reminiscent of that of an oak or of the root system visible on the clod of a pot-plant. Where the

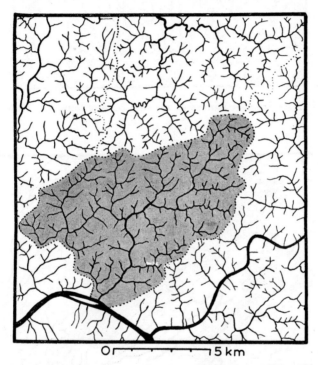

Fig. 178. Dendritic drainage pattern around Charleston, West Virginia.

dendritic pattern prevails, neither a general slope of the land surface nor an internal structure of the mountain chain has imposed any definite configuration upon the drainage system and the river has therefore been able to ramify uniformly over the whole surface.

2. *The pinnate pattern* (Fig. 179) strongly resembles the dendritic, except that all the main streams run to one side, with tributaries at an oblique angle to them, producing the pattern of a feather or a herring-bone. Usually it is the general slope of the land which induces this formation.

3. *The parallel pattern* (Fig. 180). This owes its origin to an even more pronounced inclination, resulting in both parallel main streams and tribu-

Fig. 179. Pinnate drainage pattern on the west coast of Sumatra. (After Zernitz.)

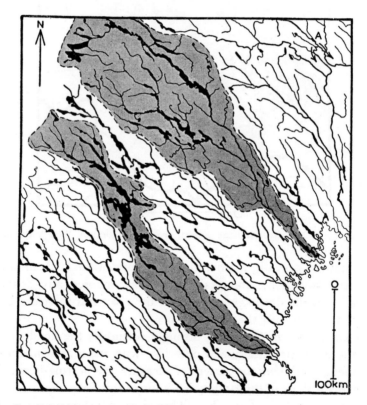

Fig. 180. Parallel drainage system in Northern Sweden. A in the north-east shows a dividing river.

taries. In other cases rivers come to lie parallel owing to the internal geological structure of the land or the ploughing of an ice-sheet.

4. *The radial pattern* (Fig. 181) consists of a number of streams radiating
from a central point. Adjacent channels, discharging into each other, form
systems of streams individually approaching the parallel type. This system
appears to have a predilection for volcanoes.

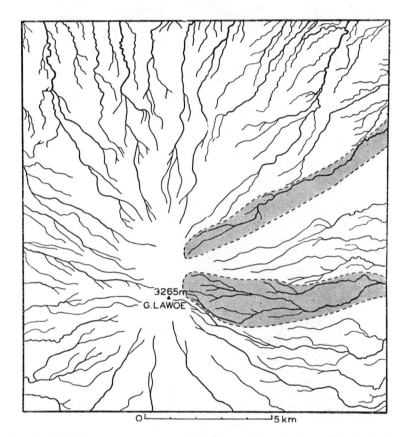

Fig. 181. Radial drainage pattern around the Lavu volcano in Java. The beginning of an
area of dividing river courses can be seen in the north-east.

5. *The trellis pattern* (Fig. 182) is distinguished by the predominance of one
particular orientation which is followed by some of the water courses
towards one side and by others to the opposite side. Other streams often
follow an orientation at right angles to this, likewise towards two opposite
directions. The internal geological structure of the area is responsible for
this behaviour. Thus, where there are parallel folds in the crust, parallel

ridges consisting of the harder rock strata will be raised in the landscape
after adequate denudation. Naturally, therefore, the valleys cut out between
the ridges will be parallel, while the water draining off the flanks of the
ridges will run perpendicular to the fold ridges.

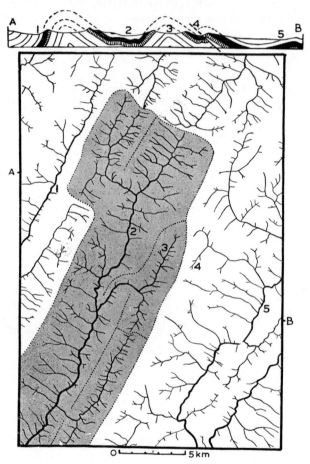

Fig. 182. Trellis-work drainage pattern around Montery, West Virginia. A vertical
section along the line A–B is shown above.

   6. *The rectangular pattern* (Fig. 183) shows two directions, approximately
at right angles, for which the rivers appear to have a preference. As a result
there are a great many 90° turns in the courses of the river with tributary
streams frequently discharging perpendicularly into the next larger generation. Two systems of faults in the crust are responsible for this. Within
each system, numerous parallel faults intersecting the rock and constituted

weak lines which attracted the stream beds step by step. Consequently, the majority of valleys follow for a certain distance the fault of one system and then abruptly jump over to a fault of the other.

The difference between this and the trellis-work pattern is that in the latter one direction predominates and a watercourse seldom takes a different direction, though it may discharge into a larger branch or be fed by smaller

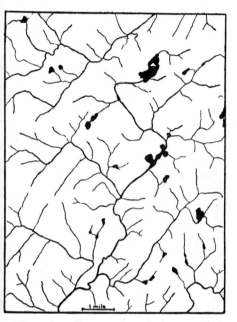

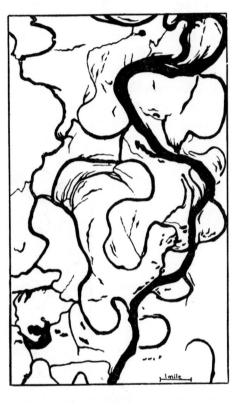

Fig. 183. Rectangular drainage pattern around Elizabethtown, N.Y. (After Zernitz.)

Fig. 184. Anastomosing drainage pattern in the Hungarian plain. (After Zernitz.)

branches following the opposite direction; while all streams running in one particular direction are of about the same order of magnitude or differ by two orders. The rectangular pattern follows no rule as to size of stream and direction, and one and the same branch may jump from one to the other direction several times in succession.

7. *The anastomosing pattern* (Figs. 184 and 185) occurs on plains, on deltas, and in tidal marshes. The rivers (or tidal channels) meander, abandoning numerous cut-off bends, while the number of watercourses and dead arms is increased by a certain tendency to braid. The differences in size of the streams, each with its own width of meander-belt, produce a highly com-

plicated pattern not unlike a jig-saw puzzle or the capillaries of the blood system.

A separate branch of earth science, called *geomorphology*, has grown around the whole body of speculation and literature, field observations and theoretical study devoted to the origin and development of valleys, both river and glacier. This science of the external features of the earth's crust, however, deals not only with the incisions cut into it, but with the topography of Mother Earth produced by uplift, faulting and folding, the action of the wind and of waves, in fact with all the internal and external geological factors which are responsible for the relief of the landscape. We have here been concerned with only one aspect of geomorphology, just as only those matters closely related to water in nature were invoked within the province of oceanography, meteorology and geology. We wish to stress this fact, maybe unnecessarily, so that the reader may realise that we lay no claim to having here surveyed the whole domain of those disciplines.

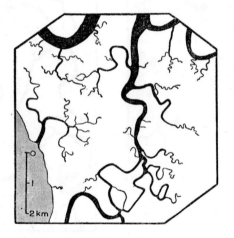

Fig. 185. Anastomosing tidal creeks in a New Guinea mangrove swamp. From an aerial photograph. The narrower branches were hidden under jungle.

VII

The Balance Sheet of Terrestrial Water

We have now completed the circle and, having studied the behaviour of water on the various stages of its journey, first in the oceans and then through the atmosphere, in glaciers and ground-water, we have returned with it in rivers to our point of departure. There are, however, three questions outstanding. One is whether there are any gains or losses in the course of the cycle, or whether the total amount of water on earth is constant. The second is whether the salinity of sea-water undergoes any change during geological history. The third is whether the distribution of water within the subdivisions of the cycle is subject to substantial variations. These are the three points to be considered in this last chapter.

The Total Amount of Terrestrial Water

The answer to the question whether water is lost to interstellar space is in the negative. While it is just possible that small amounts of light gases, like hydrogen and helium, escape from the outermost margin of the atmosphere, the heavy molecules of water vapour definitely do not. As we know, air at a high altitude is very dry; hence few, if any, water molecules occur as far out as the zone of waning gravitational force.

In theory, water could be reduced to its elements, oxygen and hydrogen, after which the light gas, hydrogen, could vanish very slowly into space. But even if this process did in fact take place the effect would be negligible in a quantitative sense.

There is, then, no loss of water from the earth. Against this, it can hardly be doubted that there is some increment on the surface. The synthesis of water from its elements cannot be more than, almost literally, a drop in the ocean; but an immense quantity of water is stored up in the hot, molten magma in the interior of the earth, and it was shown in Chapter V, dealing with ground-water, how that is eventually sweated out to the surface. This "juvenile" water makes its appearance as an ingredient of hot springs and as ejected vapour in volcanic eruptions.

The gain of water rising to the surface in this way cannot, of course, be gauged exactly, but a rough estimate shows that it is probably of the order of 1/40 of a cubic mile a year. Some consider this estimate too low but, whether it is or not, compared with the total supply of 340 million cubic miles it is virtually imperceptible. Even during a whole geological period, which spans anything from a few million to tens of millions of years, the total quantity of water on the crust does not change to any noticeable extent.

What remains to be seen, however, is whether the amount of water in the cycle outside the oceans is unvarying. It was pointed out in the Introduction that here and there water captured and held in sedimentary rocks is prevented for varying lengths of time from completing its course. For example, 20 per cent by weight of water is held within the grains of sand, and clays imprison a substantially larger quantity than that. If sedimentary rocks of this kind remain on the sea floor and fresh material is constantly being superimposed, the moisture enclosed within the pores is withdrawn from the general circulation. Most of this water is, admittedly, squeezed out again by the pressure of sedimentary deposits subsequently laid down, but some of it will be permanently out of the running. To this loss must be added the water chemically combined with clay minerals, etc., by rock weathering.

There are two ways in which the imprisoned water can be liberated. If, during folding of the crust, the sedimentary rocks are pushed deep down into the earth, they will be heated and will eventually melt. The result will be a red-hot, live melt. This molten mass may erupt or be embedded in the crust and consolidate there in the same way as genuine new igneous intrusions. The second means of escape is when tectonic forces lift the deposits to above sea-level, where they are exposed to denudation.

Hence a fraction of terrestrial water is constantly being withheld from free circulation in the manner briefly outlined but, as the perpetual breakdown and rebuilding of sediment are more or less compensatory, the variations in the quantity shunted into the sidings off the main line are minute. The average thickness of all the sediments on this planet is of the order of $1\frac{1}{2}$ miles. Assume the average volume of the water-filled voids is 5 per cent; the water thus enclosed would be equivalent to a layer of about 400 feet, which amounts to no more than some 4 per cent of the free water on earth.

It may be assumed that this confinement in sedimentary deposits was a gradual process taking place in the course of the earth's history, estimated at 3000 million years. As against the suggested increase of 1/40 of a cubic mile a year, the above reasoning suggests a yearly loss of one-third of this amount. Hence the loss is even less than the gain, itself very small indeed. Yet part of that small gain is illusory, for the above estimate did not take account of the fact that some—perhaps a quarter—of the volcanic (juvenile) water is in reality pseudo-juvenile because, as pore-space water of the remelted sedimentary deposit, it derives ultimately from the surface.

There is one aspect of this balance sheet which has been disregarded so far. It might reasonably be asked whether, in view of the immense age of the earth, the assumed small annual increment is in fact still to be regarded as of little significance. Or is it to be supposed that all the moisture on the surface is no more and no less than the gradually accumulated water sweated out and that the earth when born was completely dry? On this assumption, the earth must, according to our reckoning, have secreted 20 to 75 million cubic miles of water in the three thousand million years of its life. Though this is not the same as the present total of 340 million cubic miles, it is a figure of the same order of magnitude. As in all probability the earth had a thin crust at an early stage and was subject to stronger volcanic activity, there is very good reason to suppose that the secretion of water at that time was more intense. The inference from this is that the globe was possibly dry at first and then, rapidly at the beginning but at a diminishing rate, extravasated water which collected in the depressions on the surface, thus forming the oceans.

Five hundred million years have elapsed since the beginning of the Cambrian Period, the age from which the first rich fossilised fauna has come down to us, and from which our knowledge of the earth's history first begins to take definite shape. In that interval the increase in the quantity of water will have been two to three per cent of the total. The amount is small relatively speaking, but without that increment, sea-level would have been 400 feet lower than it is today. The consequences of this small increase appear to be of crucial significance to life on earth and the external constitution of the planet. Think only how different things would be if the surface of the sea were permanently to drop by 400 feet. The expanse of the continents would be vastly larger, the climate would be drier and the oceans would be more saline, while river erosion due to the drop of the base-line would be considerably more active.

The Salinity of Oceans

The next item on the balance sheet to be considered is the salinity of the oceans and whether this has varied. Here again there are entries both on the debit and credit sides.

The total amount of salt in the oceans is increased by the contents of river waters discharging into them. New minerals are formed by the chemical weathering of rocks. The elements of which the original minerals are composed are regrouped, often with the concurrent absorption of oxygen and carbonic acid. The element sodium, however, is redundant in the new products and is therefore ejected; dissolved in ground-water, it finds its way into rivers and is carried along towards the sea. Chlorine, too, extruded by volcanic activity from the interior of the earth, dissolves in rain-water and thus comes to be a component of river water, although in a similar manner other salts in very small concentrations travel in river water to the sea.

The salt in evaporating sea-water remains behind. Small as the salt content of rivers may be and minute the annual increment compared to the enormous capacity of the oceans, the process of the cycle itself implies a steady increase in the accumulation of salts: pure, distilled water is taken up from the sea and in return a weak solution of salt flows back into it.

There are also small losses to be shown in the account. As we have seen, the sea-water retained between the grains of sedimentary deposits is automatically returned to the sea when, through denudation, these are broken down and cleared away. Hence this salt has been only temporarily withdrawn from the oceans. Salt deposits were also sometimes formed between other sedimentary material if for some reason an arm of the sea in an arid climate was cut off from open communication with the oceans. Eventually all moisture evaporated from such a basin, leaving only a thick crust of salt at the bottom as a witness to its marine origin. Thick deposits of rock salt have been found buried under others of a later date all over the world. They provide the salt-mining industry with an inexhaustible source of supply, but the loss incurred during the building up of these reserves amounts to hardly more than one per cent of the whole capital of salts in the oceans.

It was thought at first that this picture of gradual accumulation in the oceans supplied the final answer to the whole problem. In fact, it seemed to provide the geologists with interesting and very important evidence from which they were able to infer the age of the earth's crust. The total amount of salt in the oceans can be computed with fair accuracy because the mean salt content has been determined and the total volume is also known approximately. The annual increase is likewise ascertainable, though perhaps with a wider margin of uncertainty, by multiplying the mean salt content of the rivers of the world by their mean yearly drainage.

If the total amount of salt now in the oceans is divided by the yearly increase found, the result represents the age of the oceans. This age would be equally applicable to the crust, because—so runs the argument—weathering and concentration started immediately after the formation of the rocks and the oceans. The ages found varied in accordance with the assumptions made as to the magnitude of the different factors, but were all of the order of 100 million years.

Some geologists immediately voiced their disagreement with the age suggested, declaring that a far longer period of time was needed for the development of life and the formation of all the sedimentary rocks. For all that, none were able to detect any cardinal error in the method employed. The geologists' insistence on a longer span was set aside as a gross exaggeration, with all the more conviction because physicists had, for other reasons, estimated the age of even the whole solar system at a considerably lower figure.

Subsequently, however, the physicists themselves corrected their former calculations. Radio-activity enabled them to make highly reliable deductions, with results that amply satisfied even the most exorbitant claims of the geologists. In fact, it transpired that the highest figures deduced from the salinity of the sea were short of a nought at the very least.

Finally, a serious error was brought to light thanks to the deepened insight into the geological past. One important fact had been overlooked when computing the earth's age. It had been taken for granted that during the whole geological past the rivers had brought down the same yearly amount of salt to the seas as they do now. But the crust has recently been subjected to very powerful tectonic activity, resulting in the formation of many high mountain chains and plateaux. This intensified relief has re-animated the rivers in no small degree and this, in turn, has intensified erosion and denudation.

In normal times in the geological past, the aspect of the continents was that of vast, featureless expanses of flat land through which lazy rivers wound their way and upon which a thick skin of weathered soil shielded the fresh rocks from chemical denudation. Under such conditions the liberation of sodium and the formation of new sodium chloride (i.e. salt) was necessarily a slow process. It was not until, with immense intervals of time, the dormant forces in the interior of the earth sprang to life and uplifted large tracts of the crust to high mountains, that the rivers were able to wash the face of the earth clean, and fresh rocks, now exposed to the atmosphere, became the victims of chemical attack. The present is one of these transient periods of great geological activity and the calculated values for the amount of salt being transported to the seas must be far above the average. Hence it follows that the stockpiling must likewise have taken very much longer than was at first assumed.

U

A second fact overlooked in the calculations is no less important. Although salt certainly cannot be extracted from the oceans by evaporation, yet a considerable loss to the atmosphere is regularly incurred. For, when gales whip up waves and rip off the foaming crests, the lowest layers of air are a mixture of foam, drops and air. The water evaporates and minute crystals of salt are left suspended. These, being so small that their rate of descent is negligible, are at the mercy of the air currents. The turbulent movements, which develop to the maximum in a storm, sweep the crystals high into the air, where we have already met them as very active nuclei in the formation of drops of mist and rain. Whenever that rain with its small burden of salt falls on the continents, it means that salt from the oceans is on its travels through the cycle. The implication is that some of the salt in rivers has not been freshly formed by the weathering of rocks, but is merely on an excursion from the ocean. Upon its re-entry into the sea, therefore, it has as little claim to be regarded as an increment as has water returning in this way.

It would be a mistake to think of such salt as constituting only a small percentage of that in rivers. Investigations tend to show that precipitation in the basin of the Mississippi, for instance, contains more salt than is drained away by that river. It seems fairly certain that only a small fraction of all river salt is a gain to the oceans; almost the whole of it has existed there previously.

Revised to allow for these two corrections, the estimate for the age of the oceans produces, as does also the method of radio-activity, figures running into thousands of millions of years. Quite a good case can, in fact, be made out for the contention that the major part of the salt in the oceans was already there at a very early stage and that there has only been a minor increase in the course of geological history. Speculations of this kind, however, need not detain us. The main thing is to realise that a trustworthy figure for the age of the crust cannot be deduced from increases in the supply of salt. Just as it was inferred that the wet element has increased very little comparatively since the beginning of the Cambrian, so may it also be assumed that the seas and oceans were virtually as saline as they are now in that dim past, when life was just beginning to evolve to higher forms.

The Distribution of Water within the Cycle

By and large, the distribution of water among the various sectors of the cycle will have varied very little during the geological past. It is unlikely that the atmosphere, as a whole, has ever been much drier or moister than it is now. Arid and humid periods have alternated, it is true, and desert conditions spread over vast areas, subsequently, maybe, shrivelling away till only moist climates remained; but that involved comparatively speaking little moisture. Even in an entirely saturated condition, the atmosphere could only contain a fraction of one per cent of all the water on earth.

Little as we know about the matter, it is clear that the volume of fresh water on and in the crust must have varied in the course of the ages. Depressions in the crust resulting from tectonic movements created basins in which lakes could settle. A certain amount of water was then temporarily held back in the cycle. But such fluctuations in the distribution of water must likewise have been both insignificant and transient.

There is, however, one recurrent event in the geological past which has without doubt had a more radical effect upon the location of water on this earth. The reader will immediately think of the glacial periods, when a significant percentage of all the water was switched from the oceans to gigantic ice caps. We know that the level of the sea then dropped temporarily some three hundred feet and it is reasonable to assume that the oceans then forfeited something like three per cent of their present contents. Even when the ice had for the most part melted away, as now, many basins had been formed in the liberated valleys, holding large lakes. Compared with the oceans, they contain only a few drops of water, so to speak, but, against the background of the rest of the cycle, glacial lakes are of considerable importance. Thus the North American lakes, which owe their existence to the Ice Age, contain about half of all the fresh water on the surface of the globe. A time will come when all the glacial lakes have disappeared, either through silting up with sedimentary deposits, or by drainage; when that hour strikes, the cycle outside the oceans will make do with the normal, moderate proportion of water upon and in the crust. Before that can happen, however, a milder climate will have to supervene, with higher temperatures at which all land-ice, including that of Greenland and the Antarctic, will melt away. Sea-level will then rise two hundred feet, according to recent estimates of ice volume, and many a low-lying littoral will be drowned.

The removal of a few per cent of water from the oceans to the land-ice fundamentally affected the geological trend of events. Apart from the direct effect of the glaciers, the drop in sea-level acted disruptively in a number of ways. We have already speculated on the likely consequences of such a drop. The coast shifted seawards, thus lengthening the courses of the rivers. Islands were joined on to the mainland; their fauna and flora then coming in direct contact with those of the continents, there began a lively interchange of forms. The almost complete identity between the vegetable and animal kingdoms of Britain with those of the rest of Western Europe, with only a few species missing, is largely thanks to the tongue of land which then spanned the Straits of Dover.

Of exceptional interest are the radical changes brought about in the distribution of living creatures in Indonesia by the laying dry of the extensive tract between Sumatra, Java and Borneo. One of the results was the confluence of the great rivers of Sumatra and West Borneo into one mighty drainage system, forming a gigantic river which discharged in the southern section of the South China Sea. The annual drainage must have been about double that of the Mississippi. When the waters began to rise again after the Ice Age, the low-lying land was submerged, the Java Sea was reborn and the China Sea again extended to between Borneo and Sumatra. The old river courses can still be clearly traced, like a dendritic system of channels, on the sea-floor (Fig. 186).

This recent contact is demonstrable in an elegant manner by the distribution of the fresh-water piscine fauna. In this respect there is an astonishing resemblance between the rivers of East Sumatra and West Borneo, in contrast to those of West Sumatra and of Java and the streams draining off Borneo in other directions. The distances between the sources in the central mountains of the last-named island are only a few miles, whereas the mouths of the West Borneo rivers and those of Sumatra are separated by 300 to 400 miles of sea. There is nothing in the present geographical layout of the Greater Sunda Islands that could even remotely account for the distribution of the fresh-water fish now found there.

While islands were being joined to the mainland, sea-arms of the oceans were, conversely, being cut off, so that they became first brackish and then fresh. All the coral reefs emerged above the surface of the sea, compelling the life peopling these great structures to migrate down the outer slopes with the descending waters. The limestone of the reefs, standing high and dry, for the most part fell a victim to solution, wave attack, etc. Hence, when the glaciers had melted away and the level of the sea began to rise again, the ruined reefs needed fundamental repair or complete rebuilding.

Nature has, as it were, created a small-scale model representing this course of events on a couple of small islands in Indonesia. Off the northeast coast of Borneo there are two insignificant limestone atolls, Maratua and Kakaban, inhabited by a handful of natives (Fig. 187). Seen from the sea, Kakaban looks like just one more of those rocky islands covered with an armour of reef limestone which forms part and parcel of the normal seascape in the Moluccas. The steep cliffs, everywhere undermined by the action of the waves, are covered with thick jungle and the top has the appearance of a flat plain. But if you climb up the 150-foot cliff, you will find only a

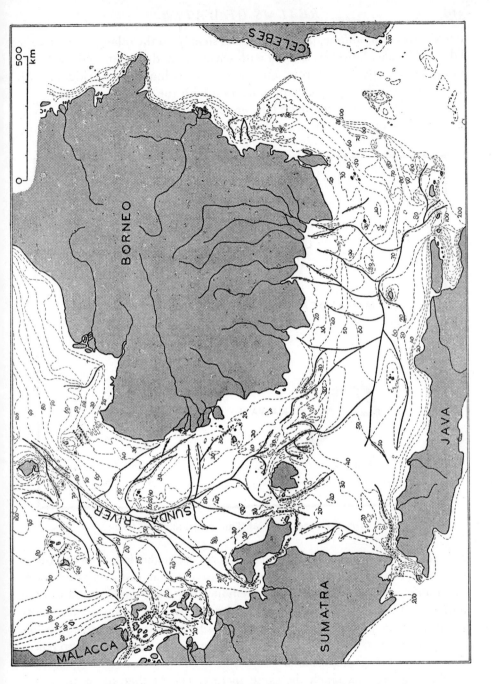

Fig. 186. Drowned river courses on the Sunda Shelf, constructed from submarine contours.
Portions indicated by heavy dotted lines have been dredged out to greater depths by tidal
currents.

narrow rim of limestone, dropping just as steeply on the other side to a large
lake. This lake, however, is filled with sea-water and rises and falls with the
tide. Apparently the narrow, enclosing wall of limestone is riddled with
apertures providing ample communication with the open sea.

The whole island must have lain under the sea at one time, until it was
built up by coral reefs to an atoll, i.e. a circular reef round a deep lagoon.

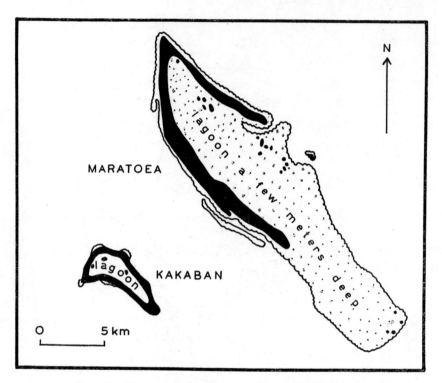

Fig. 187. Maratua and Kakaban, raised atolls off Borneo.

Subsequently it was uplifted 160 feet to form a circular island of coral-lime
soon overgrown with trees. Then for ages wave action, dissolving rain-water
and humic acid from decaying plant remains must have gnawed and scoured
and eroded it until the margin became far narrower and considerably more
porous. At the present time the limestone, after all this maltreatment, is like
a very coarse, petrified rubber sponge, with razor-like edges and sharp points
that make it almost impassable.

Maratua presents much the same picture, except that more than half
the length of the rim has already gone, so that now only a narrow sickle
borders the lagoon (Fig. 188). Only another few centuries, or at most

thousands of years, will be needed to complete the work of destruction and then the last projecting traces of the old atoll will have been worn down to sea-level. All that will remain will be a girdle of shallows with reefs around the one-time lagoon.

With these two examples before us, we have the means of visualising the fate of all atolls (and barrier reefs) of the coral seas during the low water levels of the Ice Age, and it needs little stretch of the imagination to realise subsequent events. While the ice-caps were melting away, the coral reefs subsisting along the outer margins of the truncated atolls sank deeper and

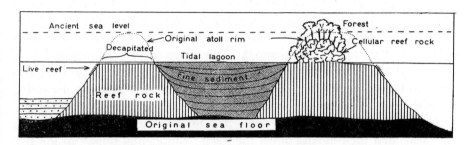

Fig. 188. Diagrammatic cross-section through an atoll of the Maratua type.

deeper and started to grow upwards again, striving to keep close below the rising surface of the sea, until in the end the present-day forms were created, viz., the circle of reefs surrounding a lagoon of considerable depth.

The arguments for and against the existence of normal atolls prior to the Glacial Period and the disputed question as to the part played by crustal subsidence in the generation of these enchanting garlands of the tropical seas are not our present concern. But it is evident that the planing down of all reefs, and that within the same period, must have made for far greater uniformity, both as to the depth of the lagoons and the width of the up-standing margins. It is to the agency of the Ice Age, therefore, that the remarkable uniformity of present-day atolls is to be attributed.

One of the most extraordinary phenomena resulting from the low sea-level was the formation of enormous valley-like gorges on the submarine continental slopes, those submarine canyons which were discussed in Chapter II. When the waters still stood at the normal level, a great deal of fine-grained sediment had accumulated on the shoals along the edges of the land masses. During the ages of low sea-level, all that silt and mud lay exposed to the action of waves. The rivers, moreover, hurriedly scouring out their valleys to adapt them to the lower sea-level, brought down huge loads of sand and mud to the new coast-line. Storm-whipped waves thus stirred a large quantity of clay and fine sand into the water until a suspension was formed of higher specific gravity than that of clear sea-water. This heavy fluid flowed down the submarine slopes until it reached the ocean floor, where it spread out. As the clouds of turbid water slowed down, the particles settled at the bottom.

In this way, these turbidity currents carried a great deal of fine silt from the continental shelves, as the result of which the shallow seas are now deeper and clearer than they would otherwise have been. We have already met such turbidity currents on the subaqueous fronts of lake deltas.

A very good notion of the mechanism can be obtained by carrying out a simple but instructive experiment, which moreover has the advantage of presenting a fascinating spectacle. Fill a soup plate to the brim with hot water so that the flat edge is also covered. This represents the continental shelf and the ocean. Wait until the water is perfectly still, then dip your fountain-pen into the water on the "coast" of this sea and squeeze a droplet of ink out of the pen. That is the counterpart of the water weighted with churned-up mud. The heavy ink slowly leaks in a tongue from the border towards the "sea" and then hurries down the steep "continental slope" to the bed of the "ocean". The larger the blob of ink is, the faster and more turbulently does it flow. On the flat bottom the ink spreads slowly into a broad tongue directed towards the centre of the plate. After a long enough wait there will be scarcely a trace of ink left on the shelf.

The speed of such currents depends not only on differences in specific gravity and angles of slope, both of which must have been small in nature, but also upon the magnitude of the phenomenon; and this, precisely, was enormous. The impetus given to the velocity of these currents of muddy water in nature can be estimated from the results of laboratory experiments and theoretical calculations. It is found far to exceed the velocity of flow of great rivers at high-water. Allowing, moreover, for the far greater dimensions of a torrent of this kind on the sea-floor, the hypothesis that deep valleys were cut into the continental slopes by them becomes comprehensible. Generally speaking, these slopes are not likely to consist of very hard and resistant deposits, a supposition which seems to be borne out by dredging operations, in which the sedimentary rocks brought to the surface were mainly only moderately consolidated.

Before accurate charts of the sea-floor had been made, the existence of a deep channel in front of the mouths of the Congo, the Hudson and one or two other rivers was known and it was also guessed that they were shaped exactly like a river valley, especially the great canyon valleys. The obvious assumption then was that these submarine canyons were former extensions

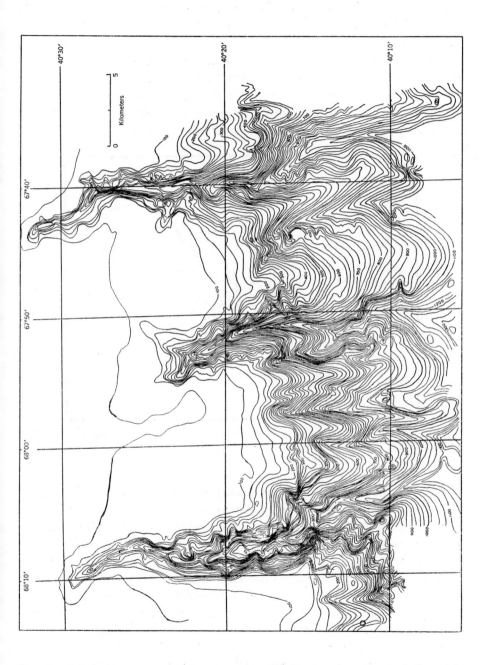

Fig. 189. Submarine canyons on the east coast of North America. Depths indicated in fathoms. (After Stetson.)

of the present adjacent rivers which somehow or other had become submerged. Matters took on an entirely different aspect when modern sounding expeditions brought home close networks of observations. The new charts showed that the continental slopes are grooved with a large number of canyon-like valleys. The very multiplicity of these submarine canyons ruled out their derivation from rivers in the hinterland, which they greatly outnumbered. This invalidated the drowned valley idea. The mechanism of turbidity currents during the Ice Age, on the contrary, could quite well

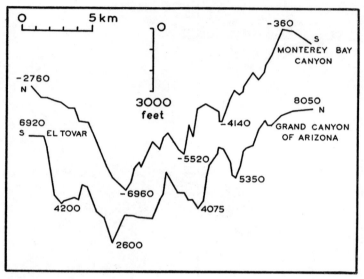

Fig. 190. Vertical section through a submarine canyon off the west coast of the U.S.A. compared with one through the Grand Canyon of the Colorado. (Vertical scale × 5.)

account for the scouring of closely juxtaposed grooves down the slopes. By no means all geologists agree with this hypothesis and there are admittedly some points to be cleared up, such as the existence of some submarine canyons with walls of hard rock.

It has been suggested that at least part of these hard-rock submarine canyons are ancient land valleys drowned long ago, smothered by sediment and re-excavated by turbidity currents during the low sea-levels of the Ice Age. Neither should it be forgotten that there was a recurrent drop in sea-level during each of the four glacial periods of the Ice Age. On the view given here, therefore, the submarine canyons may be regarded as the wheel tracks of the dust-cart which removed refuse from the shallow seas around the mainland during the Ice Age.

Half a century ago a geologist possessing a vivid imagination described how eagles used to circle above the canyon of the Hudson where dolphins now leap. He was writing at a time when the theory of a drowned river valley still held sway. While it is true that sober science now discredits this piece of fantasy, does it not in fact offer a far more colourful picture to take its place? In the mind's eye we see the mighty tide of sea-level fluctuations during the Ice Age, tempestuous storms churning up the mud, the terrific torrents dashing down the continental slopes, hewing out gigantic gorges and spreading the silt over the floor of the ocean hundreds of miles away from the coast. At the same time we are vouchsafed a glimpse of the distant past now long forgotten and of the pitch-dark depths of the ocean which the human eye cannot penetrate.

All sciences build upon a foundation of bald, sober fact and in this voyage along the ways followed by water in nature we have tried consistently to keep to observed facts and substantiated reasoning. That a modicum of speculative imagination may none the less go far towards solving elusive problems is demonstrated by the suggestions just put forward concerning the origin of submarine canyons. It may well be that, like the geologist cited, we have been lured on to a false trail. But surely it is better to stray into entrancing by-paths—with the risk, admittedly, of having to retrace one's steps, but equally with the possible chance of finding a short-cut—than, with eyes glued to the compass, to plod the safe high road, blind alike to the nearby wildflowers in bank and meadow and to the glorious distant prospects?

REFERENCES

A list of publications (marked with an asterisk) from which illustrations have with permission been adapted; together with suggestions for further reading.

GENERAL REFERENCES

J. S. COLLIS: *The Moving Waters*. Hart-Davis, London, 1955 (246 pp.).

C. A. COTTON: *Landscape*. Whitcomb and Tombs, Christchurch (N.Z.), 1948 (509 pp.).

*W. M. DAVIS: *Die erklärende Beschreibung der Landformen*. Teubner, Leipzig-Berlin, 1912 (565 pp.).

*B. G. ESCHER: *Grondslagen der Algemene Geologie*. Wereldbibliotheek, Amsterdam-Antwerpen, 1951 (442 pp.).

A. HOLMES: *Principles of Physical Geology*. Nelson, London, 1945 (532 pp.).

T. KING: *Water, Miracle of Nature*. Macmillan, New York, 1953 (238 pp.).

A. K. LOBECK: *Geomorphology*. McGraw-Hill, New York–London, 1939 (731 pp.).

*CH. LONGWELL, A. KNOPF and R. FLINT: *Physical Geology*. Wiley, New York—Chapman and Hall, London, 1948 (602 pp.).

*A. ROBIN: *La Terre, ses aspects, sa structure, son évolution*. Larousse, Paris, 1911 (330 pp.).

*I. M. VAN DER VLERK and PH. H. KUENEN: *Geheimschrift der Aarde*. De Haan, Utrecht, 1951 (373 pp.).

II

H. B. BIGELOW and W. T. EDMONDSON: *Wind Waves at Sea, Breakers and Surf*. Hydrographic Office, Publ. No. 602, Washington, 1947 (177 pp.).

R. L. CARSON: *The Sea around Us*. Staples Press, London, 1951 (230 pp.).

R. E. COKER: *This Great and Wide Sea*. University of North Carolina Press, Chapel Hill, 1949 (325 pp.).

J. Y. COSTEAU: *The Silent World*. Hamish Hamilton, London, 1953 (148 pp.).

R. A. DALY: *The Floor of the Ocean*. University of North Carolina Press, Chapel Hill, 1945 (177 pp.).

*A. DEFANT: *Dynamische Ozeanographie*. Springer, Berlin, 1929 (222 pp.).

A. DEFANT et al.: *Wind, Wetter und Wellen auf dem Weltmeere*. Mittler und Sohn, Berlin, 1940 (150 pp.).

*R. DIRCKSEN, *Das Wattenmeer*. Bruckmann, München, 1942 (220 pp.).

*A. EHRDHARDT: *Das Watt*. Ellermann, Hamburg, 1937 (96 pp.).

*D. W. JOHNSON: *Shore Processes and Shoreline Development*. Wiley, New York—Chapman and Hall, London, 1938 (584 pp.).

*PH. H. KUENEN: *Kruistochten over de Indische Diepzeebekkens*. Leopold, The Hague, 1941 (220 pp.).

*PH. H. KUENEN: *Marine Geology*. Wiley, New York—Chapman and Hall, London, 1950 (568 pp.).

317

*P. M. van Riel: *Scientific Results of the Snellius Expedition*, Vol. I, chapters I–IV. Brill, Leiden, 1937 (177 pp.).
*G. Schott: *Geographie des Atlantischen Ozeans*. Boysen, Hamburg, 1942 (438 pp.).
F. P. Shepard: *Submarine Geology*. Harper & Brothers, New York, 1948 (348 pp.).
J. A. Steers: *The Sea Coast*. Collins, London, 1953 (276 pp.).
H. U. Sverdrup et al.: *The Oceans*. Prentice Hall, New York, 1946 (1087 pp.).
*H. Thorade: *Ebbe and Flut*. Springer, Berlin, 1941 (115 pp.).
*P. D. Trask et al.: *Recent Submarine Sediments, a Symposium*. Amer. Assoc. Petr. Geol., Tulsa (Okla.)—Murby, London, 1939 (736 pp.).

III

*W. M. Davis: *The Coral Reef Problem*. Amer. Geogr. Soc., Spec. Publ. No. 9, New York, 1928 (596 pp.).
A. E. M. Geddes: *Meteorology*. Blackie and Son, London and Glasgow, 1944 (398 pp.).
*W. J. Jong: *Kern der Physischen Geografie*. Versluys, Amsterdam–Batavia, 1949 (136 pp.).
G. H. T. Kimble: *The Weather*. Pelican Books A 124. Penguin Books, Harmondsworth, Middlesex, 1951 (256 pp.).
N. Shaw: *The Drama of Weather*. University Press, Cambridge, 1940 (307 pp.).

IV

*W. A. Bentley and W. J. Humphreys: *Snow Crystals*. McGraw-Hill, New York, 1931 (227 pp.).
R. A. Daly: *The Changing World of the Ice Age*. Yale University Press, New Haven, 1935 (271 pp.).
*W. Flaig: *Lawinen!* Brockhaus, Leipzig, 1935 (173 pp.).
R. F. Flint: *Glacial Geology and the Pleistocene Epoch*. Wiley, New York—Chapman and Hall, London, 1947 (589 pp.).
*W. H. Hobbs: *Characteristics of Existing Glaciers*. Macmillan, New York, 1911 (301 pp.).
*W. Paulcke: *Praktische Schnee- und Lawinenkunde*. Springer, Berlin, 1938 (218 pp.).

V

*C. M. Bauer: *The Story of Yellowstone Geysers*. Haynes, St. Paul, Minnesota, 1937 (125 pp.).
*L. V. Bertarelli and E. Boegan: *Duemila Grotte*. Touring Club Italiano, Milano, 1926 (494 pp.).
J. B. L. Hol: *Beiträge zur Hydrographie der Ardennen*. Thesis, Utrecht, 1916 (160 pp.).
*M. Neumayr: *Erdgeschichte, I*. Bibliographisches Institut, Leipzig-Wien, 1897 (693 pp.).
W. Prinz: *Les cristallisations des grottes de Belgique*, Nouv. Mém. Soc. Belge Geol. Hayez, Bruxelles, 1908 (90 pp.).
C. F. Tolman: *Groundwater*. McGraw-Hill, New York–London, 1937 (593 pp.).

VI

*H. Boissevain: *De riviervormen in sedimentatiegebieden.* Tijdschr. Nederl. Aardr. Gen. Amsterdam, 2nd Reeks, Dl. LVIII, 5, 1941 (722–756 pp.).

L. W. Collet: *Les lacs, leur mode de formation, leurs eaux, leur destin.* Gaston Doin, Paris, 1925 (320 pp.).

*A. Ehrhardt: *Island.* Ellermann, Hamburg, 1939 (112 pp.).

A. Heim: *Geologie des Rheinfalls.* Mitt. Nat. Ges. Schaffhausen, Heft 10, 1931 (70 pp.).

*E. Krenkel: *Die Bruchzonen Ostafrikas.* Borntraeger, Berlin, 1922 (184 pp.).

E. C. Rashleigh: *Among the Waterfalls of the World.* Jarrolds, London, 1935 (288 pp.).

*A. C. Veatch: *Geology and Underground Water Resources of Northern Louisiana and Southern Arkansas.* U.S.G.S., Prof. Paper, 46, Washington, 1906.

*E. R. Zernitz: *Drainage Patterns and their Significance.* Journ. Geol., Vol. XL, 1932 (pp. 498–521).

VII

A. Holmes: *The Age of the Earth.* Nelson and Sons, London, etc., 1937 (263 pp.).

Ph. H. Kuenen: *Marine Geology.* Wiley, New York—Chapman and Hall, London, 1950 (568 pp.).

F. P. Shepard: *Submarine Geology.* Harper & Brothers, New York, 1948 (348 pp.).

*H. C. Stetson: *Geology and Paleontology of the Georges Bank Canyons,* Pt. 1, Geology. Bull. Geol. Soc. Am., Vol. 47, 1936 (pp. 339–366).

INDEX

Individual rivers, waterfalls and glaciers will be found listed under those generic headings.

36/126